THE TOADSTOOL
MILLIONAIRES

Somebody buys all the quack medicines
that build palaces for the mushroom, say rather,
the toadstool millionaires.

OLIVER WENDELL HOLMES

THE TOADSTOOL MILLIONAIRES

*A Social History
of Patent Medicines in America before
Federal Regulation*

JAMES HARVEY⌐YOUNG

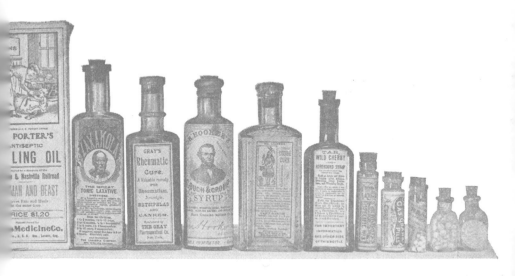

Princeton, New Jersey · Princeton University Press · 1961

Publication of this book
has been aided by the Ford Foundation program
to support publication,
through university presses, of works in the humanities
and social sciences

Printed in the United States of America
by Princeton University Press, Princeton, New Jersey

To Myrna

PREFACE

As a master's student in history at the University of Illinois, I found that my research in the early newspapers of that state was often halted by my inability to keep my gaze fixed purposefully on the news columns. My eyes inevitably sought out the patent medicine advertising, and this interest worked its way into a chapter of my master's thesis. Some years later, I yielded completely to the impulse, persuaded that medical quackery has been —and is—an important theme in American social and intellectual history. Quackery is important because through it vast numbers of our people have sought to bolster or restore their health and because it affords insight into an anti-rational approach to one of the key problems of life.

This book is a history of proprietary medicines in America, from the early 18th-century appearance of patented brands imported from the mother country to the early 20th-century enactment of national legislation intended, in part, to restrain abuses in the packaged medicine industry. Native nostrum production began during the cultural nationalism of the Revolutionary generation, expanded rapidly during the age of the common man, received a new impetus from the Civil War, and reached floodtide in the late 19th century. The critique of patent medicine quackery first became significant as part of the humanitarian crusade accompanying Jacksonian democracy. As medicine became more scientific, the anti-nostrum movement developed a sounder base. During the Progressive period, journalists and civil servants added their support to physicians and pharmacists and created an articulate public opinion in behalf of a regulatory law.

The various stages in the development of patent medicine promotion and criticism form the chapters that follow. An effort is made to relate this particular theme to broader trends in health, education, journalism, marketing, and government. In some chapters case histories are given to illustrate the patent medicine situation prevailing in the period.

Dr. Oliver Wendell Holmes knew well enough that it was difficult to tell a mushroom from a toadstool, that many promoters of nostrums were sincere and kindly men and not unscrupulous rogues, though their handiwork might be hazardous to their customers. Holmes also knew that very few patent medi-

[vii]

cine makers, whether impelled by motives good or bad, became millionaires. Most of them, nonetheless, hoped to do so.

The author, like Holmes, votes against patent medicines, casting a sad ballot against the gullible entrepreneur during the early years, when medical science and ethics were on unsure foundations and the line was hard to draw between the legitimate and the quack, casting a bold ballot against the charlatan of all ages.

The "why" of quackery is a question that runs through the book, mounting to a paradox near the close: the rise of scientific medicine and the apogee of unrestrained nostrum vending coincide. While it is hoped that in the pages that follow light is shed on this problem, it is admitted that a full answer lies hidden in the complex mystery of human motivation.

Research for this book was done, in part, while I held a fellowship from the Fund for the Advancement of Education of the Ford Foundation and, on another occasion, while I held grants from the Social Science Research Council and from Emory University. For this support, I am most grateful. So too am I grateful for the assistance given me by the many librarians, archivists, and curators at institutions named in the Note on the Sources, in which I found the materials that compose this work. Particular appreciation is due the staffs of the libraries of my own university—the Asa Griggs Candler Library, and the libraries of the Schools of Business Administration, Law, Medicine, and Theology—who have aided me imaginatively and cheerfully around the calendar. My most frequent helpers have been David Estes and Ruth Walling.

I am indebted to the publishers of *The South Atlantic Quarterly*, the *Journal of the Illinois State Historical Society*, the London *Chemist and Druggist*, the *Journal of Economic History*, the *Mississippi Valley Historical Review*, the *Journal of the American Pharmaceutical Association (Practical Pharmacy Edition)*, the *Emory University Quarterly*, and the United States National Museum Bulletin 218, *Contributions from the Museum of History and Technology*, who have given me permission to use material from articles of mine which first appeared in their pages. Gilbert S. Goldhammer and Wallace F. Janssen of the Federal Food and Drug Administration, and George B. Griffenhagen of the American Pharmaceutical Association, kindly read and criticized the first draft of Chapter 15. R. Miriam Brokaw of Princeton University Press has been most helpful with her counsel and encouragement.

Friends and acquaintances, learning of my interest, have mailed and told me about examples of patent medicine promotion they found in their own reading and research. In many conversations, colleagues have also aided me with suggestions from their own special fields of knowledge. Some, but by no means all, of my benefactors are named in the Note on the Sources. Let me here testify to my gratitude to all those whose interest has contributed to this book.

Above all, I thank my wife, Myrna Goode Young, first reader and key critic.

JAMES HARVEY YOUNG

Emory University
October 1960

ACKNOWLEDGMENTS

UOTATIONS from the following sources are used by permission: from "The Great American Fraud" series by Samuel Hopkins Adams (copyright, 1905, 1906, by the Crowell-Collier Publishing Company), by permission of the Estate of Samuel Hopkins Adams and the Crowell-Collier Publishing Company; other quotations from *Collier's*, by permission of the Crowell-Collier Publishing Company; from Jacques M. Quen's Yale University thesis, "Elisha Perkins and Perkinism," by permission of Dr. Quen and Yale Medical Library; from *Four White Horses and a Brass Band* (copyright 1947 by Violet McNeal), by permission of Doubleday & Company, Inc.; from N. T. Oliver (as told to Wesley Stout), "Med Show," in the *Saturday Evening Post* (Sep. 14, 1929), by permission of Mr. Stout; from Thomas J. LeBlanc, "The Medicine Show," in the *American Mercury* (June 1925), and from Jim Tully, "The Medicine Show," in the *American Mercury* (June 1928), by permission of the *American Mercury*; from "Good-Bye to the Medicine Show" (copyright 1942 by *Medical Economics, Inc.*), by permission of *Medical Economics, Inc.*; from Harry Leon Wilson, *Professor How Could You!*, published in 1924 by Cosmopolitan Book Corporation, by permission of Holt, Rinehart and Winston, Inc.; from the *Druggists Circular* for 1905, by permission of Topic Publishing Company; the Beveridge quotation from vol. II of Mark Sullivan, *Our Times*, by permission of Charles Scribner's Sons; from *Food Drug Cosmetic Law Journal*, by permission of Food Law Institute, Inc.

Acknowledgment for use of photographs in the section of illustrations is given there. The photographs of bottles from the author's collection used on title page and for the end-papers were taken by Wiley Perry. The photograph used for the jacket design, entitled "The Apothecary's Shelf," was taken by William Arthur Young, APSA, the author's brother.

CONTENTS

[xi]

CONTENTS

PART FOUR: LEGISLATION

PART FIVE: EPILOGUE

Illustrations following page 122

PART ONE

EARLY DAYS

𝟙

"AT THE SIGN OF GALEN'S HEAD"

Medicines approv'd by royal charter,
James, Godfry, Anderson, Court-plaster,
With Keyser's Hooper's Lockyer's Pills,
And Honey Balsam Doctor Hill's;
Bateman and Daffy, Jesuits drops,
And all the Tinctures of the shops,
As Stoughton, Turlington and Grenough,
Pure British Oil and Haerlem Ditto. . . .

—NEW YORK PACKET, October 11, 1784

𝕀N the *Boston News-Letter* for November 26, 1761, Charles Russell of Charlestown advised that "At his Shop at the Sign of GALEN'S HEAD opposite the Three Cranes and near the FERRY" he had for sale, imported on the latest ships from London, "Drugs, and Medicines, Chymical and Galenical," and certain patent medicines. These last were listed: Bateman's and Stoughton's Drops, Lockyer's, Hooper's, and Anderson's Pills, British Oyl, and Daffy's Elixir.[1]

American patent medicine history began in Britain. Its founders were certain ingenious Englishmen who combined medical lore and promotional zeal in an age when regular medicines left much to be desired. The barest of facts are these.

Anderson's Pills, a product of the 1630's, were prepared from a formula allegedly learned in Venice by a Scot who claimed to be physician to King Charles I. Daffy's Elixir and Lockyer's Pills were also first made in the 17th century, the Elixir the invention of a provincial clergyman. Richard Stoughton's Elixir

[1] Material in this chapter has appeared in a different form in James Harvey Young and George B. Griffenhagen, "Old English Patent Medicines in America," London *Chemist and Druggist,* 167 (June 29, 1957), 714-22, and in Griffenhagen and Young, "Old English Patent Medicines in America," *Contributions from the Museum of History and Technology* (U.S. National Museum Bulletin 218, Smithsonian Institution: Wash., 1959), 155-83.

[3]

was the second compound medicine to be granted, in 1712, an English patent. In 1726 a patent was also granted for the making of Dr. Bateman's Pectoral Drops: the patentee was not a physician named Bateman, however, but a businessman named Benjamin Okell, in league with a group of venturesome promoters with a warehouse and printshop in Bow Churchyard. Two decades later, Michael and Thomas Bretton patented "An Oyl extracted from a Flinty Rock for the Cure of Rheumatick and Scorbutick and other Cases." The next year a Reading apothecary, John Hooper, was given a patent for the manufacture of "Female Pills" bearing his name.

The 18th was a Cinderella century, at once an age of enlightenment and a time of superstition. As to what actually caused diseases, Sir William Osler has asserted, man knew little more at the end of the 18th century than had the ancient Greeks. This did not mean that the state of medicine was still dawn-age. Empirical discoveries of use in treating illness had accumulated, and since the Renaissance a genuinely scientific spirit had spurred individual scholars to engage in anatomical and pathological research. No earlier years had found so many forward-looking inquirers at work as did the 18th century, men anxious to transfer into the fields of biology and medicine the scientific revolution that had remade physics and astronomy. Yet the problem of disease and health was so vast and complex, the sum total of new medical knowledge still so small, and the weight of past traditions so pressing that even the keenest minds were perplexed. Or, if they were not perplexed but, in their own view, certain, they were most often wrong. Many physicians became disillusioned when biological research seemed to lead not to universal laws, like gravitation, but only to more complications and greater confusion. Anxious to get their single explanations for all disease, they did so by neglecting the scientific method, or by following it only a short way. They built vast theoretical medical schemes by speculative logic. The 18th century was a time of system-making.[2]

Many of the new systems owed much to ancient lore. It was appropriate that the shop of a Massachusetts apothecary should hang out a sign of Galen's head. For it was this Greek physician of the second century A.D. who had systematized the older path-

[2] Osler, *The Evolution of Modern Medicine* (New Haven, 1921), 208; Richard H. Shryock, *The Development of Modern Medicine* (N.Y., 1947), 3-37.

ology of the humors, holding that disease resulted when the four liquids in the body—blood, phlegm, choler (yellow bile), and melancholy (black bile)—became unbalanced. Galen's ideas, although not uncontested, were the dominant force in medical thinking into the 19th century, and remedies that would restore the harmonious relationship of the humors, called galenicals, were for sale by any British or American apothecary.[3]

So too were "chymical" remedies. These began with a 16th-century chemist-physician named Paracelsus who displayed his contempt for tradition by burning the works of Galen. He proclaimed that chemistry should forsake its forlorn effort to make gold from baser metals and devote itself to finding remedies to cure the sick. Paracelsus and his disciples added certain minerals to the materia medica.[4]

The materia medica had expanded in other ways. One touchstone that had brought appalling substances into usage was the dictum that the worse a medicine tasted the greater its curative power. Disease was an invader that must be driven from the body by a substance as abhorrent as itself. Three London hospitals in the 18th century published a dispensatory recommending dried horses' hooves and wood lice. Even such a forward-looking chemist as Robert Boyle suggested for internal medication, in the phrase of Oliver Wendell Holmes, "most of the substances commonly used as fertilizers of the soil." Thus Cotton Mather, the Puritan divine in Massachusetts, was quite in accord with the practice of his age: he devoted a chapter in his medical manuscript, "The Angel of Bethesda," to the therapeutic properties of urine and dung.[5]

Obnoxiousness often coupled with complexity in 18th-century medicines. The "blunderbuss" formula was popular, composed of many substances to cover many therapeutic bets. A good example of polypharmacy was theriaca or Venice Treacle, dating from the days of Nero, containing over sixty ingredients, one of them the

[3] Fielding H. Garrison, *An Introduction to the History of Medicine* (3rd ed., Phila., 1924), 82-83, 103-107; Edward Eggleston, *The Transit of Civilization from England to America in the Seventeenth Century* (N.Y., 1901), 50-51.

[4] Garrison, 196-200; Edward Kremers and George Urdang, *A History of Pharmacy* (Phila., 1940), 37-38.

[5] Holmes, *Medical Essays, 1842-1882* (Boston, 1892), 186-87; Charles H. LaWall, *Four Thousand Years of Pharmacy* (Phila., 1927), 434-45; Otho T. Beall, Jr., "Cotton Mather, The First Significant Figure in American Medicine," *Bull. Hist. Med.*, 26 (1952), 108, 115.

flesh of the viper. Theriaca was widely used both in England and America.[6]

Magic in medication had other facets. One was the doctrine of signatures, older than Hippocrates, perennial in folk medicine, and given so much attention by Paracelsus and his followers as to seem like a fresh idea in the years that followed. It arose from a cosmic view that God or Nature had provided remedies for the ailments of mankind and had furnished clues to direct man in his search. Thus the thistle was useful for a stitch in the side, walnut shells for a cracked skull, and pulverized mummy for prolonging life.[7]

The age of discovery had flooded Europe with new products from the entire world. Exotic plants were quickly put to therapeutic use. By 1650 the medicinal garden at Oxford University, begun in 1623, was growing 600 native species and 1,000 plants brought from beyond the seas.[8]

Medication in the 17th and 18th centuries was certainly laissez-faire, the multitude of remedies justified in terms of speculative theory or presumed empirical experience. No layman with an urge to suggest a new medicine felt any legal or moral restraint. Besides this therapeutic toleration, there were other aspects of the medical scene which encouraged the would-be medicine maker. English practitioners who possessed prestige and status were the fellows of the London College of Physicians, a body founded during the quickened scientific interest of the Renaissance but now grown arthritic. An age-old prejudice still held sway that a member of a profession should not demean himself by working with his hands. Thus surgery and experimenting in the laboratory were frowned upon. Disputation between proponents of conflicting theoretical systems was protracted and bitter. Preoccupied with questions of preferment and precedence, the physicians refused to expand their ranks even though there were over 1,300 serious cases of illness a day per every member of the College. The masses had to look elsewhere for treatment. They found it at the hands of surgeons and apothecaries, not yet fully reputable

6 A. C. Wootton, *Chronicles of Pharmacy* (London, 1910), II, 37-39, 42-50; *Boston News-Letter*, Sep. 16, 1731; Carl Bridenbaugh, *Cities in the Wilderness* (N.Y., 1938), 90.
7 Wootton, I, 28-31; Eggleston, 66.
8 Charles F. Mullett, "Overseas Expansion and English Medicine to 1800," *Bull. Hist. Med.*, 22 (1948), 667-68.

but increasingly countenanced because of the great need, and they found it at the hands of well-meaning empirics and unscrupulous quacks.[9]

It would be hard to discover a time and place in which nostrum promotion was more brazen than in 18th-century England. Therapeutic claims achieved the very perfection of extravagance. Castigation of rivals reached the summit of acrimony. Namestealing and patent-jumping were the lot of every successful proprietor. From Anderson's to Hooper's, all of the patent medicines advertised at the Sign of Galen's Head were in England the subject of intense rivalry. One enterprising woman, for example, marketed Scots Pills in boxes sealed with black wax bearing a lion rampant, three mallets argent, and the bust of Dr. Anderson. A male competitor sealed his boxes in red wax with his coat of arms and a motto strangely chosen for a medicine: "Remember you must die."[10]

Stoughton's Elixir, upon the death of the inventor, became the subject of a family feud. A son of Stoughton and the widow of another son argued in most vituperative fashion. Each claimed sole possession of the formula, and each termed the other a scoundrel. The daughter-in-law accused the son of financial chicanery; the son condemned the daughter-in-law for having run through two husbands and for desperately wanting a third. In the midst of the battle a third party entered the lists. She was no Stoughton and her quaint claim for the public's consideration lay in this: that her late husband had infringed Stoughton's patent until restrained by the Lord Chancellor.[11]

In the *Boston News-Letter* for October 4, 1708, Nicholas Boone, at the Sign of the Bible near the corner of School-House-Lane, advertised for sale: "DAFFY'S Elixir Salutis, very good, at four shillings and six-pence *per* half pint Bottle." This may well be the first printed reference in America to an English "patent medicine" (though the Elixir was not patented), and it certainly is the first newspaper advertisement for a nostrum. There had been only one gazette preceding the *News-Letter* in British America, and it had lasted but a single issue. Then its

9 Shryock, 51-54; Garrison, 396, 405-408; Kremers and Urdang, 90-93; Lester S. King, *The Medical World of the Eighteenth Century* (Chicago, 1958).
10 C. J. S. Thompson, *Quacks of Old London* (London, 1928), 256-58.
11 "Proprietaries of Other Days," *Chemist and Druggist*, 106 (June 1925), 833-34.

printer had returned to England to assume the role of nostrum vendor, selling "the only Angelical Pills against all Vapours, Hysterick and Melancholly Fits."[12] It seems a likely assumption that some 17th-century emigrant, setting forth across the Atlantic to face the hazards of life in Jamestown or Philadelphia or Boston, had brought along a bottle of Daffy's Elixir or a box of Anderson's Pills. No record to support such an incident has been found. The *News-Letter* was four years old before Boone announced his supply of the Reverend Daffy's concoction.

The Elixir entered an American medical scene different from that of the mother country. Class and professional distinctions were much less extreme or important. Medical practitioners were not averse to being physician, surgeon, apothecary, and even midwife, all in one. The first American medical school was not to open until 1765, and only one in nine 18th-century doctors went abroad to seek a degree. The rest received their medical training as apprentices, and standards were lax. "Practitioners are laureated gratis with a title feather of Doctor," wrote a New Englander in 1690. "Potecaries, surgeons & midwifes are dignified acc (ording) to success." This situation put emphasis on practical matters rather than theory, and colonial doctors largely avoided the acrimonious disputes over conceptual medical systems that involved British physicians. Untrammeled empiricism could have its weaknesses, of course, and the wiser of the apprentice-trained physicians complained of evils. In 1738 "Philanthropos" wrote to a newspaper proposing a licensing system so as to remove the "Shoemakers, Weavers, and Almanack-Makers, with their virtuous Consorts, who have laid aside the proper Business of their Lives, to turn Quacks." But control efforts that were tried proved futile.[13]

In one respect 18th-century America and England were alike: they both possessed an eager eclecticism with respect to medical remedies. Heir to the same ancient traditions, Americans dosed themselves with galenicals and chymicals, and swallowed complicated concoctions containing disgusting ingredients, in their efforts to drive away the ills that attacked them. These ills were

---

[12] Frank L. Mott, *American Journalism* (N.Y., 1941), 9-10.
[13] Daniel J. Boorstin, *The Americans, The Colonial Experience* (N.Y., 1958), 209-39; Samuel Lee to Nehemiah Grew, June 25, 1690, cited in George L. Kittredge, ed., "Letters of Samuel Lee and Samuel Sewall . . . ," Colonial Soc. Mass., *Trans.*, 14 (Boston, 1913), 142-86; Philanthropos, cited in Bridenbaugh, 403.

many. Respiratory ailments, dysenteries, and malaria were the chronic diseases, taking a greater toll year in and year out than did the more feared smallpox and yellow fever, which occasionally struck with epidemic force. A corollary of the doctrine of signatures held that God had placed specific remedies for illnesses in the very regions where the ailments flourished. This view prompted a great searching of American fields and forests for curative plants and directed respectful attention to the healing arts of the Indians. Toward the end of the 17th century, for example, it was asserted that the Pennsylvania Indians were "as able physicians as any in Europe." Much effort was expended prying botanical secrets from Indian medicine men.[14]

Thus when the English patent medicines began to appear on American shores they entered a therapeutic scene of considerable variety. Accepted in modest measure at first, to judge by newspaper advertising, they caught the public fancy beginning in the 1750's and were even more popular in the following decade. Sold throughout the colonies, the English medicines were listed over and over again in the advertising columns of papers published in Boston and New York, in Baltimore and Charleston. Zabdiel Boylston dispensed them in Massachusetts; Button Gwinnett sold them in Georgia. Nor were the imported pills and balsams confined to apothecaries' shelves for vending at the Sign of the Bible or the Sign of the Unicorn and Mortar. English remedies were sold by postmasters, goldsmiths, grocers, hairdressers, tailors, painters, booksellers, cork cutters, the post-rider between Philadelphia and Williamsburg, and by many American colonial physicians. A Virginia doctor, for example, who had migrated to America after graduating from the Royal College of Surgeons, founded a town on the frontier and dosed those who came to dwell therein with Bateman's Drops and Turlington's Balsam.[15]

American newspaper advertising of the English packaged remedies was singularly drab. The apothecary or merchant had no proprietary interest in the imported brands. There was probably not so great a surplus of supply over demand in America as

14 John Duffy, *Epidemics in Colonial America* (Baton Rouge, 1953); Kremers and Urdang, 158-60; Eggleston, 73.
15 Advertising in various papers; the Boylston ad in *Boston News-Letter*, Mar. 12, 1711; the Gwinnett ad cited in Robert C. Wilson, *Drugs and Pharmacy in the Life of Georgia, 1733-1959* (Atlanta, 1959), 108; the Virginia doctor referred to in Maurice B. Gordon, *Aesculapius Comes to the Colonies* (Ventnor, N.J., 1949), 39.

[9]

in Britain, and advertising space in the American weeklies was more at a premium than in the more frequent and numerous English journals. Thus, while the English proprietor sharpened up his adjectives and reached for his vitriol, in America, with rare exceptions, advertisers were content merely to list by name their supplies of imported English remedies. Typical was the advertisement in the *Pennsylvania Gazette* for December 1, 1768, by apothecary Thomas Preston. "At the Golden Mortar, opposite Black-Horse Alley," he announced as "Just imported from London" and for sale, "All the most useful kinds of patent medicines, as Anderson's, Hooper's and Lockyer's pills, Bateman's drops, British oil, Bostock's, Squire's and Daffey's elixirs, Stoughton's bitters, Turlington's balsam of life, Dr. James's fever powders, Godfrey's cordial."

In the whole span of the *Boston News-Letter*, beginning in 1704, it was not until 1763 that a bookstore devoted half a column of lively prose to extolling the merits of Dr. John Hill's four imported nostrums. One of them, the doctor claimed, was the restoration of a Greek secret which "convert[ed] a Glass of Water into the Nature and Quality of Asses Milk, with the Balsamick Addition." Two years earlier, in New York, a newspaper nostrum battle developed that rivaled in intensity the London feuds. Well it might, for one of the participants was Robert Turlington, the English patentee and proprietor of the popular Balsam of Life. He entered the lists late, after a handful of New York merchants had advertised his medicine for sale. They numbered among them one woman, a man at the Woman's Shoe-Store, and three male apothecaries. The dispute over who was vending the true article became so confusing to consumers that Turlington, alert to what was going on in America, decided to step in. In the pages of the *Mercury* he warned against counterfeiters, cut the Shoe-Store man off without another genuine vial, and announced he had sent a parcel of the Balsam to be sold by the *Mercury's* editor.[16]

The infrequency of fanciful newspaper promotion was compensated for to some degree in broadside and pamphlet. A critic of the New York medical scene in the 1750's condemned physicians for using patent medicines learned about from "London

[16] *Mass. Gaz. and Boston News-Letter*, Nov. 24, 1763; ads in *N.Y. Mercury* and *N.Y. Gaz.*, Turlington's in former, Nov. 9, 1761.

quack bills." Often, the doctor complained, perhaps with exaggeration, these were their only reading matter. Certainly the English promoter sought to devise ingenious pamphlets and broadsides. Turlington, for one, had issued a 46-page brochure replete with didactic text in the best 18th-century fashion. Asserting that the "Author of Nature" provided "a Remedy for every Malady," which "Men of Learning and Genius" have "ransack'd" the "Animal, Mineral, and Vegetable World" to discover, Turlington avowed that his quest had led to the Balsam of Life, "a perfect Friend to Nature." The medicine, he said, "vivifies and enlivens the Spirits, mixes with the Juices and Fluids of the Body, and gently infuses its kindly Influence into those Parts that are most in Disorder." By so doing it cured a whole host of maladies, from dropsy to sprained thumbs. Its therapeutic potency, Turlington asserted, was proved by countless testimonials. Most of them were from humble people—a porter, the wife of a gardener, a hostler, a bodice-maker. Some bore a status of greater distinction—a "Mathematical Instrument-Maker" and the doorkeeper of the East India Company. The testimonials reached out toward America. One such certificate came from "a sailor before the mast, on board the ship *Britannia* in the *New York* trade"; another cited a woman living in Philadelphia. All who spoke were jubilant at their restored good health.[17]

Promotional items like the pamphlet, now rare, may have been abundant in the mid-18th century. This type of printed matter, then as now, was likely to be looked at and thrown away. Another item of evidence survives in the records of a Williamsburg apothecary who ordered from the mother country in 1753 "3 Quire Stoughton's Directions" and "½ Groce Stoughton Vials." The broadsides served a double purpose: not only did they promote the medicine, but they also served as wrappers for the bottles in a day when labels affixed to bottles were seldom used.[18]

Whatever the amount of imported printed matter, American imprints seeking to promote English patent medicines were rare indeed. The most intriguing example is the New York reprinting of a London promotional pamphlet on behalf of Bateman's

---

[17] N.Y. critic cited in James J. Walsh, *History of the Medical Society of the State of New York* (N.Y., 1907), 31; Robert Turlington, *Turlington's Balsam of Life* (London, [1747?]), in the Folger Shakespeare Library, Washington.
[18] James Carter, Apothecary Account Book, 1752-1753, Colonial Williamsburg, Va.

Pectoral Drops. The American edition, dated 1731, may well have been the earliest work on any medical theme printed in New York. The printer was John Peter Zenger, not yet an editor and three years away from the famous trial that was to link his name inextricably with the concept of the freedom of the press.[19]

The popularity of the old English remedies, year in and year out, owed much to the fact that though the ingredients might vary (unbeknown to the customer), the shape of the bottle did not. Nostrum proprietors were blazing a trail with respect to distinctive packaging. While the Turlington bottle was pear-shaped with sloping shoulders, Godfrey's Cordial came in a truncated conical vial with steep-pitched sides. Nostrums on a shelf were so easily recognizable that even the most loutish illiterate could tell one from another. Nor to the customer was there any apparent difference between those which were actually patented and those that were not. They were all bottles on a shelf together, "patent medicines" in common speech.

Not all, by any means, of the packaged remedies—patented or not—which were produced in England were known in America. An English list published in 1748 numbered 202 proprietaries, and was admittedly incomplete. No accident determined which of the scores of English brands Americans bought. Most English exports of all kinds came to America from an area in the center of London, once the location of merchants who had migrated to New England during the 17th century. The newcomers continued to do business with erstwhile colleagues who did not leave home, starting trade channels that continued to run. In the heart of the exporting district lay the headquarters of the major medicine exporters, Robert Turlington of Lombard Street, Francis Newbery of St. Paul's Churchyard, and especially the Okell & Dicey firm of Bow Churchyard, which secured the patent for Bateman's Pectoral Drops, arranged for Zenger's reprinting of its promotional pamphlet, and vended most of the brands listed in American newspaper advertising. Out of the hundreds of patent medicines in 18th-century England, those comparatively few brands of pills and drops on the lists of the major exporters were those which ailing Americans continued to use.[20]

[19] *A Short Treatise of the Virtues of Dr. Bateman's Pectoral Drops* (N.Y., 1731), in the Library of the N.Y. Academy of Medicine; Gertrude L. Annan, "Printing and Medicine," *Bull. Med. Libr. Assoc.*, 28 (1940), 155.

[20] Poplicola, "Pharmacopoeia Empirica or the List of Nostrums and Em-

In the complexity of their composition, in the nature of their potency, the English patent medicines were blood brothers to preparations described in the various pharmacopoeias and formularies used in orthodox medicine. Indeed, there was borrowing in both directions. Richard Stoughton claimed twenty-two ingredients for his Elixir. Robert Turlington, in his patent specifications, named twenty-six botanicals, some from the Orient and some from the English countryside, digested in alcohol and boiled to a syrupy consistency. Although other proprietors had shorter lists or were silent on the number of ingredients, a major part of their secrecy really lay in having complicated formulas. Rivals might detect the major active constituents, but the original proprietor could claim that only he knew all the elements in their proper proportions and the secret of their blending.[21]

An official formula of one year might blossom out the next in a fancy bottle bearing a proprietor's name. At the same time, the essential recipe of a patent medicine, deprived of its esoteric cognomen and given a Latin name indicative of composition or therapeutic nature, might suddenly appear in one of the official volumes. The formula for Daffy's Elixir, for example, was adopted in the *Pharmacopoeia Londonensis* in 1721 under the title "Elixir Salutis" and later by the *Pharmacopoeia Edinburghensis* as Compound Senna Tincture. Two years after Turlington obtained his patent, the London pharmacopoeia introduced a recipe for "Balsamum Traumaticum" which eventually became Compound Tincture of Benzoin with the official synonym Turlington's Balsam. None of the early English patent medicines offered anything new, except new combinations or new proportions of ingredients already widely employed in medicine. Formulas of similar composition to those patented or marketed as "new inventions" can in every case be found in 17th- and 18th-

pirics," *Gentleman's Mag.*, 18 (1748), 346-50; Bernard Bailyn, *The New England Merchants in the Seventeenth Century* (Cambridge, Mass., 1955), 35-36; location of exporters found in their advertising.

21 British Patent Office, *Patents for Inventions. Abridgements of Specifications Relating to Medicine, Surgery and Dentistry, 1620-1866* (London, 1872); Thompson, 255; Philadelphia College of Pharmacy, *Formulae for the Preparation of Eight Patent Medicines, Adopted by the Philadelphia College of Pharmacy* (Phila., 1824). Bateman's Drops, Dalby's Carminative, and Godfrey's Cordial contained opium; Hooper's Pills was a cathartic and emmenagogue and included aloes, as did Anderson's Pills; British Oil and Steer's Opodeldoc were liniments, the latter also containing ammonia.

century pharmacopoeias. The English packaged remedies, whatever their advertising claims, were mostly purgatives, carminatives, opiates, emmenagogues, and liniments.

On September 29, 1774, John Boyd's *"medicinal* store" in Baltimore followed the time-honored custom of advertising a fresh supply of medicines just arrived on the latest ship from London.[22] To that intelligence was added a warning: since nonimportation agreements by colonial merchants were imminent, customers had best buy before supplies ran out. Boyd's prediction was valid. The Boston Tea Party of the previous December had evoked from Parliament retaliatory measures and, at the time of Boyd's advertising, the Continental Congress was considering a policy that soon would halt all imports from Great Britain. Trade had been interrupted before, during the decade of tension, and war was shortly to cut off altogether the importation of Turlington's Balsam, Bateman's Pectoral Drops, and their therapeutic kind.

Half a century of use had made many Americans dependent on the familiar English patent medicines. The wartime curtailment of imports accelerated a trend that had begun in a modest way at least as early as the 1750's—the compounding of English brands on American shores. The apothecary in Williamsburg, from 1752 through 1770, ordered from London sizable quantities of empty "Stoughton vials" and occasional lots of Daffy's Elixir bottles. Turlington had complained in 1761 that New York scoundrels were buying up his empty bottles and refilling them with "a base and vile composition of their own" compounding. Formulas for many of the patent medicines had been introduced into official pharmacopoeias, as well as in various unofficial formularies. John Wesley, the Methodist divine, listed a few in later editions of his *Primitive Physic.* Thus no grave problem was posed the American druggist if he had vials of proper shape to fill. During the Revolution, of course, no bottles could be imported, but the refilling of empties went on apace.[23]

In 1782 the Baltimore post office, at a time when fighting was over but peace negotiations still under way, signalized the return to the American market of made-in-Britain patent medicines by

[22] Annapolis *Maryland Gaz.*
[23] James Carter, Apothecary Account Books, 1752-1753; *N.Y. Mercury,* Nov. 9, 1761; Wesley, *Primitive Physic,* 21st London ed. of 1785, 22nd London ed. of 1788, 16th Trenton ed. of 1788.

advertising in the *Maryland Journal* half a dozen of the familiar brands. Two years later a New York apothecary turned to tortured rhyme to convey the same message to would-be customers:

Medicines approv'd by royal charter,
James, Godfry, Anderson, Court-plaster. . . .[24]

If peace brought British patent medicines back to American shops, it also made available once more imported empty bottles of the old familiar shapes. American apothecaries continued to fill them. Indeed, the British-made medicines did not win back their prewar sales ascendancy from American imitations. The records of Jonathan Waldo, a Salem, Massachusetts, apothecary, reveal the reason. The imported brand of Turlington's Balsam, Waldo noted during the 1790's, was "very dear" at thirty-six shillings a dozen bottles, whereas his "own" sold for only fifteen. It was the same with other nostrums, and in the early years of the new century American manufacturers were to increase the price differential still more by fabricating vials which undercut the cost of imported bottles.[25]

The dethroning of the old English patent medicines from their regal position in late colonial therapy, however, was not so much due to American imitations, even in American bottles. This act of rebellion came from patent medicines that were American all the way.

[24] *Maryland Jnl.*, Oct. 29, 1782; *N.Y. Packet*, Oct. 11, 1784.
[25] Jonathan Waldo, Account Book, circa 1770-1790, Library of the Essex Institute, Salem, Mass.; Joseph D. Weeks, "Reports on the Manufacture of Glass," *Report of the Manufactures of the United States at the Tenth Census* (Wash., 1883), 81-82; Thomas W. Dyott, *An Exposition of the System of Moral and Mental Labor, Established at the Glass Factory of Dyottsville* (Phila., 1833), in the Hist. Soc. of Penna.

"GALVANISING TRUMPERY"

See POINTED METALS, *blest with power t'appease,*
The ruthless rage of merciless disease,
O'er the frail part a subtil fluid power,
Drench'd with invisible Galvanic shower,
Till the arthritic, staff and "crutch forego,
And leap exulting like the bounding roe!"
—Thomas Green Fessenden, "An Address de-
livered before the PERKINEAN SOCIETY,"
1803[1]

AMERICA won her independence in the realm of pseudo-medicine not with a pill or a potion, not with an elixir or a vermifuge, but with a pair of small metal rods called tractors. The hero of this revolution was a physician in Plainfield, Connecticut, named Elisha Perkins. The critical date was 1796, in which year the government granted Perkins the first patent to be issued for a medical device under the Constitution of the United States.

Why did the revolution come so late? Why had not some shrewd colonial citizen, observing the steady sales of the old English patent medicines and sensing the gold that might lie at the end of such a rainbow, launched a competitive home-grown remedy? The answer is that there were some fumbling efforts heralding the day of native American nostrums. Yet prior to the Revolution no American entrepreneur managed to offer a real challenge to Bateman's Pectoral Drops or Hooper's Female Pills.

American quackery dates back to 1630. In that year Nicholas Knopp, a resident of Massachusetts Bay, was fined five pounds, or was whipped, for vending as a cure for scurvy "a water of no

[1] Cited in Fessenden, *Terrible Tractoration!! A Poetical Petition against Galvanising Trumpery, and the Perkinistic Institution* (1st Amer. ed., N.Y., 1804), xxxiii-xxxiv. Some material in this and the next chapter has appeared in the author's "The Origin of Patent Medicines in America," *Chemist and Druggist,* 172 (Sep. 9, 1959), 9-14.

[16]

worth nor value," which he "solde att a very deare rate."[2] How Nicholas marketed his water is not known, but certainly not with the exaggerated printed promotion that attended the origin of the English nostrums in the same century. Nor did Americans, during the colonial years, ever achieve either the flamboyant advertising or the distinctive packaging that characterized the English patent medicines.

Mountebanks wandered up and down the colonies persuading the gullible to buy their wares. One Charles Hamilton, for example, appeared in Chester, boasting of his excellent education and marvelous cures. Somehow the townspeople got suspicious and examined the pretender. Charles was found to be a woman, and Charlotte Hamilton was put in jail. Another itinerant, calling himself Francis Torres, came to Philadelphia, selling "Chinese Stones" for the cure of toothache, cancer, and the bites of mad dogs and rattlesnakes. A fortnight later, one Acidus gave counsel to the poor who could not afford Monsieur Torres' twenty-five-shilling charge. "Go to a Cutler's Shop," he wrote, "there you'll find a Remnant of the Buckshorn, cut off probably from a Piece that was too long for a Knife Handle, saw and rasp it into what shape you please, and then burn it in hot Embers; and you will have Mons. Torres's Chinese Stone." The wandering Frenchman with his Oriental remedy showed up in other colonial cities. But, unlike many British contemporaries, he did not settle down in one place, wrap his potent stones in identical packages, ship them to shops in other towns, and advertise their curative blessings in numerous papers simultaneously.[3]

Nor was such a sophisticated scheme of promotion employed in behalf of American-made medicines hardly so suspect as Monsieur Torres' wares. Humble men and women, most of them probably sincere, went into the market place with remedies taken over from folk medicine, and even advertised them. But the efforts were local, sporadic, and limited.

The text of an advertisement from a Philadelphia newspaper under date of August 19, 1731, read: "The Widow READ, removed from the upper End of Highstreet to the *New Printing-Office* near the Market, continues to make and sell her well-known Ointment for the ITCH. . . . It is always effectual for that

<hr/>

[2] *Records of the Governor and Company of the Massachusetts Bay in New England* (Boston, 1853), I, 83.
[3] *Pa. Gaz.*, July 16, 1752, Oct. 17 and 31, 1745.

purpose, and never fails to perform the Cure speedily. It also kills or drives away all Sorts of Lice. . . . It has no offensive Smell, but rather a pleasant one; and may be used without the least Apprehension of Danger, even to a sucking Infant. . . . Price 2 *s.* a Gallypot containing an Ounce." It may be doubted that this advertisement cost the ointment maker a penny, for the newspaper was the *Pennsylvania Gazette*, the *Gazette's* publisher was Benjamin Franklin, and the Widow Read was publisher Franklin's mother-in-law.

Many of the herbal concoctions in the pharmacopoeias had begun in the empirical experimentation of laymen. In America as in England, Nature was continuing to yield her secrets, whether sound or not, to the prying of all people, professional or not. An interest in one's own health and that of relatives and friends was enough qualification—then as now—to set up in business as a lay prescriber. According to an ancient and perverse tradition, under which disease was regarded as a curse from offended gods, cures could not be found through human intelligence but in a secret lore of an occult order, a kind of magical knowledge more dramatic and potent when possessed by the unschooled. Thus remedies advanced by widows and maiden aunts, simpletons and slaves, were by some regarded with especial favor. Traditions handed down, the slightest bent toward haphazard tinkering, provided dozens of therapeutic possibilities. Almanacs, newspapers, diaries, correspondence, bear testimony to the universal concern over sickness, the widespread interest in cures, and the plethora of gratuitous counsel. The line between free health hints and marketed remedies was often crossed, with economic need, perhaps, the major stimulus. The Widow Read might have desired the sense of independence which selling her itch ointment could provide. Certain "Dutch Ladies" of Charleston might have vended their "Choice Cure for the Flux, Fevers, Worms, bad Stomach, [and] Pains in the Head" because this was the only way they could support themselves. Doubtless a similar economic explanation lies behind the cordials of a New York carpenter, the eye-water of a Charleston goldsmith, the cough cure of a Boston grocer.[4]

[4] *Va. Gaz.*, Dec. 22, 1738; *S.C. Gaz.*, Mar. 7, 1743, and July 12, 1735; *N.Y. Post*, Dec. 19, 1748, cited in Rita S. Gottesman, *The Arts and Crafts in New York, 1726-1776* (N.Y., 1938), 192; *Boston News-Letter*, Feb. 24, 1743.

But seldom do these colonial notices have even the verbal vigor of the Widow Read's announcement. Advertisements for American remedies are shy and circumspect beside those appearing in England for their bolder English cousins. Compared with British Oyl, the Widow Read's ointment did not get around, even in America Lack of capital may be one explanation. The fact that trade ties were tighter between each colony and Britain than between colony and colony may hold a clue.

The colonial years offered one concoction that has often been termed the first patent medicine in American history. It was named Tuscarora Rice and its maker was a woman. First to tell Mrs. Sybilla Masters' tale in print, so far as can be found, was John F. Watson, who in 1844 published his *Annals of Philadelphia and Pennsylvania, in the Olden Time*. From Indian corn, asserted chronicler Watson, Mrs. Masters prepared her Tuscarora Rice which she recommended as a fare especially beneficial for promoting the recovery of consumptive and other sickly persons. In 1711 she and her husband went to England with her remedy to seek her fortune. While there she got a patent. Back in America, Thomas Masters set up a water-mill and a processing plant near Philadelphia to make Tuscarora Rice in more abundant quantities.[5]

Watson's tale is substantially true. In 1715, after an initial rebuff, Thomas Masters managed to secure letters patent for "A New Invencon found out by Sybilla his Wife, for Cleaning and Curing the Indian Corn Growing in the severall Colonies in America." This was the first patent granted in Great Britain to anyone dwelling in America. A drawing accompanying the petition shows a device for pounding maize in mortars with stamps operated by cog-wheels attached to a large cylinder turned by horse or water-power. Besides providing a "wholesome Food" in a

---

[5] Garrison, *Introduction to the History of Medicine*, 402; LaWall, *Four Thousand Years of Pharmacy*, 412-13; and James T. Adams, *Provincial Society, 1690-1763* (N.Y., 1927), 126, call Tuscarora Rice a patent medicine. Mrs. Masters' story is drawn from Watson, II, 388-89; *Alphabetical List of Patentees of Inventions* [1617-1852], (London, 1854), 368; George Ramsey, "The Historical Background of Patents," *Jnl. Patent Office*, 18 (1936), 13; Samuel H. Needles, "The Governor's Mill," *Pa. Mag. Hist. and Biog.*, 8 (1884), 285-87. Photostats of the Letters Patent from Chancery, Patent Rolls (C.66/3511, No. 29), of Mrs. Masters' petition from State Papers Domestic, Entry Books (S.P.44), vol. 249, and of the sketched specification of the invention, from the Specification and Surrender Roll (C.210/1), have been supplied by the Public Record Office, which has also reported on several other references to the Masters in the British records.

more convenient form for export, according to Sybilla's petition, "the said Corn so refined is also an Excellent Medicine in Consumptions & other Distempers."

Having secured her patent, did Sybilla vend her food-medicine in the American colonies? The record is dim. She did petition the officers of Pennsylvania requesting that the patent be noted in the colony's records. How much maize she ground and how zealously she promoted it among the ailing are unknown. The Masters' mill of Watson's account, indeed, seems to be a case of mistaken identity.

Thus Sybilla is one of the mystery women of American patent medicine history. Inventive, ambitious, desirous of protecting the fruits of her ingenuity, she is the type of woman who might grind corn, call it rice, and market it as a consumption cure. Whatever the truth, Mrs. Masters' Tuscarora Rice did not make the therapeutic impact in the colonies that Mr. Turlington's Balsam did.

Even the prodding of nascent patriotism in the years leading to the Revolution did not bring forth a real American competitor to the English patent medicines. Advertisements might tell of made-in-New-England mustard, "superior . . . to any imported," of colonial tobacco pipes, "equal in Goodness" to any from abroad, and of "American Grindstones . . . esteemed vastly superior to those from Great-Britain, the Grit being smaller." But no fervent patriotic pride inspired the advertising of hair-restorers and cure-all dentifrices made and marketed in the colonies.[6]

Ironically, the first patent medicine to stress in its name its American origin, a product of the final tempestuous decade before the outbreak of war, was made in England. The proprietor was the vigorous Dr. John Hill, he who could change water into asses' milk. In 1770 ,Dr. Hill marketed an American Balsam. Truthfully or not, he said that the medicine was made from American plants which had been taken to the king and queen some years before by an American botanist—who really existed—named William Young, Jr. The new remedy, its proprietor asserted, would cure everything from whooping cough to the *"hypochondriacal disease."* And, of course, being compounded from American plants, it was "no wonder" that "it must have the

6 *Mass. Gaz.*, Oct. 23, 1766, and Aug. 17, 1769; *Boston News-Letter*, Apr. 13, 1769.

best effect in that country." Out of gratitude to young Mr. Young, Dr. Hill declared, he had appointed the botanist's venerable father as the only "capital vender" of the American Balsam in the American colonies.[7]

Comparable ingenuity on the part of Americans themselves did not come until after the fighting was over. It was part of the great fire of cultural nationalism, kindled during the war and fanned into higher flame by the pride of victory. The United States gloried in new American textbooks, American maps, American Bibles, American machines. Reputable medicine reflected the trend. There was a renewed search by American physicians to discover American herbs which could relieve the American sick of "unrepublican dependence" on European medicines. Efforts were begun to compile an American pharmacopoeia. Benjamin Rush, signer of the Declaration of Independence and most distinguished physician in the new nation, argued that there were twenty times more intellect and a hundred times more knowledge in America in 1799 than there had been before the Revolution.[8]

Amidst this atmosphere made-in-America patent medicines also were proudly launched. But the first American-made product in the annals of quackery to provoke a national mania was the metallic tractors of Dr. Elisha Perkins. More than that, the tractors went eastward across the Atlantic and earned the first considerable repayment from Britain toward balancing the debt accrued through a century of American colonial dependence on the English patent medicines. The tale of this Connecticut Yankee and his remarkable device must precede the account of American ingenuity in filling pill-box and vial.

Perkins was a man from whom something remarkable was almost sure to come. Nature had endowed him with tremendous energy, persistent curiosity, and a commanding presence. His vigor was revealed in the way he conducted his practice in and around Plainfield. Perkins often rode his horse sixty miles a day. For weeks on end he got along on three or four hours of sleep a night. Sometimes he grew so weary that he would lie down at the home of a patient, but the busy doctor demanded that he be

---

[7] *Pa. Gaz.*, Oct. 11, 1770, and Jan. 23, 1788; *N.Y. Jnl.*, Sep. 5, 1771.

[8] Whitfield I. Bell, Jr., "Suggestions for Research in the Local History of Medicine in the United States," *Bull. Hist. Med.*, 17 (1945), 465; Rush cited in Holmes, *Medical Essays*, 192.

[21]

allowed to nap exactly five minutes and no more. In an age in which hard liquor was viewed as the antidote to weariness, Perkins refused to touch a drop. Despite such Spartan devotion to duty, the doctor found time to take an active role in community affairs. He established and helped support an academy. He held office in his county medical society. It was no wonder that he earned the respect of his professional colleagues and the esteem, even the adoration, of his patients.[9]

Perkins was not a physician content to practice by rote. He had learned medicine, after a brief matriculation at Yale, through apprenticeship to his father. His career had begun precociously before he was twenty. As he went his rounds, he speculated on the cases which came under his care. He found some time to read, too, acquiring raw data and pieces of theory to mix with his own empirical observations. This curiosity led Perkins to certain conclusions with respect to therapy, and he was a man who had the courage to try them out.

The doctor was a tall man for his day, six feet in height, powerful and well proportioned. His manner was decisive, forceful, confident, yet not too aloof to mar sociability. Perkins' person strengthened the impact of his good works in the community. He also had a native shrewdness that may well have won admiration from his fellow-residents of the Nutmeg State: Perkins supplemented his medical fees—he had a family of ten children to support—by buying, selling, and trading mules.

This, then, was the man who invented Perkins' metallic tractors. His son Benjamin, who was closely associated with the venture, asserted later that Elisha long had held the view that metals possessed an influence on the body not fully recognized up to his day. He had observed that during surgery, when the scalpel touched a muscle, the muscle would contract. He had been convinced that when he applied a lancet to separate the gum

---

[9] The account of Perkinism is drawn from Jacques Marc Quen, "A Study of Dr. Elisha Perkins and Perkinism" (unpublished thesis, Yale Univ. School of Medicine, New Haven, 1954); Fessenden's poem, including its introduction and notes; James Thacher, *American Medical Biography* (Boston, 1828), I, 422-25; *Certificates of the Efficacy of Doctor Perkins's Patent Metallic Instruments* (New London, [1796]), in the Amer. Antiquarian Soc., Worcester, Mass.; *Certificates of the Efficacy of Doctor Perkins's Patent Metallic Instruments* (Newburyport, [1797]), and *Evidences of the Efficacy of Doctor Perkins's Patent Metallic Instruments* (Phila., [1797]), both in the N.Y. Public Library; Holmes, 15-38; Walter R. Steiner, "The Conflict of Medicine with Quackery," *Annals Med. Hist.*, 6 (1924), 60-70; Morris Fishbein, *Fads and Quackery in Healing* (N.Y., 1932), 9-18.

from a tooth before extraction, the ache in the tooth came to an end. With these observations in his mind, his son indicated, Perkins read of the experiments of Galvani. The Italian scientist had found that the leg of a frog contracted when a nerve and muscle were linked with two different metals placed in contact one with the other. This information from abroad, said Benjamin Perkins, tended to confirm his father's hypothesis.[10]

Electricity certainly was in the air in the late 18th century, and it was playing a dramatic if uncertain role in medicine. Before the American Revolution, in Charleston, electrical tropical fish were being used to fire charges into palsied patients. In the mid-1780's a Philadelphia bookseller lauded the panacea properties of electrical treatments—especially if taken in conjunction with cephalic snuff. Thirty years earlier, Benjamin Franklin, though skeptical, carried his notable interest in electricity to the point of helping a physician employ it in treating a woman suffering from convulsions.[11]

Franklin's shadow also fell across the trail of Franz Antoine Mesmer, who dealt in electricity of another form. This dynamic young physician had come from his medical training in Vienna to Paris. There he set up a lavish establishment at which he healed by the power of animal magnetism. Wearing a lilac suit, carrying a metal wand, playing solemn music on a harmonica, Mesmer ministered to his patients and admirers. They sat gripping thumbs around a wooden tub, or "battery," from which came jointed metal rods to touch the ailing parts of their bodies. The tub was the condenser and conductor of the universal fluid that flowed through all those in the circle and wrought the cure. Mesmer walked about enhancing the magnetic potency by touching the afflicted with his rod or by a laying on of hands. The healing seance went on for hours, amid a growing tension accompanied by shouts, tears, hysterical laughter, and convulsions.[12]

In 1784, while Franklin was representing the United States at the French court, Louis XVI ordered a commission appointed

---

10 Cited in Quen, 11-12.

11 *S.C. Gaz.*, Oct. 31, 1748, cited in Hennig Cohen, *The South Carolina Gazette, 1732-1775* (Columbia, S.C., 1953), 81; *Pa. Gaz.*, Oct. 20, 1784; Carl and Jessica Bridenbaugh, *Rebels and Gentlemen* (N.Y., 1942), 270-71; I. Bernard Cohen, "How Practical Was Benjamin Franklin's Science?" *Pa. Mag. Hist. and Biog.*, 69 (1945), 292.

12 Carl Van Doren, *Benjamin Franklin* (N.Y., 1938), 713-17; James J. Walsh, *Cures, The Story of Cures That Fail* (N.Y., 1930), 88-96; Garrison, 382.

to investigate Mesmer. Franklin was chosen to serve, and among his colleagues were the chemist Lavoisier and a physician-inventor named Guillotin. After observations and experiments, some of which were held at Franklin's estate, the commission concluded that they could discover no electricity in Mesmer's tub. Nor could they detect, with any of their senses, that current known as animal magnetism. Mesmer was forbidden to continue his healing seances. Taking his spoils, he sought in England a comfortable retirement. Animal magnetism sank below the level of public concern.

Was it revived a decade later by Dr. Elisha Perkins? This charge was to be leveled and in turn denied. Two things are sure. Perkins did see a connection between disease and an electrical "fluid." And the tall, powerful, decisive physician from Connecticut, though different from Mesmer in many ways, could stand comparison in one essential trait, the magnetism of his personality.

An account of the steps by which Perkins came upon his great discovery that is more circumstantial than his son's after-the-fact explanation can be pieced together from surviving letters. It was in 1795 that this curious doctor was called upon to treat a woman afflicted with pains in her ankles. Spurred by an impulse, he took the blade of his penknife and drew its point downward from the middle of his patient's calf. What Perkins said to her as he performed this simple act is not a matter of record. But to the lady's joy and the doctor's gratification, the pains departed forthwith. The matter called for more experimentation and more thought. Later in the same year Perkins discovered that he could cure a headache by wielding a japanned iron comb. Just as important was his conviction that he knew why. Most of the discomfort, he wrote in a letter at the time, came from "a surcharge of electric fluid in the parts affected." The comb drew the fluid off.[13]

The next crucial step in Perkins' progress is clouded in mystery. This was the shift from simple objects ready at hand as the agents of therapy to the more elaborate fabricated devices he called tractors. The new invention looked like nothing else under the sun. It was a pair of small metal instruments, each about three inches long and both of the same shape, flat on one side, rounded on the other, and tapering from a hemispherical head to a sharp point. One of the tractors was gold in color, the other

[13] Perkins' letters are cited by Quen, 13.

silver. Perkins and his son averred that the former was an alloy of copper, zinc, and gold; the latter of iron, silver, and platinum.[14]

From the pinnacle of success, Elisha Perkins insisted that nothing but his tractors would work. Perhaps he had come to believe this doctrine. Buried in his correspondence lay his initial triumphs with the more modest penknife and comb. At the time of the transition, the doctor's use of different metals might have been a cue taken from Galvani. The new project might also have gained from lessons the shrewd doctor had learned in trading mules.

Later in 1795 Perkins made the first public announcement of the tractors. To his fellow physicians assembled in state convention, he revealed his important discovery and told of the cures it was performing. Nor was the power of the tractors confined to cases in which they were wielded by their inventor. Others, too, it had been found, could use them with success, if certain therapeutic rules were adhered to strictly. The points must be drawn or stroked, one after the other, across the afflicted surface of the body, always being moved from the center toward the extremities. Otherwise the patient's condition might worsen. Even when properly employed, Perkins warned, the tractors were not "a catholican"; nonetheless he would "cheerfully hazard" his "honor and reputation" on their "ultimate success." They were most useful, the doctor said, in local inflammations, pains in the head, face, teeth, breast, side, stomach, and back, in rheumatism and similar ailments. Drawing off the noxious electrical fluid that lay at the root of the suffering, they brought blessed relief.[15]

From the Connecticut doctors to whom he first announced his discovery, Perkins noted at the time, he had received many compliments. Indeed, he had been invited to read a paper on the subject at the next year's meeting of the state society. But this particular day of glory was not to come. Events of the ensuing year changed the minds of many of the physicians. When they convened in 1796, instead of listening to Perkins as he extolled his metal points, the doctors condemned the tractors as a device "gleaned up from the miserable remains of animal magnetism" and resolved that any member using them faced expulsion from

[14] A pair of the tractors may be found at The Mütter Museum of the College of Physicians of Philadelphia.

[15] Quen, 14; *Evidences of the Efficacy of Dr. Perkins's Patent Metallic Instruments* (Philadelphia ed.); Thacher, 423.

the society. The next year this threat was made good. Perkins was ousted for violating the society's taboo against nostrums.[16]

By 1797 Elisha Perkins did not particularly care what his erstwhile colleagues thought or said or did. Indeed, he insisted, their action in expelling him would make him two friends for every single foe. He was too busy to pay much heed to his critics. He was a man with a mission. The tractors were now protected from the envious by a patent from the government, and the busy physician was occupied day and night in forging the instruments in a furnace hidden behind panels in his Plainfield home. Supply was hard-pressed to keep up with demand. And the retail price was twenty-five dollars a pair.[17]

The tractors, indeed, bade fair to grip the imagination of the whole country. Electricity, that dramatic, potent, and mysterious force, might yet unlock the door to health, and perhaps Perkins had found the key. This was certainly the impression which he himself wanted to create. He issued a series of pamphlets to speed the good word. Not only humble citizens, but politicians, ministers, college professors, and many doctors gave ecstatic testimony. Not all of the members of the clergy who had tractors and certificates stating they had paid for them had in fact laid out any money. It was deemed prudent by Perkins to make a number of strategic gifts. Perhaps it was one of this number, a divine who taught at one of New England's colleges, who wrote for Perkins to print: "I have used the Tractors with success in several other cases in my own family, and although, like Naaman the Syrian, I cannot tell why the waters of Jordan should be better than Abana and Pharpar, rivers of Damascus; yet since experience has proved them so, no reasoning can change the opinion. Indeed, the causes of all common facts are, we think, perfectly well known to us; and it is very probable, fifty or a hundred years hence, we shall as well know why the Metallic Tractors should in a few minutes remove violent pains, as we now know why cantharides and opium will produce opposite effects."[18]

To lend his personal persuasion to the impact of the printed word, Perkins went on the road. At the moment the medical con-

[16] Quen, 14-15; Fishbein, 14-15.
[17] Quen, 19; William S. Miller, "Elisha Perkins and His Metallic Tractors," *Yale Jnl. Biology and Med.*, 8 (Oct. 1935), 43.
[18] Perkins' pamphlets; Walsh, 102-103; quotation cited in Holmes, 25.

vention in Hartford was expelling him, he was holding forth in triumph in Philadelphia.

Franklin was no longer living to cast a baleful eye. The newspaper he had founded accepted advertising for Perkins' product. At the Alms House, the board of managers were so carried away with enthusiasm that they bought the rights of distribution for the city. Philadelphia was still the nation's capital, and Congress was in session. Several members of the House of Representatives were among the inventor's zealous recruits. Perkins also sold a pair of tractors to the Chief Justice of the Supreme Court. Legend has it that he made a customer of President Washington himself. With the three branches of their national government thus leading the way, the citizens of America followed gladly. The boom was on.[19]

Franklin had brought down electricity from the sky, and now Perkins had found a way, so it seemed, to bring forth from suffering men and women its evil influences. Could it be that a new America would provide the whole world not only with an example of freedom but also with the means to health?

Such, alas, was not to be. Elisha Perkins, nonetheless, died a martyr to his own delusion. In 1799 the city of New York was ravaged by a severe epidemic of yellow fever. All Americans, perplexed at the cause of this disease, were aware how dangerous such a scourge could be. Perkins especially had reason to know: six years before, in the terrible Philadelphia epidemic, he had lost a daughter, a son-in-law, and two grandchildren. It took courage of a high order for the Connecticut doctor to go to New York to tend the sick. Persuaded of the efficacy of his tractors, and of a remedy he had made from marine salt, vinegar, and water, Perkins went out from a boarding house room to serve. Within a few weeks he caught the fever, suffered, and died. With the haste necessary during such mass disasters, Elisha Perkins was given summary burial in a potter's field on the present location of Washington Square.[20]

The fad for metallic tractors in America did not long survive their inventor. In the meantime, however, Benjamin Perkins had borne them across the ocean to England.

[19] *Pa. Gaz.*, May 3, 1797; Francis R. Packard, *History of Medicine in the United States* (N.Y., 1931), I, 248; Holmes, 23; Quen 18.
[20] Quen, 25-29.

Unlike Elisha, Benjamin was no physician, but his father's talents at promotion he had inherited in double measure. Arriving in London, Benjamin secured a British patent for the metallic points under the title, "Application of Galvanism as a curative agent." He then arranged for the rendering into English of a German translation of a Danish book. The wife of a Danish diplomat, returning from a sojourn in the United States, had introduced the tractors into Copenhagen, where they had become the therapeutic rage. A dozen distinguished physicians swore to their effectiveness and permitted themselves to be quoted in the most extravagant terms. These words rendered into English, as well as Benjamin's own asseverations, kindled a fire of enthusiasm in England, even with the tractors selling at five pounds a pair. Many could afford to buy such a wonder and did so. On the plea that the deserving poor could hardly be expected to pay so high a sum, Benjamin launched a campaign to establish in London a charity clinic, the Perkinean Institution. On its list of officials were a number of peers of the realm and the son of Benjamin Franklin. The endowment, secured by public subscription, surpassed that possessed by any London hospital of the day.[21]

As Benjamin Perkins soared to new heights of fame and fortune, he enlisted the aid of an American ally. In London at the time was a Yankee lawyer, tinkerer, and poet named Thomas Green Fessenden. Down on his luck, Fessenden took little persuading when asked by young Perkins to expound the merits of the metallic tractors in verse. From the poet's quick pen came a bombastic satire called *Terrible Tractoration!! A Poetical Petition against Galvanising Trumpery, and the Perkinistic Institution.* Adopting the guise of Christopher Caustic, a regular English physician angry at having his income threatened by the tractors, Fessenden had his stormy hero stir up a war to the death against this dire threat, which was

> . . . begotten
> In wilds where science ne'er was thought on;
> And had its birth and education
> Quite at the fag-end of Creation!

21 Fessenden, *Terrible Tractoration!!*; Quen, 19-21, 30-32; Holmes, 18-36; Porter G. Perrin, *The Life and Works of Thomas Green Fessenden, 1771-1837* (Orono, Me., 1925), 47-77.

Terrible Tractoration!! speedily sold out a first edition and went into a second. But this record was nothing compared with the sale of the tractors themselves. One Perkinean pamphlet cited testimonials from eight professors in four universities, twenty-one physicians, and thirty clergymen, twelve of them equipped with D.D. degrees. By March 1803, the pamphleteer asserted, some 5,000 English cures had been reported. "Supposing," he exulted, "that not more than one cure in three hundred, which the Tractors have performed, has been published, and the proportion is probably much greater, it will be seen, that the number . . . will have exceeded one million five hundred thousand!" Since the tractors also were being widely employed in the treatment of ailing horses and dogs, the totals doubtless soared higher still.[22]

Already the critics were active. A physician from the provinces proclaimed that he had achieved cures just as marvelous with tractors carved from wood and painted to resemble the costly metal ones. Indeed, nails, pieces of bone, tobacco pipes, all worked as well. There was the case of the girl who long had suffered pain in the right arm and shoulder. After five minutes of treatment with wooden tractors, she pronounced herself cured. "Bless me!" she exclaimed, "why, who could have thought it, that them little things could pull the pain from one. Well, to be sure, the longer one lives, the more one sees; ah, dear!"[23]

The five-pound tractors could not live long under such treatment. Without popular belief in the secret and exclusive efficacy of the patented metallic points, the vogue hung on a while and then vanished.

Benjamin Perkins, in the meantime, sailed home to America. With him he brought two things he had not had when he went abroad. One was adherence to the Quaker sect. The other, representing the profits from England's contribution to American quackery, was £10,000. Perkins settled in New York as a seller of books, joined the New-York Historical Society, and used his wealth to aid libraries, help hospitals, and forward the abolition crusade.[24]

[22] Cited in Fessenden, 113.
[23] *Ibid.*, 83-85; Holmes, 36.
[24] Quen, 32.

It has been suggested that certain stalwart physicians in the Connecticut Medical Society and some members of the faculty at Yale were greatly shocked by the galvanising trumpery that had arisen in their midst. From this sense of outrage, at least in part, was to come the founding of the Yale Medical School. This unintended result may be viewed as the most lasting legacy of Dr. Perkins' metallic tractors. Four decades later, Dr. Oliver Wendell Holmes, preparing for a lecture on the theme, only by great effort managed to find a pair to show his audience.[25]

The tractors may have well-nigh disappeared. But the frantic hopefulness with which thousands of ailing people had greeted them lived on.

[25] Steiner, 69; Holmes, 15.

VIALS AND VERMIFUGES

And when I must resign my breath,
Pray let me die a natural death.
And bid the world a long farewell,
Without one dose of Calomel.

—*The Granite Songster; Comprising*
the Songs of the Hutchinson Family,
1847

ELISHA PERKINS was laying plans to patent his metallic tractors when, in the mid-1790's, there arrived on American shores from England a poor druggist's apprentice named Thomas W. Dyott. The young migrant settled in Philadelphia and began to earn his living at blacking shoes. By day Dyott applied the polish which by night he made, and he performed so conspicuously, doing his daubing in the wide window of his small shop, that he attracted attention. Soon he was manufacturing more polish than he himself could daub on other men's boots. The surplus he sold to others. In time Dyott accumulated enough capital to undertake a larger venture. The field of enterprise he chose was patent medicines. At first he opened a store. Early in the new century he acquired a "warehouse." Before long he moved to an even larger establishment which he called the American Dispensatory. Early in his career as nostrum monger, Dyott had drawn on his experience as an apprentice pharmacist and had begun making his own brands of patent medicines. This new departure was a very shrewd move indeed.[1]

---

[1] Material on Dyott is drawn from newspaper advertising and the following: *Phila. Med. Museum*, 6 (1809), 58-62, and ns 1 (1811), 52-56; Joseph W. England, ed., *The First Century of the Philadelphia College of Pharmacy* (Phila., 1922), 19; George S. and Helen McKearin, *American Glass* (N.Y., 1941), 468-70; Dyott, *An Exposition of the System of Moral and Mental Labor, Established at the Glass Factory of Dyottsville*; M. I. Wilbert, "America's First Cutter," *Bull. Pharm.*, 18 (1904), 237-38; Carmita de Solms Johns, "Thomas W. Dyott," *Pa. Museum Bull.*, 22 (1926), 226-34; *Dictionary of American Biography*, (N.Y., 1928-1958), v, 586-87; obituary in *Phila. Press*, Jan. 19, 1861.

That same wave of cultural nationalism that lifted Perkins' tractors to such a dizzy height launched many packaged nostrums, Dyott's among them, on less sensational but longer lasting careers. As early as 1800, with the trend barely begun, an observing newspaper editor was to note it. "Perhaps no past age in the history of this country," he wrote, "has teemed with such a multitude of medical mountebanks as the present. The venders of patent medicines in almost every capital town in the United States are fattening on the weakness and folly of a deluded public."[2]

The medicine men, of course, put entirely another face on the matter and posed as savers of mankind, and salvation was possible in abundance. Whereas a 1771 Philadelphia drug catalog had listed no American proprietary brands, a New York catalog for 1804 devoted by far the majority of its eighty to ninety nostrums to American names.[3] The nature of advertising copy was changing too. Some of that boldness which had marked the London prose of Dr. Hill now began to assert itself in behalf of American nostrums. The localism of colonial days gave way, as several proprietors, anxious to sell their remedies far and wide, began to insert column-long advertisements in papers throughout the expanding nation. Few colonial products had borne distinctive names—the most vivid in seventy years of the *Boston News-Letter* was The Noble Mummy, and it designated a remedy not for people but for trees.[4] Now greater ingenuity was displayed, and Sovereign Ointments, Grand Restoratives, and Damask Lip-Salves came on the market.

Illustrative of this first independent generation of American patent medicine promoters are four men, all of whom bore, strangely enough, a surname famous in the annals of American history. The name was Lee.

First in the field was Samuel Lee, Jr., of Windham, Connecticut. This Lee won the distinction of being the first American to patent a medicine. In 1796, a few months after Perkins had patented his tractors, Lee applied for and secured governmental protection for an invention that bore the name of "Bilious Pills." The specifications for this remedy were burned in a patent office

[2] *N.T. Daily Advertiser*, Sep. 18, 1800, citing *Gazette of the U.S.*

[3] *Catalogus Medicinarum, et Pharmacorum* (Phila., 1771); Joel and Jotham Post, *A Catalogue of Drugs, Medicines & Chemicals* (N.Y., 1804). Both are in the Library of Congress.

[4] *Mass. Gaz. and Boston News-Letter*, June 20, 1765.

fire, but a later dispensatory gave the ingredients as gamboge, aloes, soap, and nitrate of potassa. This list conformed in one respect to a point the proprietor kept repeating insistently: his pills contained no mercury. Lee was positive as well as negative, and the list of diseases which the pills would cure ran on and on. Guarded proudly by the American eagle, Lee's remedy went forth to battle not mere biliousness, but yellow fever, jaundice, dysentery, dropsy, worms, and female complaints.[5]

Samuel Lee is a shadowy figure, but some traits of his character may be deduced. He had ingenuity, since he was the first American to patent a pill. He possessed vigor, for he made a success of his patent by marketing techniques scarcely exploited by American entrepreneurs. He was equipped with imagination, as the cleverness of his advertising attests. One more trait is evident from the scanty record. Samuel Lee had an abundant capacity for indignation. Well he might, for three years after he had begun selling his pills, another Samuel Lee began to trespass on his preserve.

Samuel H. P. Lee was a physician from the same Connecticut town where Elisha Perkins lived. Lee, indeed, had been cited in praise of the tractors in one of Perkins' early promotional brochures. In 1799 this Dr. Lee also secured a patent, and the name of his medical invention was "Bilious Pills." The coincidence seemed too great. The original Samuel, obviously angry, addressed the public on the subject of his upstart rival. After the launching of his own pills, he wrote, "the demand soon became so great and benefits . . . so amply demonstrated," that the New London scoundrel, thinking to "take advantage of the similarity of names and of the credit of my Pills," obtained his patent. The public needed warning. "If people incautiously purchase his Pill for mine," cautioned Samuel, Jr., "I shall not be answerable for their effects."[6]

The New London brand was composed of more ingredients than was the Windham brand of bilious pills, the potent mixture containing, according to the dispensatory, aloes, scammony, gam-

[5] Material on the four Lees is drawn from newspaper advertisements, Baltimore city directories, broadsides in the Amer. Antiquarian Soc., and from these works: Lyman F. Kebler, "United States Patents Granted for Medicines during the Pioneer Years of the Patent Office," *Jnl. Amer. Pharmaceutical Assoc.*, 24 (1935), 486-87; *Dispensatory of the United States* (10th ed., Phila., 1854), 75n.
[6] *Columbian Museum & Savannah* [Ga.] *Advertiser*, Sep. 29, 1802.

boge, jalap, soap, syrup of buckthorn, and calomel. Both pills were potent purgatives. Samuel, Jr., did not let the public overlook Samuel H. P.'s calomel, a form of mercury.

The national appetite for bilious pills proved to be enormous. Drug catalogs listed both varieties, and the Connecticut rivals fought each other from nearby newspaper columns with an acerbity worthy of their English ancestors. The vigor of the competition may have boosted the sale of both brands. When fourteen years had expired, each patent was renewed, and the battle raged on. Nor was it limited to Connecticut and the surrounding states. Early in the 19th century, bilious pills were being sold in Georgia and in the newly-acquired territory west of the Mississippi River.

The fight against biliousness was not monopolized by the two Connecticut Lees, not even within the Lee clan. Two other Lees marketed bilious pills. By 1800 a Richard Lee & Company was operating a patent medicine store in Baltimore, both for the city trade and for a regional market. Several years later Richard Lee moved on, bearing his brands with him, to the greener pastures of New York City. At the same time a Michael Lee came on the scene in Baltimore. It is tempting to speculate that Richard and Michael were members of the same family and that the former, in departing, left the latter to carry on the nostrum business at the old stand.

Whether or not this surmise be so, Michael in time became Richard's competitor. A Washington paper for 1813 reveals the New York Lee seeking to persuade the sickly in the nation's capital to buy Hamilton's Grand Restorative, his Genuine Essence and Extract of Mustard, his Elixir, his Worm-Destroying Lozenges, whereas the Baltimore Lee bade them purchase Lee's Grand Restorative, his Genuine Essence and Extract of Mustard, his Elixir, and his Lozenges.[7]

Not all American entrants in the promising field of nostrum promotion were Lees. A man named Church, for example, coined a pretty phrase for his vegetable lotion: "Cream drawn from Violets and Milk from Roses!!"[8] A man named Dyott surpassed all his rivals during the first generation and became the king of nostrum makers in the American republic.

[7] *Wash. National Intelligencer*, Jan. 7 and Aug. 7, 1813.
[8] *N.Y. Spectator*, Aug. 31, 1799.

At the start Dyott relied heavily on a compound for the cure of "a certain disease," but soon he was producing a long line of remedies similar to those of Richard and Michael Lee. Most of these creations bore the name of a Dr. Robertson. This worthy, Dyott asserted in his advertising, was his own grandfather, a distinguished physician in Edinburgh. The enterprising editor of a Philadelphia medical journal, looking into the matter, discovered that there had been no noted Dr. Robertson in Edinburgh for nearly two centuries.[9] This intelligence did not disturb Dyott in the least. He went on vending Robertson's Infallible Worm Destroying Lozenges and the other priceless preparations devised by his honored progenitor, and he made bold to claim a more lofty dignity himself, assuming the title of Doctor of Medicine and fabricating a tale of long experience as a physician in London, the West Indies, and Philadelphia.

Business boomed. Dr. Dyott's advertisements were displayed prominently in daily papers of the Eastern cities and occupied columns of space in the rural weeklies of the hinterland. Better to service his far-flung market, Dyott established agencies in New York, Cincinnati, New Orleans, and other cities. His advertisements featured drawings of large Conestoga wagons being loaded from his capacious warehouses with nostrums for the South and West. Besides his own brands, Dyott distributed the old English patent medicines, and the pills and potions of his rivals, among them the bilious pills of Samuel H. P. Lee.

As Thomas Dyott, early in his career, had expanded from blacking to nostrums, so later he enlarged his enterprises again and again. Living in the day of a barter economy, the shrewd merchandiser accepted produce for patent medicines. Soon he was dealing in such things as tobacco and turpentine, peach brandy and rum, candles and castor oil. The scope of his nostrum sales required thousands of bottles, an article he had first required while vending blacking, so Dyott acquired, first, an interest in a glass works, and then full ownership of a large factory on the Delaware River near Philadelphia. Dyott not only undercut the prices of imported British glassware, but soon was turning out the best grade of bottle glass in America. One product of his factory, preserved in the Smithsonian Institution, was a

9 *Phila. Med. Museum*, ns 1 (1811), 52-54.

double portrait flask, honoring those two distinguished adopted sons of Philadelphia, Benjamin Franklin and Thomas Dyott.[10]

By the 1830's Dyott was living extravagantly on a princely income of $25,000 a year. His personal estate was said to be worth $250,000. He dressed oddly and drove about in style, with four horses attached to his elegant English coach and several outriders in attendance. A man with such expansive vision who had achieved so much was perhaps bound to fancy himself a humanitarian. A pioneer at price-cutting, Dyott had offered to sell his remedies to the "laboring poor at one-half the usual price." For his own laborers he sought to turn his factory into a sort of model community. Whatever the proportion of alcohol in his remedies, the nostrum king permitted no spirituous liquors in Dyottsville. He made this clear in a high-toned pamphlet composed by his own hand and garnished with classical quotations. Nor was his establishment to be disgraced by swearing, fighting, or gambling. Infractions brought deductions from pay. The former druggist's apprentice decreed that his own hundred apprentices, who lived on the grounds, be taught reading, writing, arithmetic, and singing. They must also bathe and go to Sunday School. They worked a ten-hour day.

The benevolent baron of Dyottsville owed his success to other factors besides his own business skill. Fundamental, of course, was the fact that people were still getting sick. The status of medical knowledge was little advanced over that of the colonial years, and the status of therapy was, if anything, worse. These were the days of "heroic" medication. This circumstance was due most of all to the patriotic Benjamin Rush. In 1793 Rush had valiantly stayed by Philadelphia while his native city was ravaged by the most terrible yellow fever epidemic in its history, the disaster that had taken the lives of Perkins' daughter and her family. Rush tried many remedies, but none of them helped. Overburdened and despondent and ill, desperately anxious to find a cure for the mysterious affliction, Rush can scarcely be blamed for not being cold-bloodedly scientific. The distraught physician, like many contemporary European doctors, speculated his way to a monistic theory of disease. He grasped at the conclusion that all fevers, indeed all diseases, were caused by excess excitability of the blood vessels. Hypertension being the sole cause, relief of this

10 **Division of Medical Sciences, Smithsonian Institution.**

pressure was the sole cure. Rush raised the use of bleeding and purging—ancient treatments—to phenomenal heights. At times, he said, it might be necessary to remove eighty per cent of the body's blood. Rush's enormous influence, coupled with the self-confident way in which he advocated his theories, won the day over rival claimants and dominated American medicine for more than a generation. Throughout the country Rush's disciples deliberately bled the ill to unconsciousness—and now and then to death—and prescribed such tremendous doses of calomel that patients lost teeth and even jawbones.[11]

Confronted with this demand for heroism, many Americans responded with timidity. They eschewed the rugged regimen of regular doctors and listened to patent medicine vendors who promised them an easier way. A mild and pleasant mode of treatment was a stock appeal in nostrum advertising. Very early, promoters began to decry the excessive use of mercury. The rigorous "mercurial disease" was included in the long list of ailments that their remedies would cure, and they swore solemnly—whether it was true or not—that there was no calomel in their concoctions. Samuel Lee, Jr., boasted that Samuel H. P.'s bilious pills contained mercury whereas his own did not. Dyott's remedy for "a certain disease" was touted as non-mercurial. Indeed, according to a cynical observer, one requisite for the success of any patent medicine was for its maker to attack the brutal therapy of the regular doctor. The nostrum salesman must "pronounce the surgeon's lancet a Bowie or an Indian scalping-knife, and calomel equal in properties to a mixture of arsenic, cicuta, and verdigris."[12]

As to palatability, patent medicine makers were sometimes pioneers. Swaim's Panacea, as we shall presently see, owed much of its success to a delicious flavor. Sugar-coated pills, far easier to swallow than the crude and often horrid-tasting concoctions prepared by physicians, were given their large-scale introduction into American dosage by patent medicine makers like Zadoc Porter and C. V. Clickener. "Heretofore," Clickener advertised, "medicine in almost all its forms was nearly as disgusting as it was beneficial." But "CLICKENER'S PURGATIVE PILLS, being completely enveloped with a COATING OF PURE WHITE SUGAR

---

11 Richard Shryock, *Development of Modern Medicine*, 3-4, 30-31; James T. Flexner, *Doctors on Horseback* (N.Y., 1944), 101.

12 W. Euen, *An Essay in the Form of a Lecture, on Political and Medical Quackery* (Phila., 1843), 34.

(which is as distinct from the internal ingredients as a nut shell from the kernal) HAVE NO TASTE OF MEDICINE."[13]

While the "heroic" age of medication still held sway, new problems of health arose to plague the citizen and prompt the nostrum maker. Industrialization and urbanization, in their early stages, had serious consequences for man's well-being. The urban worker labored long hours, with low pay, tending unprotected machines, endangered by physical exhaustion, emotional tension, and financial insecurity. He and his family lived in the early crowded filthy slums. After 1815 mortality began to rise and, despite better control of smallpox and greater publicity given to personal hygiene, adult death rates did not decline. Tuberculosis was on the increase, as were the dread fevers—typhoid, typhus, and yellow—and in 1831 cholera began to stalk the American landscape.[14]

All this was fertile ground in which the seeds of quackery might grow. The market was flooded with pulmonic syrups and pectoral lozenges, and many were the warning voices like that of the Rev. Dr. Bartholomew. Under the ominous heading, "Last Day," the proprietor of this Expectorant Syrup asserted that consumption "usually sweeps into the grave, hundreds of the young, the old, the fair, the lovely and the gay," and he pointed a hypothetical finger at the reader. "Have you a cough?—Do not neglect it!—Thousands have a premature death from the want of a little attention to the common cold." It was not only medicines that sold well: there was a brisk market in such items as Waterproof Anti-Consumptive Cork Soles and Medicated Fur Chest Protectors. The slow course of pulmonary consumption, the ups and downs along the way, made the disease one for which quacks could prescribe with less risk than for swift epidemic diseases with more clearcut symptoms. Nevertheless, even for such a scourge as cholera, nostrum promoters were eager to try. One remedy was heralded as made from a formula recorded in hieroglyphics on a papyrus scroll found under the mummified head of an Egyptian pharaoh. Another was promoted as a famous Near

13 Glenn Sonnedecker and George Griffenhagen, "A History of Sugar Coated Pills and Tablets," *Jnl. Amer. Pharmaceutical Assoc. (Practical Pharmacy Ed.)*, 18 (1957), 486-88.

14 Shryock, 103-104, 212-17, 228-34; Lemuel Shattuck, *Report of the Sanitary Commission of Massachusetts, 1850* (Cambridge, Mass., 1948), 104.

Eastern cure, which had wrought wonders in Bethlehem and Jerusalem, in Sodom and Gomorrah.[15]

Other features of the complex interrelationship between disease, regular physicians, and nostrum makers will merit consideration in the chapters which follow. The sale of nostrums expanded not solely for causes strictly within the medical domain. There were non-medical developments in early 19th-century American society which helped the patent medicine man.

One was the spread of newspapers. The great expansion of the press between the day of Jefferson and that of Lincoln, from some 200 to 4,000 papers, is both an evidence and a cause of the nostrum boom that accompanied it. The nostrum promoter counted on the press as the most likely vehicle to carry his message to potential customers, and the papers depended on patent medicine advertising for needed revenue. Rural weeklies sprang up as the frontier moved westward, and virtually every county boasted its own gazette. In the growing towns, mechanization revolutionized the business of publishing. The America of 1800 had some 20 daily papers. By 1860 there were 400. Cheaper paper and larger presses turned by steam power were necessary before Benjamin Day, in 1833, could bring out in quantity a penny paper for the urban masses. Day's *Sun* and its imitators in New York and elsewhere employed a more vivid style in handling more sensational themes than had the staid political party organs of an older day. The frenetic tone of news story and editorial in the new penny press was echoed in the advertising columns. Nostrum promoters found a new and susceptible class of urban patrons to read their appeals.[16]

During these same years common schooling was imparting the ability to read to an ever-greater proportion of the American populace. New England and New York began to provide free schooling to the children of the poor, and by 1860 the principle of educating the common man was well established in the North and West. Constantly diminishing was the number of humble citizens too illiterate to puzzle out the gory symptoms and the

15 *Springfield Ill. State Register*, Oct. 12, 1839; Harcourt, Bradley & Co. brochure, Oct. 1854, in author's collection; Anodyne ad cited in John W. Allen, "Cholera," 1955 mimeographed news release in series, "It Happened in Southern Illinois"; *Frederick* [Md.] *Weekly Times*, Oct. 4, 1832.

16 Mott, *American Journalism*, 167, 220-44; S. N. D. North, *History and Present Condition of the Newspaper and Periodical Press of the United States* (Wash., 1884), 81, 187, 100-104.

glorious cures described in plain blunt English by Thomas Dyott and his competitors.[17]

The federal government helped promote the nostrum boom, mostly unwittingly. In 1793 Congress enacted a law under the Constitutional provision permitting legislation to "promote the Progress of Science and useful Arts" by granting patents to inventors, and the anti-bilious Lees demonstrated that this law applied to pills. Few aspiring nostrum promoters, however, availed themselves of this opportunity. Despite the laxness of the law, which did not require that an applicant show either the novelty or utility of his wares, only some seventy-five patents for pills, ointments, salves, bitters, and other medicinals were granted before a newer and tougher measure was passed in 1836, and few of the patentees came even close to the Samuel Lees in the scope of their sales. Most applicants were humble and obscure, sending in their requests from hamlets like Crawford, Arkansas, and Rattlesnake Springs, Georgia. One name on the list was well known around the country, that of Lorenzo Dow, an itinerant evangelist, not a quack doctor, who patented a Family Medicine to dispense along with the Christian faith. By and large patent applications came from simple-minded folk unused to the clever ways of the commercial world. The shrewd could secure other forms of governmental protection for their nostrums without revealing, as a patent application required, the ingredients in the remedies.[18]

Manufacturers of packaged medicines patented not the medicine or its method of composition but the distinctive shape of the container. They secured copyrights on the label, on promotional literature wrapped around the nostrum, and on display posters to be affixed to tree and fence. A copyright, under a federal law of 1831, lasted for twenty-eight years and was renewable for fourteen more. Another form of promotion permitted one badge of proprietorship to live presumably forever: the trade-mark. The subject was not yet a federal matter, being a product of the common law. But the distinctive symbol could be defended in the courts. The fiercely competitive patent medicine industry, with a

17 Merle Curti, *The Growth of American Thought* (N.Y., 1943), 360-61.
18 Kebler, 487; *Patent Medicines*, House Report No. 52, 30 Cong., 2 ses. (1849), 4-29; Charles C. Sellers, *Lorenzo Dow, The Bearer of the Word* (N.Y., 1928), 200-202.

history of upstart challenging established proprietor, made judicial history in this domain.[19]

In the 1840's, after years of agitation, Congress enacted markedly lower postal rates. Since a free press was a bulwark of democracy, editors were permitted to use the mails to send their papers without postal charge to subscribers who lived within the county of publication. This prompted an increase in subscriptions and enlarged once more the readers who could learn about the healing virtues of cathartic and catholicon. The new postal laws also helped medicine makers by letting them mail more cheaply than before their brochures, simulated newspapers, and other "direct mail" promotion.[20]

Patent and copyright legislation, the expansion of means for advertising, rapid growth in the population of the country, the unabated suffering from many ailments, the spirit of therapeutic laissez-faire in a democratic age—all these were factors broadening the market for vendors of packaged remedies. It was a tempting prospect. Nor was making the panacea a major obstacle. It was a simple task, as an Ohio editor pointed out, for "Any idle mechanic" to launch a nostrum. He "by chance gets a dispensatory, or some old receipt book, and poring over it, or having it read to him. . . , he finds that mercury is good for the itch, and old ulsers; that opium will give ease; and that a glass of antimony will vomit. Down goes the hammer, or saw, razor, awl, or shuttle—and away to make electuaries, tinctures, elixirs, pills, plasters and poultices."[21]

Promotion was much more difficult than production. For every Thomas Dyott there were a hundred small proprietors who lacked a certain business acumen to enable them to push a small venture into an outstanding success. Some hopeful proprietors failed altogether. Others plugged ahead on a village basis. Only a few became titans of the industry, men whose products were household words across the land.

[19] John S. Billings, "American Invention and Discoveries in Medicine, Surgery, and Practical Sanitation," *Celebration of the Beginning of the Second Century of the American Patent System at Washington, D.C.* (Wash., 1892), 414; Richard R. Bowker, *Copyright, Its History and Its Laws* (Boston, 1912), 35-37; Amasa C. Paul, *The Law of Trade-Marks* (St. Paul, 1903), 22-24, 56.
[20] North, 137-54.
[21] *Portsmouth* [Ohio] *Jnl.*, cited in Madge E. Pickard and R. Carlyle Buley, *The Midwest Pioneer: His Ills, Cures & Doctors* (N.Y., 1946), 286.

The big-scale patent medicine maker, during the early decades of the 19th century, blazed a merchandising trail. He was the first American manufacturer to seek out a national market. He was the first producer to help merchants who retailed his wares by going direct to consumers with a message about the product. He was the first promoter to test out a multitude of psychological lures by which people might be enticed to buy his wares. While other advertising in the press was drab, his was vivid; while other appeals were straightforward, his were devilishly clever. The patent medicine promoter was a pioneer, marching at the head of a long procession of other men with ships and shoes and sealing wax to sell.

Thomas Dyott was one of these giants, but the benevolent baron of Dyottsville suffered a sad fate. Once again branching out, he established a bank. Moved by the same philanthropy that had prompted his model factory, Dyott promised "to give to the meritorious working man the full legal interest which he ought always to obtain for his savings." But this laudable aim could not be long fulfilled. In 1837 financial disaster struck the nation, and panic engulfed the bank. To save his various holdings, Dyott parceled out his stock among relatives and took refuge in bankruptcy. Creditors persuaded Pennsylvania state officials to sue the nostrum maker for fraudulent insolvency. Dyott's conduct, the prosecuting attorney told the jury, could be summed up as "systematic wholesale cheating." After hearing the evidence, the jury agreed. The moral elevation and the virtuous habits Dyott had sought to inculcate in his employees did not save him. Nor did the fact that he had once given money to build a church. A man in his late sixties, Dyott was sentenced to from one to seven years at hard labor. He was pardoned before the expiration of his term.[22]

Such a blow from fortune might have caused the one-time bootblack to wish that he had limited his sphere of business action to manufacturing patent medicines. This at least was safely within the law. It was to this more circumscribed career of nostrum vendor that Dyott returned after his release from

[22] F. Cyril James, "The Bank of North America and the Financial History of Philadelphia," *Pa. Mag. Hist. and Biog.*, 64 (1940), 76-77; *The Highly Interesting and Important Trial of Dr. T. W. Dyott, the Banker, for Fraudulent Insolvency* (Phila., circa 1839), in the Hist. Soc. of Penna.; *Phila. Press*, Jan. 19, 1861.

prison. He had lost his throne as nostrum king and he did not win it back. His post-depression activities were restricted in size and geographical compass. But he did have time to acquire another modest fortune before he died, during his ninetieth year, in 1861.

Dyott's career spanned more than half a century, the years in which the native American nostrum trade became soundly established. Some phases of this early history deserve more detailed investigation. Let us next inquire into the career of patent medicine making's most dedicated disciple of democracy.

4

"THE OLD WIZZARD"

Blind!—Leaders of the blind! lift up your eyes
And seek for light, that leads from ruins brink!
Your Calomel, and all your deadly drugs, reject!
The world is wakening round you! Botanic
Doctors (sounding the majesty of truth)
Gain ground: the mercurial craft declines!
Thick darkness flies before Thomsonian light,
Bursting in glory on a long benighted world!

—THE THOMSONIAN RECORDER, 1834[1]

OF all the medical patents issued in the early decades of American independence, the patent with the greatest impact on society was granted to a New Hampshire farmer named Samuel Thomson. Influenced by the same forces that boomed the sale of packaged remedies, Thomson patented a system of medical treatment that made every man his own physician, a system destined to sweep the nation.

The road to the patent office, however, was arduous, and Thomson's own account of it grim. He was born on the frontier in 1769. His parents were poverty-stricken. His father was stern and severe. The boy's own labor on the unyielding acres began when he was five. Lame from birth, Thomson was often sick. He had one month of schooling, at the age of ten. His main pleasure came from wandering through the woods and fields testing the products of nature's bounty. One herb the lad discovered brought him perverse delight. "I . . . used to induce other boys to chew it," he remembered, "merely by way of sport, to see them vomit."[2]

His interest in plants, bolstered by popular medical lore learned from a neighborhood widow, almost brought Thomson's re-

[1] Cited in Alex Berman, "The Thomsonian Movement and Its Relation to American Pharmacy and Medicine," *Bull. Hist. Med.*, 25 (1951), 405.

[2] Samuel Thomson, *New Guide to Health; or Botanic Family Physician . . . to Which Is Prefixed, A Narrative of the Life and Medical Discoveries of the Author* (Boston, 1835), 14-95.

lease from the hated farming. He longed to go and live with a
nearby root doctor, but his father could not get along without his
son's labor and the doctor could not accept his lack of schooling.
So Thomson toiled wretchedly on. When the young man was
twenty-one, his father deeded him half the family farm and
moved off to Vermont. His mother and sister were left in Samuel's
care, but soon the mother died, a victim of measles turned into
"galloping consumption." Several doctors had done her no good at
all, Thomson was persuaded, whereas he himself, suffering from
the same maladies, had managed to restore his health with botanical concoctions. A year later a new experience strengthened
Thomson's convictions. He had married, and his wife, following
childbirth, became gravely ill. Seven regular physicians rendered
their conflicting treatments in vain. In despair the anguished
husband called in two root doctors. One day later his wife was
cured. This event turned Thomson's attention in earnest to the
hobby he had never ceased to pursue. In the next several years he
used herbs to cure a daughter, a son, then several neighbors.
His fame spread. In time he was too busy healing to continue
farming. He moved about from town to town in eastern New
England, practicing the medical theories that by now he had
formulated.

Samuel Thomson's ideas were neither complex nor new. He
was convinced "that all disease is the effect of one general cause,
and may be removed by one general remedy." The cause was
cold, the remedy heat. Like the Greeks, Thomson believed "that
all animal bodies are formed of four elements, earth, air, fire,
and water." An imbalance of these elements which diminished
"the power of heat," brought on an illness. The proper cure,
therefore, was "to restore heat to its natural state." The whole
thing could be summed up in a quatrain:

> My system's founded on this *truth*,
>   Man's Air and Water, Fire and Earth;
> And death is cold, and life is heat
>   These *temper'd* well, you are complete.

Thomson sought to do this "tempering" directly, by means
of steam baths and "hot" botanicals like red pepper, and indirectly, by the use of emetics, purgatives, enemas, and sweat-
producing herbs, which would clear the body of all "obstruc-

tions," let the stomach function properly, and thus preserve the natural heat-balance among the body's basic elements. "All the art required to do this," Thomson believed, "is, to know what *medicine* will do it, and how to administer it, as a person knows how to clear a stove and pipe when clogged with soot, that the fire may burn free, and the whole room be warmed as before." Early in his career, Thomson hoped that one plant alone might prove to be the universal remedy. His choice was the very same herb, *lobelia inflata*, that had set his boyhood companions to vomiting. The Indians had used lobelia as a smoke, and others before Thomson had mentioned it as an "Emetic Weed." But Thomson made it the keystone of his system of therapy. Lobelia did not work out as the sole cure—Thomson ended up with some sixty-five botanicals, chosen in accordance with the "strikingly obvious" dictum "that the medicinal vegetables of our own country must be more congenial to the constitutions of its inhabitants, and better suited to the diseases incident to our climate, than imported drugs." Lobelia remained No. 1 in the numbered list of six remedies which Thomson was to patent.[3]

Thus an unschooled frontier farmer had propagated a one-cause, one-cure theory of disease, performing a feat of speculative medical logic not unlike the theorizing of leading European and American physicians during the same years. Almost simultaneously with Thomson's musings, indeed, Benjamin Rush was working out his hypertension pathology that ushered in America's "heroic" age.

It must not be assumed that, by contrast, Samuel Thomson's system of therapy lacked courage. Lobelia alone required a certain hardihood. There were other brave aspects of the regimen, as made clear by a surviving account of the first of at least eleven Thomsonian treatments given a Maryland man some years later for an unspecified disease. The day began with "a steam bath 30 minutes in duration. When the sweat rolls off as thick as your

[3] *Ibid.*, 43-45; Thomson, *The Constitution, Rules and Regulations* (Portsmouth, N.H., 1812), 13, 22, and Thomson, *Address to the People of the United States* (Boston, 1817), 4, in the Amer. Antiquarian Soc.; John Uri Lloyd, *History of the Vegetable Drugs of the Pharmacopeia of the United States* (Bull. Lloyd Libr., No. 18, 1911), 55-56; Berman, 413; "Restored Patents," 28 (1836), 93-96, in the Patent Office Library; Philip D. Jordan, "The Secret Six, An Inquiry into the Basic Materia Medica of the Thomsonian System of Botanic Medicine," *Ohio State Archeological and Historical Quarterly*, 52 (1943), 347-55.

finger the body is washed with cold water and the patient straightway put to bed with hot bricks to bring back the heat. Then a powerful vomitive is administered, composed of *bay berry*, of cayenne (red pepper) and lobelia, and all these herbs are mixed in 40 proof brandy, after which warm water is drunk until there has ensued the most extraordinary vomiting." After a second steaming, a second cold bath, and a second session with hot bricks, the patient "takes two injections [enemas?] of penny royal, cayenne pepper and l'obelia [*sic*] and the treatment is over for the day."[4]

The experience of this patient bolsters the assertion of a Virginian who described the "spirit" of Thomsonianism as "that of our restless, dauntless, active, western backwoodsmen, who even judge their 'physic' by the amount of labor it is capable of performing."[5]

If the New Hampshire farmer's system had its own form of rigor, it was distinguished from Rush's Philadelphia "heroism" in two significant ways. Thomson's approach to therapy did not include bleeding and it did not prescribe mineral medicines. Indeed, it not only did not include them, it forthrightly condemned them. Thomson was a frank foe of regular physicians. They had killed his mother, he felt, and had brought his wife to the brink of death. Their methods were anathema.

> They are like Javas deadly tree
> Whose sland'ring poisonous breath,
> Are nuisance to society
> A pestilential death.

It was not long after Thomson had launched his practice that he incurred the enmity of the doctors in his vicinity. The trained professionals were outraged by the presumption of this ignorant country bumpkin with his steam baths and his herbs. Thomson's growing popularity among the people made things worse. His outspoken castigations stung the doctors to white-hot anger. All that physicians ever learned about the nature of medicine, Thomson said, was "how much poison [could] be given without causing death," and considering "their instruments of death, *Mercury,*

[4] Frank C. Halstead, "A First-Hand Account of a Treatment by Thomsonian Medicine in the 1830s," *Bull. Hist. Med.*, 10 (1941), 681-82.
[5] *Stethoscope and Va. Med. Gaz.* (1851), cited in Wyndham B. Blanton, *Medicine in Virginia in the Nineteenth Century* (Richmond, 1933), 196-97.

Opium, Ratsbane, Nitre and the *Lance*," they often gave too much. Soon a bitter feud was under way.[6]

Thomson's temperament, as well as his ideas, led him into conflict with other people. One may imagine the reaction of the boyhood companions who had been persuaded to chew lobelia. After a quarrel, one of Thomson's later associates spoke of him as "illiterate, coarse in his manners and extremely selfish." The botanical doctor's face, to judge by an engraved portrait, was severe. He had a square head with an extremely high forehead, close-cropped hair, large eyes under heavy brows, and straight-set lips. He did not have the engraver remove from his likeness a conspicuous wart on his large nose. This high-domed head was naturally of interest to a leading practitioner of another sect, the phrenologist Orson S. Fowler, who made a personal examination of Thomson's cranium. Based on this—and doubtless on observation of the steam doctor's career—Fowler described Thomson's character. The three largest "organs" on his skull were "Firmness, Approbativeness and Causality." He was quick to anger, vigorous in his animosity, "obstinate, even to mulishness." "Nothing daunted him." His social "organs" also were large, especially amativeness, so that Thomson was "beloved or hated in the *extreme*." He "had no deception; loved and spoke the *truth*, and was not naturally cunning or double faced." "Benevolence stood out conspicuously, indicating that he had the good of his fellow-men at heart." Still, his "organ" of money-making was also markedly developed. And he had an unmistakable love of praise.[7]

Thomson's enemies began by calling him names. He was labeled, he said, "the sweating and steaming doctor; the Indian doctor; the old wizzard; and sometimes the quack." His lobelia was called such things as "screw auger," "bull-dog," "belly-my-grizzle." Thomson denied that this plant was a poison, even in large quantities, and insisted he had the instinct of the wild beast permitting him to discover by tasting "what is good for food, and what is necessary for medicine." But regular doctors began to circulate the rumor that lobelia had killed some of Thomson's

6 Thomson, *New Guide to Health*, 24-95; Thomson, *Constitution*, 24; Thomson, *Address*, 5; Wilson G. Smillie, "An Early Prepayment Plan for Medical Care," *Jnl. Hist. Med. and Allied Sciences*, 6 (1951), 253.

7 Berman, 528; engraved portrait as frontispiece in Thomson, *New Guide to Health*; Fowler's examination of Thomson made in 1838 or 1839 is given in *Phrenological Almanac, and Physiological Guide, for . . . 1845*, 45-48, in the N.Y. Public Library.

patients and in 1809 Thomson was arrested and charged with murder.[8]

The instigator of this attack was a regular physician named French who long had been the most vindictive of Thomson's medical critics. "I had considerable practice in his neighborhood," the herb doctor wrote later, "and was very successful in every case; this seemed to excite his malice against me to the greatest pitch; he . . . took every opportunity to insult and abuse me both to my face and behind my back." Witchcraft and trafficking with the devil were among the charges hurled. Thomson had fought back, haling the doctor before a magistrate to answer for his threats. French countered with the murder charge, insisting that two years previously the botanical doctor had killed a patient with lobelia. Thomson was thrown into a Newburyport jail to await trial.[9]

This "dungeon," in Thomson's memoirs, was horrible indeed. There was no heat against the winter's cold. The thin November sunshine had no means of entrance, nor was a candle provided for light. The first meal was hard corn bread, stale coffee, and "the nape of a fish." The air was heavy with filth. Lice crawled about the floor. Thomson's sole companion was a man convicted of assault upon a girl of six. Release did not seem possible. Bail could not be granted for a murder charge and no court would meet regularly to try the case for nearly a year. "This was the policy of my enemies," Thomson was sure, "thinking that they could keep me in prison a year, and in all probability I should not live that time."

But Thomson survived a month in his foul jail to face his principal accuser in a special court convened at Salem through the intercession of friends. The herb doctor pleaded not guilty to the murder charge. He had been called to treat a dying man, he said, afflicted with the same severe cold, possibly typhus, that shortly before had killed his mother. Thomson's treatments had brought relief, so that the young man had gotten out of bed. Foolishly he had gone outdoors into the bitter cold of a December day. There was a relapse, accompanied by delirium. Called back to the bedside, Thomson told the family there was no hope.

8 Thomson, *New Guide to Health*, 27, 53, 95-96.

9 *Ibid.*, 37-38, 66, 95-105; Theodoric R. Beck and John M. Beck, *Elements of Medical Jurisprudence* (12th ed., Phila., 1863), II, 735-36.

He requested the patient's father to call in other doctors. This was done, but Thomson's prediction proved correct. The next morning the young man was dead.

A parade of prosecution witnesses at the trial gave a different twist to the interpretation of events. The botanical doctor had been called, they said, to treat the youth's cold. The therapy had consisted of three powders of lobelia within half an hour, which produced the most violent vomiting. On each of the next two days, Thomson administered two more doses of this powerful plant. Then he went off, leaving the patient prostrate with weakness. Several days later, Thomson returned and gave several more doses. The young man went out of his head and became so convulsed that it took two men to hold him down. Once again, Thomson insisted on giving two more lobelia powders. This was the last straw. The youth worsened and died. Such was the testimony of Thomson's accusers.

Then came a moment of high drama. A medical witness for the prosecution showed the court a plant he called the poisonous lobelia. One of Thomson's attorneys took the herb and calmly and deliberately chewed and swallowed it. The nation's leading botanist, Manasseh Cutler, then took the stand. The plant introduced in evidence by the prosecution, he said, was not lobelia at all, but marsh rosemary. The jury quickly found the defendant innocent.

A liberated Thomson failed in a suit for libel against the physician responsible for bringing the murder charge, but soon was pleased to note that his evil persecutor had been convicted of stealing a dead body from a graveyard.[10]

French's discomfiture and Thomson's exoneration did not end the battle between the steam doctor and the regulars. As a result of Thomson's continuing popular success, his renewed blasting of bloodletting and mineral medication, and his advocacy of republican principles in a region where everyone who counted was a die-hard federalist, his enemies grew more determined and sought new weapons. Even before the Revolution, physicians in various colonies had secured legislative enactments, although they proved futile, to control quackery. Now doctors renewed their efforts, inspiring state laws which forbade the Thomsonian practice. This attack angered the botanical doctor and led him to

10 Thomson, *New Guide to Health*, 105-107.

patent his system. "I finally came to the conclusion," he wrote, "that there was only one plan for me to pursue with any chance of success; and that was to go on to Washington, and obtain a patent for my discoveries; and put myself and medicine under the protection of the laws of my country, which would not only secure to me the exclusive right of my system and medicine, but would put me above the reach of the laws of any state."[11]

Patent procedures when Thomson went to Washington in 1813 were still lenient, requiring proof of neither the novelty nor the utility of an invention. Even at that the unschooled Yankee had a hard time getting the clerk to approve his application. Finally, after a former governor of Vermont had helped him re-draft his specifications, Thomson succeeded. It was comforting to know that he now had a document giving him "the exclusive right of preparing, using and vending to others the use of this Medicine, signed by the *President, Secretary* [of State], and *Attorney-General*, of the United States." Thomson in time would expand the actual truth and suggest that the President had guaranteed the medical potency of his system. "Oh! to take medicine 'by authority,' " a critic would chide, "and that, too, of the President, who would recommend nothing that he had not tried on himself, and found useful for the people."[12]

Patent in hand, Thomson headed hopefully back to New England. On his way he stopped in Philadelphia to meet the most distinguished physician in America and to ask his advice about introducing the newly patented system to the world. Benjamin Rush was very busy, and he handed Thomson on to a professor of materia medica. This at least was graciously done, for Thomson remembered the Philadelphian's personal politeness at the same time that he recalled his own astonishment at learning to what lengths Rush went in bleeding his patients.[13]

Thus did Rush and Thomson briefly meet. The untutored botanical doctor had hardly left the city before the urbane physician was dead. But Rush's system of heroic treatment lived on in

11 *Ibid.*, 122; Alexander Wilder, *History of Medicine . . . and Especially a History of the American Eclectic Practice of Medicine* (New Sharon, Me., 1901), 457, 464-65.
12 Kebler, "United States Patents Granted for Medicines during the Pioneer Years of the Patent Office," 486-87; Thomson, *Address*, 6; Pickard and Buley, *The Midwest Pioneer*, 180; Daniel Drake, *The People's Doctors* (Cincinnati, 1829), 10; Thomson, *New Guide to Health*, 123-26.
13 *Ibid.*

the practice of most American doctors. Against it Thomson was pledged to fight with renewed vigor, since he was now supported by the power of the United States itself.

There still were lean years ahead. In a suit for trespass against an interloper, Thomson found that his specifications had not been drawn concretely enough to serve as a foundation for legal action. So he got a second patent in 1823. Nor did these patents give Thomson the protection he had hoped for against the "Black Laws" passed by state legislatures. The lobbies of regular doctors continued active and successful through the decade of the twenties. Nonetheless, Thomson's medical ideas spread. He advertised in the papers. He issued pamphlets. He traveled up and down the country promulgating his doctrine in person. Opposition only led to more rapid acceptance, Thomson wrote, "like whipping fire among the leaves."[14]

The years ahead were troubled ones for orthodox disciples of Aesculapius. In 1828 Andrew Jackson was elected to the presidency, a result of broadened suffrage, a signal that the common man was coming increasingly into his own. One foible of the ordinary citizen was a grave suspicion of too much book-learning. This pervasive feeling made it difficult for members of all the learned professions. "The priest, the doctor, and the lawyer," Samuel Thomson wrote, all were guilty of "deceiving the people." Doctors especially came under attack. Many a speech by a physician and many a resolution by a medical society began to reflect the tumbling authority of the doctors and their belief that this unhappy state of affairs was due to an excess of democratic individualism improperly aimed. "The people regard it among their vested interests," wrote a New York doctor, "to buy and swallow such physick as they in their sovereign will and pleasure shall determine; and in this free country, the democracy denounce all restrictions upon quackery as wicked monopolies for the benefit of physicians." A committee of the New-Hampshire Medical Society reported "so strong an antagonistic feeling" between physicians and the public that the people considered "their reliance upon nostrums and quack administrations of medicine more valuable than any dependence upon a learned profession. The profession to them is 'pearls before swine.'" The patronizing of pseudo-doctors and quacks, opined a book re-

14 *Ibid.*, 165-66, 180-81; Wilder, 465-66.

viewer, "is incident to the character of our institutions. . . . It is the result of too much liberty."[15]

The popular distrust of doctors led to all sorts of wild charges. Ancient suspicions were refurbished as weapons for the renewed battle. Imbued with zeal for the common man's religions, which stressed fervor and decried intellect, state legislatures opposed the practice of dissection. Anyone who would desecrate the temple of the soul, ran the common belief, was bound to be an atheist. In the face of such laws, adequate medical education could not continue unless grave-robbing occurred. Samuel Thomson's medical foe had run afoul of such a statute. Imprisonment was the least danger faced by doctors and students of anatomy. A mob assault at a small Illinois medical school led to the death of a student and the serious wounding of a teacher. Nor were the anatomy professors at even Harvard and Yale immune from such dangers.[16]

With atheism went immorality, and one more hoary suspicion was bruited again in the age of the common man. An Ohio agent for botanical medicines, who doubled as a Radical Methodist preacher, was quoted as saying: "The practice of employing physicians to officiate in Midwifery cases was so demoralizing that he believed, that any woman who would willingly submit to have a Doctor to deliver her of a child, would let that same Doctor afterwards get her with child, if he chose to do so."[17]

Such an assertion was patently absurd. But what made it difficult for reputable physicians and easy for untutored doctors and outright quacks was that much of the popular criticism, though it had its excesses, was to the point. Medical science was immature, and many people instinctively revolted against the heroism of noxious emetics and violent bleeding. Medical ethics had only the most tenuous authority among run-of-the-mill practitioners. The "Black Laws" did look like special privilege. And the pseudo-doctor was devilishly clever in parading the physician as an aristocrat before the eyes of the common man. "Every quack is, indeed, a *demagogue*," explained Daniel Drake, the

[15] Thomson, *New Guide to Health*, 201; David M. Reese, *Humbugs of New York* (N.Y., 1838), 124; N.H. Med. Soc., *Trans.*, *1856*, 36; "Quackery and the Quacked," *Ntl. Quarterly Rev.*, 2 (1861), 355.
[16] Pickard and Buley, 137-38; Linden F. Edwards, "Resurrection Riots during the Heroic Age of Anatomy in America," *Bull. Hist. Med.*, 25 (1951), 178-84.
[17] Belmont Med. Soc., *Trans.*, *for 1850-51* (Bridgeport, O., 1851), 57-58.

most keen-minded doctor in the Midwest, in 1829, "and relies, for his success, on nearly the same arts, with his political and religious . . . brethren." The botanical doctor poses as "one of the *people*," as "pre-eminently the guardian of the *people*," and he accuses trained doctors of being "not *of* the *people*, but arrayed against the *people*, and bent on killing them off." The people were "charmed" by this appeal, Drake said, and "crawl[ed] into the serpent's mouth."[18]

The system that Samuel Thomson patented was the ultimate in the democratic approach to health. There was no need of doctors; every man could treat himself. Thomson sold, or had agents sell, family rights to use his system. For twenty dollars a family could buy a book of directions and the privilege of preparing and using the remedies described, although Thomson sought to maintain a monopoly of the sale of the basic botanical ingredients. Purchasers in a given area belonged to Friendly Botanic Societies and could share their experience and counsel, but no member was to give away secrets to non-members.[19] Only the most trustworthy physicians and medical students were to be admitted, and they only after having paid $500 each and having sworn before a justice of the peace to keep their lips properly sealed.

Such a strange mixture of medication and salesmanship would never have been granted a patent under any but the most ludicrously laissez-faire of patent policies. The regular doctors, of course, were quick to point this out. To be granted a patent for the "clumsy" and "dangerous" methods by which Thomson prescribed his vegetable remedies, said Daniel Drake, was like getting a patent for vaccinating not the arm but the nose.[20]

Drake even debated against Thomson when the steam doctor brought his gospel to Ohio, realizing full well that his own criticism, and that of other educated physicians, helped the prestige of "the artful demagogue and mischievous imposter" with the credulous. The scope of this triumph was amazing, even if it did not take quite the form which Thomson would have wished. By 1839 he claimed to have sold 100,000 of his family rights. Sec-

[18] Drake, 59-60.
[19] Thomson, *New Guide to Health*, 126-42; Berman, 415; Thomson, *Constitution*, 1-5; a copy of the certificate a purchaser secured is reproduced opposite p. 158 in Kremers and Urdang, *History of Pharmacy*; Smillie, 253-57.
[20] Drake, 21-24.

[54]

tions of rural New England, the South, and the West were won over to botanical medicine. The governor of Mississippi asserted that half the people of his state were treated according to Thomsonian principles, and in Ohio the regular physicians admitted botanical recruits to be at least a third of the population.[21]

The vast sweep of this botanical tide did not make Samuel Thomson happy. Indeed, his movement had gotten quite out of hand. It was supposed to be his. He had a patent for it. But "mongrel Thomsonians" kept stealing the booty. Rascals pirated his medical manual. Agents he had hired went off on their own. Unauthorized manufacturers compounded "Thomsonian" botanicals. There were even those who defied the master's motto, "The Study of Patients, Not Books—Experience, Not Reading," and sought to make his concepts the basis of medical school education. Even in a democratic age, many Americans, anxious to be treated by Thomsonian principles, wanted a "doctor" to do it rather than relying on a book. About all these troubles, despite constant law suits, and violent diatribes, Thomson could do but little.[22]

On one thing botanical practitioners of all persuasions did unite. They launched a vigorous drive to secure the repeal of the "Black Laws" discriminating against them. One of Thomson's own sons led the fight in New York state. On one occasion he pushed to the state capital a wheelbarrow containing a petition bearing so many signatures it was thirty-one yards long. The tone of the campaign is caught in the words of a senator in the course of the debate. "The people of this state have been bled long enough in their bodies and pockets," he said, "and it [is] time they should do as the men of the Revolution did: resolve to set down and enjoy the freedom for which they bled." Another New York solon spoke for the age of the common man: "A people accustomed to govern themselves, and boasting of their intelligence, are impatient of restraint. They want no protection but freedom of inquiry and freedom of action."[23]

Medical democracy, indeed, was what Americans seemed to desire. They might not decide to treat themselves, but they wanted no restrictions on their right to choose the method by

[21] *Ibid.*; Jordan, 349; Berman, 415; Pickard and Buley, 178-79.
[22] Thomson, *New Guide to Health*, 133-36, 165-66, 170-72, 181; Wilder, 497; Berman, 424-26, 523-24; Paul, *The Law of Trade-Marks*, 22-23.
[23] Wilder, 468-71; Berman, 423; Henry B. Shafer, *The American Medical Profession, 1783 to 1850* (N.Y., 1936), 210; Shryock, *The Development of Modern Medicine*, 262.

which they would be treated. The New York law was modified and then repealed. Medical control statutes in almost every other state likewise fell before the pressure of botanical lobbies and public opinion. Before mid-century, in those few states which still had laws in their codes, only three made any pretense at enforcement. The judicious might grieve, but the people and the people's doctors had won their way. In a pioneering and long-unheeded report on the public health in Massachusetts, Lemuel Shattuck wrote in 1850: "Any one, male or female, learned or ignorant, an honest man or a knave, can assume the name of physician, and 'practice' upon any one, to cure or to kill, as either may happen, without accountability. It's a free country!"[24]

Another token of the Thomsonian victory was the way many members of the regular medical profession broke ranks. "We must adopt the Thomsonian medical agents, or lose our practice." So argued a professor at the Pennsylvania Medical College. Many physicians, seeing the booming popularity of botanical medicine, followed this counsel. Other doctors, not willing to go so far, found it advisable to let up on the bloodletting and mineral medication which were the major objects of Thomsonian attack. This pressure helped to mitigate the excesses of "heroic" therapy. Thomsonianism was not the only force for reform. It was joined in due course by another strange sect, homeopathy, with its emphasis on infinitesimal doses. There came, moreover, the inevitable reaction within the ranks of regular medicine, originating in France and brought to America by such students as Oliver Wendell Holmes. This literary doctor condemned bloodletting and asserted that, except for a few specific drugs, opium, and anesthesia, "if the whole materia medica, *as now used*, could be sunk to the bottom of the sea, it would be all the better for man-kind,—and all the worse for the fishes."[25]

Many forces worked toward the replacement of the excessive "heroism" associated with Rush's theories by the new vogue of therapeutic nihilism. In the contest, the role of Thomson was that of primacy. He was, in the words of a sympathetic medical historian, "the first to publicly attack Allopathy in America."[26]

24 *Ibid.*, 261; Wilder, 468-81, 503-10; Shattuck, *Report of the Sanitary Commission of Massachusetts*, 58.
25 Wilder, 498; Holmes, *Medical Essays*, 39-102, 173-208; Shryock, 151-64, 170-71; Pickard and Buley, 199-218; King, *Medical World of the Eighteenth Century*, 157-91.
26 Wilder, 455.

Whatever its role for good, Thomsonianism was no sound system for the American people, even though, in a democratic age, they might desire it. In 1837 a Thomsonian practitioner in New York suffered the fate which Thomson himself had luckily escaped, being convicted of manslaughter for causing the death of a patient by excessive use of lobelia. The impact of such sobering episodes, the continuing criticism by physicians, the bitter feuding within botanical ranks, and the arrival of new popular enthusiasms, brought the waning of the doctrine. There was a legacy of more judicious and fruitful study of the medicinal resources of American fields and forests than Samuel Thomson had had the skill to provide. But the simple body-heat theory of the founder passed away. The patent, which had been renewed in 1836, expired in 1852. By then Thomsonianism was moribund. Six years earlier Daniel Drake had said that "STEAM-ERY" was out of fashion, and in 1859 a Tennessee physician asserted that the day of the steam doctors was over. Many of them, he said, had been preachers who now had returned to that calling.[27]

The career of Samuel Thomson does not escape paradox. He hated the "heroism" of bloodletting and massive mineral doses, but he failed to realize that his own torrid baths and vigorous botanicals required enormous courage on the part of the patient. He denied the monistic pathology which Rush and his followers believed in, but he spun out a speculative one-cause explanation of his own based on a misconception harking back to ancient Greece. He fought the licensing restrictions by which regular physicians became a privileged class, but he sought to monopolize his own remedies and methods of treatment by recourse to the patent office.

Thomson died in 1843. His last years were no happier than his boyhood. He had managed to secure neither the loyalty of his followers nor the profits from his patent which he felt he deserved. In the end, even his own medicines failed him. He died taking them in vain.[28]

[27] Halstead, 683; Kremers and Urdang, 161-62; Berman, 420; reprint from an 1858 journal containing an 1846 letter by Drake, in the Toner Collection, Rare Book Div., Library of Congress; R. Snead, "Quackery in East Tennessee," *Nashville Jnl. Med. and Surgery,* 16 (1859), 485-87.
[28] Fishbein, *Fads and Quackery in Healing,* 35.

HERCULES AND HYDRA

"The increase of empiricism and of patent medicines within the 19th century, is an evil over which the friends of science and humanity can never cease to mourn."

—HOUSE REPORT NO. 52, 30TH CONGRESS, 2ND SESSION, 1849

CONFLICTING versions often arise concerning the circumstances of momentous discoveries, and so it is with the Panacea of William Swaim. The inventor was a resident of New York or Philadelphia. He was a harness maker or a bookbinder. He either encountered the recipe which was to make him famous in the pages of an old volume he was repairing or had it handed him in the prescription of a doctor whom he had consulted because of an ailment.[1]

When Swaim got the formula, at any rate, he knew what to do with it. His success, particularly the techniques he employed in gaining it, brought forth against him the most vigorous campaign America had yet witnessed in pitting the ranks of regular medicine against an individual maker of a packaged medicine. These events took place during the age of Jackson, not only an era in which the common man insisted on medical democracy but also a time in which no seeming evil of society went unchallenged, no inhuman practice unrebuked.

According to the most probable of the varying accounts of his career, William Swaim was pursuing the craft of bookbinding in New York when, afflicted with some illness, he consulted a highly reputable physician with the inappropriate name of Quackinboss. After a period of taking the remedy prescribed, Swaim recovered his health. He was much impressed, and some-

[1] *Reports of the Medical Society of the City of New-York, on Nostrums, or Secret Medicines* (N.Y., 1827), 35; Drake, *The People's Doctors*, 31; England, *The First Century of the Philadelphia College of Pharmacy*, 73; *Rowell's American Newspaper Directory, 1870* (N.Y., 1870), 173.

[58]

how managed to discover from his physician the nature of the curative agent. A more exact formula he found printed in the pages of a New York medical journal. Giving up bookbinding, Swaim moved to Philadelphia with his recipe to become a medicine manufacturer. His first concoction was launched in 1820. He christened it with a powerful word. Not, he was to explain modestly, that he intended anything "ostentatious or empirical" in the designation he selected. The word "panacea" had often been employed "both by the ancients and moderns, in the restricted sense of a remedy for *a large class* of diseases, and not in its literal and more comprehensive meaning." Nonetheless, Swaim felt, this name for the nostrum, of all he could find, "would best express its peculiar merit."[2]

In the same spirit, we may assume, the ex-bookbinder went about choosing a symbol for his product. Not that Hercules had performed all the labors in the world, but the twelve he had accomplished were more than sufficient to establish his lasting reputation for strength. The adventure in which he killed the many-headed Hydra could serve with especial vividness to signify the valiant potency of the Panacea in successful conflict with the many evil faces which disease presents to a suffering mankind. Therefore, Swaim had America's leading wood engraver— a man trained as a physician, at that—design for him a block showing the husky hero with knotted club upraised to dispatch with devastating blow the hideous Hydra.[3]

From his former profession Swaim brought to his new pursuit a respect for the authority of the book. He began in 1822 to issue a series of small volumes—most of them bound, it would seem— to make known the merits of his product. The edition published in 1824 bore the title, *A Treatise on Swaim's Panacea; Being a Recent Discovery for the Cure of Scrofula or King's Evil, Mercurial Disease, Deep-Seated Syphilis, Rheumatism, and All Disorders Arising from a Contaminated or Impure State of the Blood.* The Hydra, unquestionably, was grim enough, and Swaim's Hercules notably ambitious. The book contained not only persuasive promotional prose, not only page after page of

[2] N.Y. Medical Soc. Report, 35; *A Treatise on Swaim's Panacea* (Phila., 1824), vii.

[3] A copy of the Hercules trade-mark may be found in a proof book of Alexander Anderson, in the N.Y. Public Library; Frederic M. Burr, *Life and Works of Alexander Anderson, M.D., the First American Wood Engraver* (N.Y., 1893).

triumphant case histories, but also commendations from some of the most distinguished physicians in America.

"I have within the last two years," wrote Dr. Nathaniel Chapman in 1823, "had an opportunity of seeing several cases of very inveterate ulcers, which, having resisted previously the regular modes of treatment, were healed by the use of Mr. Swaim's PANACEA; and I do believe, from what I have seen, that it will prove an important remedy in scrofulous, venereal, and mercurial diseases."[4]

Dr. Chapman was one of the most illustrious students of Benjamin Rush. He had also pursued his medical training in Edinburgh and London. Proprietor of a medical journal, author of a text on the materia medica, professor of the institutes and practice of physic at the University of Pennsylvania, Chapman was destined to become the first president of the American Medical Association.[5]

One of Chapman's colleagues at the medical school, Dr. William Gibson, testified in behalf of the Panacea with equal enthusiasm. He had used it "in numerous instances," had found it especially useful "in secondary syphilis and in mercurial disease," and had "no hesitation in pronouncing it a medicine of inestimable value." Dr. Gibson, indeed, had brought to a lecture hall crowded with medical students two patients who had been afflicted with frightful ulcerations. All the regular methods of treatment, Gibson had told the students, were unavailing, but Swaim's Panacea had restored them to perfect health.[6]

The testimonials of Chapman and Gibson were genuine and sincere. Swaim cited many others from "among the brightest ornaments of our country." The ex-bookbinder also could say, truthfully, that his remedy had been employed in the Philadelphia Hospital and the Philadelphia Alms House Infirmary. At the latter institution, Swaim himself had held at least a quasi-position on the staff. A promoter who could elicit such recommendations from medical dignitaries, and who, moreover, could entice a doctor on the Alms House staff to resign and go to Europe as his merchandising agent, was indeed gifted in the arts of persuasion. It was no wonder that the Panacea, even at

4 *A Treatise on Swaim's Panacea*, [7].
5 R. French Stone, *Biography of Eminent American Physicians and Surgeons* (Indianapolis, 1894), 81-83.
6 *Ibid.*, 182; *A Treatise on Swaim's Panacea*, [7], [56].

three dollars a bottle, was doing famously on the market. It was no wonder that a host of imitators sprang up to seek a share of the profits.[7]

Three of the ingredients in Swaim's golden liquid require attention. The first of them is sarsaparilla. Basically the Panacea was a syrup of sarsaparilla. Swaim's use of it was by no means new. An extract from the roots of certain plants native to Latin America, sarsaparilla had been one of the first American botanicals imported into Europe and used for medicinal purposes. In the 16th century the root acquired a vast reputation as a cure for syphilis, then fell into disuse, to be revived in the mid-18th century as a remedy for venereal disorders, scrofula, and ailments of the skin. Regular doctors blessed its healing properties, and nostrum makers turned its fame to their profit. About 1811 the sarsaparilla revival reached America. A New York physician created a sensation by using a French proprietary version, called "the rob of Laffecteur," to cure, so he said, "the case of a gentleman labouring under a loathsome complication of disease, the sequelae of syphilis, and the repeated and irregular use of mercury." Many other New York doctors adopted the vogue, one of them the physician consulted by William Swaim, and another the author of the article in which Swaim found the Laffecteur formula. The ambitious bookbinder had doubtless noted well that the French proprietary was retailing for seven and eight dollars a bottle.[8]

Sarsaparilla syrup was thus a reputable weapon in the arsenal of regular medicine when Swaim sought to market his version of it. Indeed, in the year that his first bottles appeared, the first edition of the *Pharmacopoeia of the United States* was issued, and it contained a formula for sarsaparilla syrup. The Panacea's clever proprietor, by acknowledging that his remedy contained the wonder root, could profit from the public interest spurred by the enthusiasm of regular medicine. This too helps explain Swaim's initial success in appealing directly to doctors. Here was a version of a remedy that was all the vogue, at less than half the price of the imported French article. Try it out, Swaim

[7] *Ibid.*, [5], [7]-[10]; *First Report of the Committee of the Philadelphia Medical Society on Quack Medicines* (Phila., 1828), 5-7, 28.

[8] N.Y. Medical Soc. Report, *passim*; Wootton, *Chronicles of Pharmacy*, II, 118-19; *Dispensatory of the United States* (24th ed., Phila., 1950), 1,007-1,010.

could say, observe the results. Physicians who were convinced that the French proprietary had cured the ailing, were as easily persuaded that the Panacea would work wonders. Several delegates to the convention which had framed the *Pharmacopoeia* were among Swaim's enthusiastic supporters.[9]

Swaim's hope for success lay in large sales direct to the public. In the purses of the common people lay his fortune. To make his appeal the more effective, he wanted the testimonials from leading physicians. But he had no hesitation in exaggerating. Regular doctors used the syrup of sarsaparilla for a restricted list of diseases. Although asserting that his Panacea was not necessarily sovereign over all illness, Swaim strove valiantly to suggest that it did not miss by much. The mystery of its composition was not dispelled by publication in a medical journal. Indeed, Swaim sought to make secrecy itself appealing. His remedy, he said, had powerful healing ingredients not known to any published formula, absent from all competing syrups of sarsaparilla. As a result, the Panacea could cure a longer list of diseases and cure them more effectively.[10]

In Swaim's formula there was indeed an ingredient new to medicine. It is the second of the three constituents in the complex composition of the Panacea that must be noted. In place of the sassafras in the published formula which Swaim appropriated, he substituted gaultheria, or oil of wintergreen, derived from the bark of the sweet birch and from the roots, stalks, and berries of other plants. Where the bookbinder came upon this idea is not known, but it proved sheer inspiration. The oil added immeasurably to the sales appeal, not, of course, because it healed hitherto incurable diseases, but because it had a very pleasing taste.[11]

It was not the oil of wintergreen in Swaim's concoction that began to worry some orthodox physicians, nor was it the sarsaparilla, nor even an as yet unsuspected third ingredient. Swaim's methods of promotion got him into trouble. He himself had noted that the regular doctors who had praised his medicine had done so without regard "to the oblique censure which their more fastidious brethren might choose to cast upon them."[12] A Phila-

[9] N.Y. Medical Soc. Report, 31; Kremers and Urdang, *History of Pharmacy*, 240-41; England, 302.
[10] *A Treatise on Swaim's Panacea*, [11]; N.Y. Medical Soc. Report, 40-45.
[11] Lloyd, *History of the Vegetable Drugs of the Pharmacopeia of the United States*, 38-41.
[12] *A Treatise on Swaim's Panacea*, [6], [145].

delphia medical journal had raised doubts soon after the Panacea
had first appeared. But the ranks of the fastidious were not
augmented to the point of making much show until 1827. Then
the Medical Society of the City of New-York created a Committee
on Quack Remedies.

Condemnation of quackery was not new in America. Even in
colonial days an occasional voice was upraised against the
wandering mountebank or the fantastic claims made in behalf of
some packaged nostrum. The *Virginia Gazette* had copied a
flight of satirical fancy from a London paper, describing an ointment made by a Chinese sage five millennia before the "Mosaick
Creation," which would bring about a regeneration in five days
when applied to the stump of an amputated arm or leg.[13] Perkins
had had his critics. Dyott had been disparaged. Thomson was
even yet under heavy attack from the embattled regulars. As
patent medicines expanded in American life, their enemies saw
even greater dangers against which to sound the alarm. The
report of the New York committee may be regarded as an opening salvo in a heavier barrage of criticism that was to assail
quackery in the age of Jackson during the broader battle for
reform.

Insofar as Swaim was the target, the New York committee's
salvo was not unduly devastating. Hopes were still high as to the
curative powers of sarsaparilla. The physicians of Swaim's
former city admitted, more or less, that the Panacea would work
as well as other forms in treating certain ailments, including
secondary conditions of syphilis. The trouble was that Swaim
made too sweeping claims for his remedy and kept his formula
secret. On his list of diseases within the curative scope of the
Panacea, its proprietor included cancer, scrofula, rheumatism,
gout, hepatitis, the early stages of syphilis. For these ailments,
noted the New York doctors, a sarsaparilla syrup was not
effective.[14]

More reprehensible was the "air of mystery and concealment"
in which Swaim enveloped his nostrum. This was, the New York
committee acknowledged, effective as a sales device. The very
remedies which, in the hands of the trained doctor, "never excited
much attention," could, "in the hands of the pretending empiric,

[13] P&D *Va. Gaz.*, July 4, 1771; see *Mass. Gaz.*, Apr. 16, 1773.
[14] N.Y. Medical Soc. Report, 28-47.

. . . perform miracles, command the confidence of the public, and call forth the encomiastic approbation of reputable physicians." Such a state of affairs, the committee warned, injured the public welfare and degraded the character of the profession. "If the untaught empiric could be permitted to seize upon the approved remedies of the art, and, in order to speculate on suffering credulity, veil them under the specious garb of secrecy, their partial successes will confer upon their order, an importance and character that could not be otherwise attained, to the serious detriment of the healing art."[15]

If Swaim's Hercules wore a disguise, and if his Hydra had too many heads, what could be done about it? Let every physician abstain from prescribing such a secret nostrum, advised the New York committee, and let them warn the public constantly against risks involved in its use.[16]

In Philadelphia, Swaim had enlisted champions from the ranks of the most eminent medical practitioners. There was, therefore, a certain temerity involved, on the part of the Philadelphia Medical Society, in appointing a committee on quack medicines and setting its members upon Swaim's trail. Some months after its New York counterpart, the committee delivered its report. By this time, in late 1827, the new prophet was no longer so honored as he had first been in the land to which he had come to make his medicine. The Philadelphia doctors condemned William Swaim with spirit and with force.

The Panacea, they said, was neither effective nor safe. The case histories which Swaim had quoted so glowingly were much less than the whole truth. One by one the committee recounted these tales to indicate that the cures were either nature's work, or else not cures at all. One of the most famous of Swaim's testimonials, based on an Alms House case, ended not in recovery but in death. The ex-bookbinder's assertions that his remedy might "be administered to the tenderest infant" was a callous falsehood, charged the committee of doctors, and there were cases on record in which the Panacea might be considered the primary cause of death. The ingredients in the nostrum were badly mixed, so the Panacea was not of uniform quality. This was a particular hazard because "in an evil hour, the plan of mixing corrosive sublimate

15 *Ibid.*, 28, 51-52.
16 *Ibid.*, 52.

with at least certain parcels of the Panacea was adopted; and ignorance, vexatious before, was then armed with an instrument of mischief and destruction."[17]

Corrosive sublimate was the most rigorous medical form of mercury. Here, then, was the third key ingredient in the Panacea, and Swaim claimed his bottled nostrum as a cure for mercurial poisoning! The Philadelphia committee assumed the presence of this potent metal on the basis of the physiological symptoms of patients who had taken the medicine. Although the angered proprietor was to swear an oath that the Panacea contained no mercury, three separate chemists, within a year or so, were to prove by analysis that he lied. The pharmacist from whom Swaim had gotten his mercurial supply was also to be made known.[18]

Swaim's guilt must be shared, the committee said, by physicians who had sanctioned his nostrum. But here the Philadelphians trod lightly. There was no need unduly to embarrass their fellow doctors, especially since they had recanted of their heresy. Indeed, the most telling evidence in the report consisted of new quotations from Dr. Chapman and other repentant physicians.

Chapman did penance. He admitted to having once "overrated the value of the Panacea," but now "for a long time" he had "entirely ceased to prescribe it." He had in his files, moreover, not a few cases relating to Swaim's remedy in action which were "eminently calculated to alarm the public on the subject." In like fashion, Swaim's other early enthusiasts changed their optimistic tune in light of sober experience. As to the Alms House and the Philadelphia Hospital, the committee discovered, the Panacea had not been used at the former since 1825, and at the latter it had been employed in but a single case.[19]

"The Panacea by Swaim," the committee was forced to conclude, was "on the same footing with all the quack medicines." Hercules was, after all, a myth.[20]

In answer to the committee's 37-page attack, the unchastened proprietor offered a 52-page rebuttal. "I have not passed through life without making some observations," he wrote, more aptly,

[17] Phila. Medical Soc. Report, *passim.*
[18] *Ibid.*, 23; Swaim, *Some Remarks upon a Publication by the Philadelphia Medical Society concerning Swaim's Panacea* (Phila., 1828), 19-21; *Amer. Jnl. Medical Sciences*, 4 (1829), 530; *Jnl. of Health*, 1 (1830), 222-23.
[19] Phila. Medical Soc. Report, 4-7.   [20] *Ibid.*, 25.

doubtless, than he was aware, "and among others, that assertions, however broad and unfounded, if permitted to pass into the mind of the hearer, without contradiction, will frequently be received with the acquiescence due only to established truth."[21]

It was clear too that, for Swaim, even assertions that had been contradicted were not devoid of merit. In his answer to the doctors, the medicine man boldly reprinted the very testimonials they had criticized, including the original commendations from the physicians who had changed their minds. But he sought to profit with the laity not only by continuing to use the now-repudiated medical praise. The clever promoter tried also to turn the newer condemnation to his account. Swaim boasted that most empirics had been "merely despised" by orthodox medicine, whereas he had "risen to the dignity of being hated." He was no ordinary quack. He was a prophet condemned by the Pharisees. "Is it not a singular spectacle—," Swaim asked of the man in the street, "a learned body striving with all the might of authority to crush an unsupported, unfriended individual, who has risen to notice, not by occult arts, but by curative miracles, performed in open day?"[22]

As time went on, Swaim had even more reason to adopt the role of martyr. Other physicians and chemists joined the ranks of his persecutors from as far afield as his Panacea was selling. Out in the West, Daniel Drake, an inveterate foe of the untutored in medicine, added Swaim to his gallery of quacks.[23] Indeed, the condemnation of Swaim's Panacea was but part of a vigorous crusade against medical quackery in all its forms. The year after the New York City society report was printed, the state medical society in New York adopted one of the first formal codes of medical ethics in America, which termed patent medicines incompatible with the duties of a physician and hence not to be "professionally countenanced." Scores of resolutions, addresses, articles, even a Phi Beta Kappa oration, echoed the same sentiment.[24]

21 Swaim, *Some Remarks*, 3.
22 *Ibid.*, 3-4, 24-45.
23 *Jnl. of Health*, 1 (1830), 222-23; Drake, 30-32.
24 *Statutes Regulating the Practice of Physic and Surgery in the State of New-York . . . Also a System of Medical Ethics, as Adopted by the New-York State Medical Society* (N.Y., 1828), 49; Caleb Ticknor, *A Popular Treatise on Medical Philosophy; or, An Exposition of Quackery and Imposture in Medicine* (N.Y., 1838) is the Phi Beta Kappa oration.

The American imitations of the old English patent medicines also came under attack. So chaotic was the situation in this field that the newly organized Philadelphia College of Pharmacy created a committee to look into the matter. When this group gathered recipes by which these English nostrums were being prepared by American apothecaries, they found confusion twice confounded. In some cases two formulas bearing the same English name did not contain one single ingredient in common. After considerable study, the committee issued a pamphlet in 1824 stating the ingredients and their proportions which, the members felt, eight of these old English patent medicines *ought* to contain. Turlington's Balsam of Life, for example, had been intended originally as "an elegant and rich balsamic tincture," and the committee prepared a formula seeking to respect this purpose, while reducing the number of ingredients from the twenty-seven listed in the 1744 English patent specifications to nine.[25]

It may be ironic that the first significant action of the first American college of pharmacy was to sanction the preparation of patent medicines. But the step had been undertaken for a worthy end, to strip the various imitations on the market of "their extravagant pretensions."

The proprietors of American nostrums of secret composition came in for even harsher rebuke. These men, in Dr. Oliver Wendell Holmes' phrase, were "the mushroom, say rather, the toadstool millionaires."[26] Holmes and his colleagues condemned them as greedy, dishonest, obscene, and heartless. There was no end to the quack's effrontery. He pretended to be a trained physician when he was not. He fabricated testimonials. He created diseases. He gave his nostrums foreign names and said they were imported from abroad. He asserted they were made of rare and expensive ingredients. He used the poor as decoys for the rich, trumping up a false philanthropy in claiming to treat the indigent for nothing. He crept under the mantle of all the persecuted scientists of history, asking self-righteously if Galileo and Harvey, Copernicus and Franklin, had not been treated with skepticism by the learned of their day. He faked statistical evi-

25 *Formulae for the Preparation of Eight Patent Medicines, Adopted by the Philadelphia College of Pharmacy* (Phila., 1824); Kremers and Urdang, 178.
26 Holmes, *Medical Essays*, 186.

dence of alleged cures. He insisted that his nostrums could cure with dispatch diseases that could be cured only slowly. He boasted that his remedies could cure with certainty diseases that could not be cured at all.[27]

Quacks were adept at prescribing for general symptoms as well as for specific diseases. Whatever the illness, if it became chronic, certain conditions were apt to appear, such as general weakness, ill-defined pains in the back and sides, sick headache, fluttering about the heart, night sweats, an oppressive fullness of the stomach, irregularity of the bowels, loss of weight, nervousness, despondency. Patent medicine promoters listed dozens of such symptoms, some of which indeed might occur in a person not really sick at all. These afflictions, as a doctor pointed out, seemed "very definite and clear to a patient or his friends, but beautifully indefinite to a penetrating and acute physician."[28]

All this had the most disastrous consequences. People who were not really sick were frightened into the medicine habit. Once started, they kept on, if only to get their money's worth from what they had bought. The continued use of laxatives was especially dangerous. "Few patients among the lower classes," wrote a doctor, "now apply to a physician, who have not previously aggravated their complaints by swallowing numbers of these pretended specifics."[29] Another habit that nostrums might engender was alcoholism. The temperance crusade was in full swing, and many Americans were signing the pledge. But some of them, unknowingly, were imbibing quantities of alcohol in the remedies they relied on, including many patent medicines advertised as containing none. A fate even more dire lay in the opium habit. Nothing could be more cruel than the fastening of this insidious monster on the backs of innocent men, women, and children. To make things worse, the disease often became more

[27] The summary of the critique of quackery is based on many articles, printed orations, and resolutions. A few representative titles are: Ticknor; Holmes; John Morgan, *A Warning against Quackery* (Boston, 1851); Lewis H. Steiner, *Oration before the Medical and Surgical Society of Baltimore* (Balt., 1859); Paul F. Eve, *The Present Position of the Medical Profession in Society* (Augusta, Ga., 1849); William O. Baldwin, *Physic and Physicians* (Cambridge, Mass., 1866); "Quackery and the Quacked," *Ntl. Quarterly Rev.*, 2 (1861), 355, *Jnl. of Health*, 1 (1830), 348-50; Reese, *Humbugs of New-York*; William A. Alcott, *Dosing and Drugging* (Boston, 1839).

[28] J. R. Black, "Thoughts on the Prevalence of Quackery," *Cinc. Lancet and Observer*, 4 (1861), 58-62.

[29] Cited in Walsh, *History of the Medical Society of the State of New York*, 134-35.

serious while the patient, his pain deadened by the narcotic, acquired a false impression that he was on the road to recovery.

The delay in consulting an expert physician that often resulted from the use of nostrums, the critics charged, could amount to murder. The "most usual effect" of the employment of patent medicines, according to one doctor, was "to convert medicable into incurable disease, with its train of domestic distresses and bereavements." Sometimes the threat of life was even more direct. Many nostrums contained poisonous ingredients in high proportion, or in small quantities but badly mixed. All in all, one doctor was convinced, "nothing is more certain . . . than that quackery kills a larger number, annually, of the citizens of the United States than all the diseases which it is pretended to cure, together with all the explosions that take place on our steamboats, all the accidents which occur on our railroads, and all the houses that tumble down on their inmates."[30]

For such a dire threat to the life and health of the American people, the nostrum maker was not alone to blame. He had allies, if often unwitting ones, who must share the awful responsibility. There were the "old aunt Betsies," the "female would-be missionaries," who went from door to door giving bad advice about patent medicines to the sick. The clergy, in this respect, were a positive menace. Their motives might be commendable, but in suggesting nostrums to ailing members of their congregations, ministers were ducks sadly out of water. When the recommendation came in the form of an endorsement to adorn advertisements spread across the pages of the nation's press, the situation was ten times worse. "How often," inquired one doctor, "do we see the filthy patent nostrums rendered palatable and find ready sale by the indorsement of some minister of the Gospel?" What if the shoe were on the other foot, asked another physician, and doctors of medicine went around recommending books filled with "the subtle poison of infidelity"? In such a case, "would not every pulpit, from Maine to Mexico, thunder forth with anathemas against the medical profession"? And would not the charge of "warring against Christianity" be absolutely just?[31]

Others besides the clergy were rebuked by physicians for providing testimonials for patent medicines. "Men may be wise

[30] *Jnl. of Health*, 1 (1830), 348; *Ntl. Quarterly Rev.*, 2 (1861), 357.
[31] Baldwin, 63; *St. Louis Med. and Surg. Jnl.*, 4 (1846), 244.

and just princes, proud and wealthy lords, . . . sagacious and eminent statesmen, and shrewd and wily lawyers," observed an Alabama doctor, "and yet fail to be the best possible judge of a medical doctrine."[32] There was the continuing problem of the black sheep within the medical fold: the regulars who behaved so badly they drove their patients into the arms of quackery; the editors who accepted nostrum advertising for the pages of medical journals; the doctors who wrote testimonials as eloquent as those of the veriest clergyman; worst of all, the physicians who themselves made and vended secret remedies. In the orations and in the resolutions about such erring brethren, the tone was perhaps more often pleading than execrating. But it was criticism nonetheless, it kept on and on, and medical societies took action against the worst offenders.

The masses of the American people, noted the critics, were fundamentally responsible for the magnitude of the patent medicine evil, for they bought the medicines. Yet they were more sinned against than sinning, ignorant victims of their own credulity. The common man could not handle evidence rationally. The vigor of an argument rather than its sense seemed to persuade him. Man's reasoning seemed to flounder particularly when the issues related to things medical, which constituted, one doctor felt, the "most difficult, obscure, and complicated" of all branches of human learning.[33] In such a confusing field, people tended to hearken to the voice of authority, whether or not it was qualified to speak. Hence nostrum testimonials were so effective. Common-sense logic often persuaded a man of the value of a patent medicine. He was sick, he dosed himself with a nostrum, he got well—ergo, the patent remedy cured him. It was so easy to feel sure that an event which came first in time was therefore a cause. That nature healed most illnesses, sometimes in spite of nostrums, was not easy to perceive. Most people adhered stubbornly to their privilege of making their own medical decisions and acting on them. "A man's [medical] ignorance," said Dr. Holmes, sadly, "is as much his private property, and as precious in his own eyes, as his family Bible."[34]

All these hazards to sound judgment were made more frightful, anti-nostrum writers indicated, when illness was present.

32 Baldwin, 25.   33 Eve, 22.   34 Holmes, 380.

People "tortured by pain, or distressed by affliction," were very prone to look to "delusive sources for relief." They preferred to hear what was hopeful and agreeable rather than what was true, "and the flattering and confident promises of the empiric, often out-weigh[ed] the cautious and candid decisions of the physician." This was particularly true when the disease was grave, and honest doctors could offer little hope. Then the quacks gave forth their most deceptive assurances. What of the young man whose parents, brothers, and sisters have died of consumption, when he detects the first symptoms of this dread affliction? He sees an advertisement promising a cure. "His heart is cheered, his fears are in a measure dispelled, and with eagerness he procures and takes the medicine." For several weeks he may feel better, since the nostrum is doubtless "of a stimulating nature." Then he declines, and "with four-fold rapidity the poor victim is hurried into eternity."[35]

Some medical observers were gloomy. The credulity of the people, they believed, was an inborn trait which nothing could change. Quackery, therefore, was "peculiar to no particular age, or country, or state of society." "It has existed," proclaimed one of the discouraged, "from the earliest periods, and will continue to exist as long as human beings are found upon the earth."[36]

In the age of the common man, it was the aristocratic die-hard who was thus pessimistic about human potentialities. The weight of opinion, even of the medical opinion that made itself heard, was hopeful. If man could be shown the error of his ways, he would improve. "Quackery . . . is the legitimate offspring of ignorance," asserted an orator at the opening of a new medical school in the West, "and can only be abridged by elevating the standard of medicine, and disseminating a correct public sentiment." In "an intelligent community," the orator was persuaded, "quackery could not flourish."[37] Optimistic doctors set about trying to make their communities intelligent. The very volume of the anti-nostrum literature is a token of the confidence of the critics, for the articles and orations—often printed to give them a

[35] 1809 address by Nicholas Romayne, cited in Walsh, 101; Eve, 6; Morgan, 15-17.

[36] John M. Beck, *An Historical Sketch of the State of Medicine in the American Colonies* (2nd ed., Albany, 1850), 22.

[37] *Addresses Delivered by Professor* [Charles K.] *Winston* and [Paul] *Eve*, *at the Opening of the Medical Department of the University of Nashville* (Nash., 1851), 9-10.

wider circulation—were themselves a part of the campaign to enlighten. The public did not realize the magnitude of the evil and must be taught. "If the people were aware of the immense amount of such [patent medicine] sales, and of the impaired health, the ruined constitutions, and the premature deaths, which they occasion, they would be astounded."[38] So wrote Lemuel Shattuck in his pioneering report on the public health. Scores of physicians agreed with him, and with voice and pen sought to specify the hazards to purse and health posed by nostrums.

Over and over again, doctors sought to shock the common man into common sense by asking some variation of this theme: "Who would employ a blacksmith to repair a watch, a barber to shoe a horse, a ship-carpenter to make bonnets, or a milliner to build a church? Or who would send a son to a dumb man to learn elocution, or to one born deaf to be taught music? And yet it is quite as reasonable and philosophical to do one of these things, as to expect that the human system should be repaired by one who knows nothing of it."[39]

Some physicians were willing to combine a little legislating with the educational crusade. On the national level, the step proposed was negative rather than positive, to repeal or modify the patent law so that compound medicines could no longer receive this form of governmental protection. This was the recommendation of a select committee of the House of Representatives after an investigation in 1849, but Congress took no action. Still some physicians did not give up hope. "The time will come," predicted one doctor, "when that system of legislation which allows unprincipled men, for their private benefit, to send forth patent medicines under the great seal of the nation, will be seen to be no other than a licensed imposition on the public."[40] That the time would come when Congress would legislate positively against patent medicines was a possibility not yet dreamed of.

Nor was anti-nostrum legislation on the state level a real possibility during the age of the common man. While laws prescribing the standards for medical practitioners were being repealed in wholesale fashion, other laws controlling the doctor's competition from patent pills and potions stood little chance of

---

[38] Shattuck, *Report of the Sanitary Commission of Massachusetts, 1850*, 219.
[39] Ticknor, 131.
[40] *Patent Medicines*, House Report No. 52, 30 Cong., 2 ses. (1849); Shafer, *The American Medical Profession, 1783 to 1850*, 220.

passage. The most frequent of the vain proposals made by physicians would have required that the names of ingredients and suggested dosage be plainly printed on the label of every patent medicine. This was a sort of enlightenment by fiat. "Let but the composition of secret remedies be once known to the community," insisted one physician, "and the death knell to empiricism will have sounded."[41] But no laws were passed to put such a hopeful prediction to the test.

The educational crusade against the nostrum evil may have deterred some potential purchasers from dosing themselves with alcoholic elixirs and pain-killing opiates. Nonetheless, all the pamphlets, articles, and resolutions by the opponents of quackery were too small a dike to stem the mighty flood of patent medicine advertising. The sale of nostrums grew and grew.

Take the Panacea of William Swaim. The medical societies of the two leading cities of the nation had attacked this remedy and the proprietor's methods of promoting it. Other critics had spoken out against him. Had he been seriously hurt?

In the same year that he issued his pamphlet reply to the attack, Swaim opened in Philadelphia some public baths, with separate apartments for women and men, the latter equipped with a bar room, and a total of fifty tubs, some tin-plated copper, some Italian marble.[42] Was the nostrum proprietor fearful of a decline in the sale of his Panacea, and hence diversifying his economic interests? Or were the baths financed out of the profits from his remedy?

Swaim also cut the price of his Panacea. Did this act stem from a falling market caused by the public reaction to the doctors' condemnations? Or was Swaim fighting the competition created by his own success?

Truth to tell, Swaim was prospering. He might, in fact, have been less angry at the medical committees than he was at the effrontery of a rival, who stole for his own use in advertising the now-repudiated testimonial of Dr. Chapman, merely changing the name Swaim to Shinn. Competition was a problem for the ex-bookbinder. Many sarsaparilla nostrums came on the market, some of them flavored with oil of wintergreen. With regular

41 Eve, 16.
42 Harold D. Eberlein, "When Society First Took a Bath," *Pa. Mag. Hist. and Biog.*, 67 (1943), 46-47.

physicians, the root was to lose caste in a short time, and compound sarsaparilla syrup was to continue in the *Pharmacopoeia* only because it served as a vehicle for truly active drugs and as a mask for such flavors as castor oil. In the realm of pseudo-medicine, however, the sarsaparilla vogue was to be vast and persistent, reaching its apogee in the concoctions of Brandreth and Ayer and Hood.[43]

William Swaim, in the good old 19th-century tradition, triumphed over all obstacles. Neither competition nor criticism seriously deterred his rise to wealth. By mid-century his worth was estimated at half a million dollars, and he later spent considerable time abroad. Decades after its original proprietor had passed from the terrestrial scene, the squat octagonal bottles of the Panacea were still enjoying a brisk sale.[44]

Hercules was still hoisting his knotted club to do battle with the Hydra.

[43] *A Treatise on Swaim's Panacea*, vi, [156-57]; Lloyd, 39; *U.S. Dispensatory, 1950*, 1,007-1,010.

[44] Herman L. Collins and Wilfred Jordan, *Philadelphia* (N.Y., 1941), III, 157; Henry Holcombe, "Private Die Proprietary Stamp Notes," *Wkly. Philatelic Gossip*, Mar. 25, 1939, 39-41. A bottle of the Panacea bottled after the 1906 Pure Food and Drugs Act is in the author's possession; evidence in the Swaim folder in the Dept. of Investigation of the Amer. Med. Assoc. in Chicago suggests the remedy was made at least into the 1930's.

PURGATION UNLIMITED

*"This is the whole subject in a nut-shell.
Whatever makes bad digestion breeds disease;
whatever makes good digestion cures disease."*

—BENJAMIN BRANDRETH, 1862[1]

GLOBULES of sarsaparilla are identical with globules of blood. Such was the astounding discovery of the distinguished German chemist, Justus von Liebig. At any rate, so asserted an advertising pamphlet issued in 1860. Great as was this achievement, the pamphleteer argued, the Teutonic scientist did not deserve sole credit. Liebig had merely proved what an English immigrant in America had found out a quarter of a century before. Peering through a microscope, Benjamin Brandreth had detected the similarity between the two kinds of globules. Brandreth now put a drawing in his pamphlet to demonstrate to the most casual observer that he and Liebig were right, that blood and sarsaparilla were the same.[2]

The medical implications of such a discovery were clear. If the concrete alkaloid of this ancient American plant, which Columbus himself had first carried back to Europe, could be bound up in a pill, then that pill was certain to impart "extra vitality" to the blood of any man, woman, or child wise enough to take it. Dr. Brandreth had performed this medical miracle, and the result was his Life-Addition Pills.

Thus was a new change rung on the perennially popular sarsaparilla theme. Dr. Brandreth's devotion to the American root was fervent and long-standing, and he was likewise wholly committed to the blood. The blood's vast significance to man, indeed, was made manifest in Holy Writ, and Brandreth was

[1] *Dr. Benjamin Brandreth's Vegetable Universal Pills* (N.Y.?, 1862), Rare Book Div., Library of Congress.

[2] *Dr. B. Brandreth's Life-Addition Pills and Quintessence of Sarsaparilla* (N.Y., 1860), Rare Book Div., Library of Congress.

[75]

fond of citing Leviticus 17:11: "The life of the flesh is in the blood." This vital fluid must at all costs be kept pure. The Life-Addition Pills could aid in this task, to be sure, but major reliance must be placed, for reasons we shall observe, upon the Vegetable Universal Pills. These were another, and an earlier, contribution of Dr. Brandreth to the therapeutics of America, although not his invention. He had learned their composition—which included sarsaparilla—from his paternal grandfather.

Dr. William Brandreth, a physician who practiced in Liverpool, had devoted thirty years in the mid-18th century to perfecting this combination of herbs. His own son was not interested in matters medical; as a young man he gained renown as a musician, but conversion to the Society of Friends caused him to abandon music for a mercantile career. It was the merchant's sixth and youngest son, Benjamin, born about 1808, who followed in the footsteps of his grandfather. As a lad at Dr. William's knee, Benjamin began to learn his medical secrets. Soon he was compounding the vegetable pills and, according to family record, distributing them gratuitously among the poor. Upon the death of his grandfather, Benjamin, a young man in his late teens, inherited the formula and began to market the pills over a wider area. Perhaps he applied merchandising talents observed in his father. Things went rather well, but English opportunities presented the ambitious Brandreth with an inadequate challenge. In 1835 he came to America and rented a house on Hudson Street in the city of New York. "Brandreth," opined a critic, "could never have succeeded in his own country; but he saw that the people of the United States, like young birds in their nest, were holding their mouths wide open for something new."[3]

Brandreth was nearing twenty-five when he crossed the ocean. He brought with him, besides his grandfather's formula, a wife, three children, and a modest amount of capital. The first American production of the Vegetable Universal Pills was a family venture. The father mixed the ingredients; the mother pasted the

3 *Ibid.; N.Y. Tribune*, Feb. 20, 1880; Holcombe, "Private Die Proprietary Stamp Notes," *Scott's Monthly Journal*, 20 (1939), 120-21; information provided by Mrs. Laurance D. Redway, Ossining Hist. Soc.; Dan King, *Quackery Unmasked* (Boston, 1858), 295. Sources differ on the date of Brandreth's birth, from 1807 to 1809. *Rowell's American Newspaper Directory, 1870*, 173, says that at the time Brandreth began making pills rumors had it that his formula had really come from an elderly man he met either on his voyage over or soon after arriving in New York.

labels on the boxes; the eldest son counted out the pills. The cost of raw materials and advertising drained the family purse. As a granddaughter recounted the tale, Benjamin Brandreth nailed his last three gold pieces to the counter before any money came back across it in payment for pills.[4]

The lean years, however, were less than seven. Prosperity, indeed, came with a rush. The very next year after his arrival, Brandreth was forced to add two sales outlets to the house on Hudson Street, and this dwelling no longer doubled as the family residence. In 1837 still another sales office was opened, and the pill doctor took the major step of moving his manufacturing operations away from the city to a village up the Hudson River. Its name was Sing Sing. There Brandreth found a large tract of land containing a grain mill, which he bought and refashioned to his purposes. While the pills poured out in an ever-increasing flood, Brandreth began to build a larger factory. Across its doorway, according to a later chronicler, the entrepreneur placed a Latin motto, "Cavando Tutus," meaning, said the chronicler, "Tested and Not Found Wanting." A better rendering, since it might serve as a tribute peculiarly appropriate to the active principle of Brandreth's popular product, would be "Safe in Evacuating." For he had made a panacea of a purgative.[5]

Within five years the vigorous Englishman became the *ne plus ultra* of American nostrum-making. Coins came back across his counter so rapidly that in 1839 his wealth was estimated at $200,000. The next year a rival paid him this grudging tribute: "Dr. Brandreth figures larger in the scale of quackery, and hoists a more presuming flag, than all the rest of the fraternity combined."[6]

Brandreth had indeed chosen a most propitious time to hoist his flag. The dietary dark ages still prevailed when the English pill man came to America. Well into the 19th century the belief was popular that all foods contained one "universal element" which kept life going. Over-eating was a national scandal, as foreign visitors to the nation kept repeating, an evil compounded

[4] Information from Mrs. Redway; Holcombe, 121; J. Thomas Scharf, *History of Westchester County, New York* (Phila., 1886), II, 359-61.

[5] Holcombe, 121-22; *Longworth's American Almanac, New-York Register, and City Directory*, 1835-1838.

[6] *Graham Jnl. of Health and Longevity*, 3 (1839), 245; William Euen, *A Short Expose on Quackery* (Phila., 1840), 7.

by a diet stressing starchy dishes, salt-cured meats, fat-fried foods and lacking in fresh fruits and vegetables. Americans also ate too fast. The national motto, one European traveler said, was "gobble, gulp, and go."[7]

Many of these conditions had prevailed for generations, but a rural mode of life, replete with fresh air, sunshine, and vigorous physical labor, had tended to mitigate the consequences. Now, in town and city, people lived at a faster pace and under more pressure, often without proper exercise. "We are fast becoming . . . a nation of invalids," an author charged in *Harper's Monthly* during 1856. "Foreigners already effect to see in us a degenerate offspring of a nobler race, and with them a skeleton frame, a yellow-dyed bilious face, an uncomfortable dyspeptic expression, an uneasy spasmodic motion, and a general ghost-like charnel-house aspect, serve to make up a type of the species Yankee." Such physical traits were embodied in the symbolical Uncle Sam.[8]

Purges of various potencies were a popular prescription by regular physicians. The quacks too, as a New York doctor pointed out, had fastened on the "almost universal prevalence of indigestion." But no one who read the advertisements had to be told. There were scores of remedies on the market "whose chief mission," as a pharmacist saw it, "appear[ed] to be to open men's purses by opening their bowels." It was no wonder that one nostrum which failed when promoted as a cold cure should achieve success as a stomach remedy.[9]

In these years, however, laxatives were not content to perform a simple role. Their service to mankind must be glorified and elevated. The ways in which nostrum makers sought to make indigestion and constipation the source of all illness were explicit and ingenious. Benjamin Brandreth was merely the most successful of a numerous tribe. His Universal Vegetable Pills, besides sarsaparilla, seem to have contained aloes, gamboge, and colocynth, among the most powerful cathartic cannon in the botani-

[7] Richard O. Cummings, *The American and His Food* (Chicago, 1941), 4, 23-24; Arthur M. Schlesinger, *Paths to the Present* (N.Y., 1949), 240-42.

[8] *Ibid.*, 242; "Why We Get Sick," *Harper's Monthly*, 13 (1856), 643.

[9] Shafer, *The American Medical Profession, 1783 to 1850*, 99-100; Reese, *Humbugs of New-York*, 121; George D. Coggeshall, "Address . . . ," *Amer. Jnl. Pharm.*, 26 (1854), 205; Frank Presbrey, *The History and Development of Advertising* (Garden City, N.Y., 1929), 297.

cal armory,[10] and with the theme of purgation Brandreth seemed genuinely obsessed.

In long advertisements in newspaper and magazine, in special pamphlets, even in books, Brandreth reiterated that "purgation may be set down as the magnet, the guide, the star of safety." The logic leading to such a conclusion began with the familiar premise that all disease had but one cause. This was "an alteration or vitiation of the blood." Many were the evil forces that might upset the digestion and render the blood impure. It might be bad food, it might be grief, it might be overwork, anxiety, impure water, contagion, a hundred things. Especially vicious was polluted air, a result of "the artificial conditions in which society has placed the human race," which was inhaled, adding corrupt particles to the blood. Bits and pieces of worn-out muscles and nerves were another hazard. They became separated from the body solids and, unless eliminated, corroded and produced disease. Disease had various forms: pleurisies, consumptions, dropsies, rheumatisms, blotches, plagues, fevers, "great nervousness and debility, accompanied with anxiety and dread that some sad event is about to occur."[11]

The human body, indeed, was a constant battleground between the forces of life and death. If the pollutions and decompositions could be gotten rid of with sufficient speed through the natural outlets, life went on and man was healthy. This, alas, too seldom happened. Much too often the tide of battle turned in favor of the "death-disposing influences." "It is a remarkable and incontrovertible fact," Brandreth insisted, "that not one person in a thousand dies of old age." Nay, fewer than that. In all his life he had actually known but three. But such sad statistics need not be. "Premature death in nine hundred and ninety nine cases out of a thousand is the consequence of disease being allowed to progress unchecked in the body, whereas by timely *pergation* [*sic*] it might have been successfully nipped in the bud, and finally removed."

With Brandreth, as with the monistic regulars, it was one cure as well as one cause. "The doctrines of the unity of disease and of

10 Holcombe, 120; Charles W. Oleson, *Secret Nostrums and Systems of Medicine* (5th ed., Chicago, 1894), 18-19.

11 Brandreth's doctrines are taken from *Dr. Brandreth's Vegetable Universal Pills; Purgation: or The Brandrethian Method* (N.Y., 1840); *The Doctrine of Purgation* (N.Y., 1867; 3rd ed., 1873); and various advertisements.

one method of cure," he said, "are but the two halves of one great truth." Purgation was not enough, of course. It must be purgation by Brandreth's Vegetable Universal Pills. The proprietor recognized that there were other cathartics on the market. The "owls and the bats of the learned faculty" had their poisonous mineral purgatives, and such dangerous drugs as mercury, arsenic, antimony, and hemlock might be found in rival advertised remedies. Brandreth scorned his competitors, and left them "to banquet on their own envy." He could not be "confounded with the promiscuous crowd of medicine venders that infest our streets." His pills were vegetable and had been used for a century without one "fatal consequence." They might be taken safely in any quantity. "A dose more of Brandreth's Pills than required, will never hurt you, but not taking a dose when required, may cost you your life." A New York female had doubtless saved hers by taking, in twenty-fours hours, no less than sixty-six. She, and all users, could be assured that the small pellets possessed "the great advantage . . . that *they never make any mistakes.*"

"Purge then, ye wise," exhorted one of Brandreth's pamphlets, "before your sickness is too far advanced, and by the blessing of God, and Brandreth's Pills, insure your safety and your life."

Other purgatives were purveyed by similar theories, but there was a certain distinction to Brandreth's treatment which his rivals could not emulate. He had an arrogant tone, a literary flavor, an historical sweep in his advertising copy which were unique. His assertions were so pontifical, sometimes bolstered by the Latin phrase. His authorities were so respectable, including William Harvey, Benjamin Rush, and Benjamin Franklin. And his grasp of the past was so daring. Who else would think of publishing a volume of 224 pages, bearing such an imposing title as *The Doctrine of Purgation, Curiosities from Ancient and Modern Literature, from Hippocrates and Other Medical Writers* —some two hundred sages were cited—*Covering a Period of Over Two Thousand Years, Proving Purgation Is the Corner-Stone of All Curatives*? Who would guess that such a volume, once compiled, would pass through three editions?

Benjamin Brandreth paid not only for the solid bound volumes and the flimsy pamphlets, but for thousands of columns of newspaper space. The quantity of his advertising, as well as its peculiar quality, sets the pill maker apart and helps to explain his outstanding success.

Brandreth sent his copy into the hinterlands, where new counties and new county weeklies continued to proliferate. In Illinois and Michigan—so he boasted in his Indiana advertising—people rode sixty miles through the woods for Brandreth's Pills. City-dwellers did not have to go so far, and Brandreth was particularly attracted to the new sensational penny press.[12]

Brandreth was a lavish advertising patron of the first-established of these papers, Benjamin Day's *New York Sun*, as he was of Day's even more flamboyant rival, James Gordon Bennett's *Herald*. Indeed, Brandreth began to produce and distribute his purgative in the same month that Bennett began to print and distribute his paper. Later stories had it that a thousand dollars of advance advertising from Brandreth was a welcome part of Bennett's initial capital, and that some months later, when a fire destroyed the plant of the new penny paper, the Brandreth account permitted Bennett to start in again. The first tale is probably false, the second more likely. There is no doubt, at any rate, that Brandreth paid thousands of dollars to the *Herald* for hundreds of columns of space.[13]

Brandreth and Bennett were not unlike. Both were immigrants, Bennett from Scotland, Brandreth from England, and their association began as both were in the early stages of phenomenal careers. Bennett once called himself one of the "Napoleons of the press." With equal justice Brandreth might have adopted the title of Napoleon of the nostrums. Both men lived by words. Bennett's leaders and editorials were frank, saucy, spicy, often accused of being in bad taste. The same was true of Brandreth's advertisements, whether or not he wrote them himself. Both men were also successful. As the *Herald* grew in circulation and in the revenue it brought its proprietor, so did the pills.[14]

Both men were interested in profits. Responding to a criticism of the pill maker's advertising copy, the publisher replied: "Send us more advertisements than Dr. Brandreth does—give us higher

[12] Pickard and Buley, *The Midwest Pioneer*, 284.
[13] *N.Y. Sun* and *Herald*, 1835-1840, *passim*; M. R. Werner, *Barnum* (N.Y., 1923), 26; information provided by Mrs. Redway.
[14] *Herald*, Aug. 18, 1836; Oliver Carlson, *The Man Who Made News, James Gordon Bennett* (N.Y., 1942).

[81]

prices—we'll cut Brandreth dead—or at least curtail his space. Business is business—money is money."[15]

This sort of defense has been termed the *caveat emptor* alibi for advertising. It was not infrequently resorted to when the press was attacked for the scandalous nature of some of the copy it accepted for pay. The same year that Bennett so tersely excused himself, the *Philadelphia Public Ledger* printed a more elaborate expression of the doctrine. "We admit any advertisement of any things or any opinions, from any person who will pay the price," the *Ledger* explained, "excepting what is forbidden by the laws of the land, or what, in the opinion of *all*, is offensive to decency and morals." Nor did the paper hold itself responsible for any ad. "In allowing Peter Pill Garlic to puff his pills, or Long-legged Legget to laud his lotion, or Oliver Overreach to be orator for his opodeldoc, we do not indorse for the disease-dispelling potency of any of these drugs." Any competitor was free to advertise, pointing out the weakness of rival remedies. "Besides," the *Ledger* argued, "our advertising is our revenue, and in a paper involving so many expenses as a penny paper. . . , the *only* source of revenue, and we get our living honestly by permitting our advertising columns to be a stage for the whole public to act upon, we excluding all actors unlicensed by the law of morals or the law of the land."[16]

What was true for the penny sheet in the city was true for the country weekly. Without nostrum advertising, an Ohio village editor pointed out, his paper would require a paid circulation of two thousand copies rather than just a few hundred. "The bones," he said, "are sold with the beef."[17]

Under these circumstances, that there was any criticism of nostrums at all in the pages of the press seems a matter for remark. The young Kaskaskia *Illinois Intelligencer*, in 1820, reprinted from an Eastern newspaper a denunciation of quackery in general, "from the humble villager who vends the infallible cure for agues, to the political quack who would fain persuade us that every temporizing expedient is the political panacea." A decade later the *Intelligencer* returned to the attack by citing from a Philadelphia journal the argument that patent medicines were antithetical both to science and philanthropy.[18]

[15] *Herald*, June 26, 1836.
[17] Pickard and Buley, 269.
[16] *Ledger*, Sep. 26, 1836.
[18] Sep. 16, 1820, and Sep. 11, 1830.

The borrowed words in this Illinois weekly indicate that the large dailies of the East were not entirely silent on the evils of quackery, but there was little consistency in the matter. In 1805, after a young girl had been killed by a patent medicine, the *Post* in New York denounced "the quack advertisements which . . . so much distinguish and disgrace the city." Yet not a month went by that did not witness some quack advertising in the same paper. Two decades later a similar incident occurred. When the Philadelphia Medical Society issued its criticism of Swaim's and similar panaceas, the *Post* printed excerpts from the report. Nonetheless, in the very same issue, the paper began to run an advertisement for one of the condemned nostrums. Such a schizoid policy was even stranger than the incident involving a weekly paper in Fort Wayne, Indiana. When a temporary editor wrote that "Every village newspaper from the North to the South, and from the East to the West, is filled with . . . [the nostrum maker's] trash," the regular editor, resuming control, promptly repudiated such a rash assertion.[19]

In 1835 a quack dentist, peeved by some jibe at his expense in the *New York Sun*, challenged one of the paper's reporters to a duel. The journalist accepted and was called upon to name the weapons. Syringes, he said, filled with a nostrum of the dentist's own manufacture.[20] This symbolizes the larger duel between press and patent medicines during the first half of the 19th century. The participants ran about the same degree of risk. Certainly the newspapers, though a watchdog of the public interest, were not apt to bite with vigor the hand that fed so lavishly. So the quantity of criticism was small, the tone often mild, and the purpose frequently not so much a sincere attack on quackery as a means of lambasting a rival journal.

In New York especially, most of the condemnation of nostrums that was printed in the papers sounds as if it were penned for use as a weapon in the tempestuous rivalry that characterized this age of personal journalism. The great dailies were the sharp shadows of their editors, and competition was keen and bitter. Horace Greeley, soon to launch the *Tribune*, avowed his hatred of "the immoral and degrading Police Reports, Advertisements,

[19] Alfred M. Lee, *The Daily Newspaper in America* (N.Y., 1937), 316; Willard G. Bleyer, *Main Currents in the History of American Journalism* (Boston, 1927), 148; Pickard and Buley, 270.
[20] Frank O'Brien, *The Story of the Sun* (N.Y., 1928), 35.

and other matter which have been allowed to disgrace the columns of many of our leading Penny Papers." Several weeks after the *Tribune* had begun publishing, Greeley loosed a vitriolic attack on Day's *Sun* and Bennett's *Herald* for accepting advertising from a notorious abortionist. "By constant publication and puffing in *The Sun*," Greeley stormed, "backed by puffing Editorials in the *Herald*, the dreadful trade of this wretch was made to thrive and gold flowed in streams into her den, and thence to the pockets of her newspaper accomplices. Must not this blood-money prove a curse to its receivers? . . . What demoniac practices shall be next resorted to, to glut the avarice of these vampyres?"[21]

The *Tribune* did not accept advertisements for abortionists or venereal cures, but it opened its columns to a horehound candy good for "spitting of blood, [and] contraction of the lungs," and Indian remedies which would cure consumption, scrofula, cancer, piles, painful menstruation, and falling of the womb. When a reader wrote Greeley objecting to the tone of some of these ads, the editor sought refuge in the *caveat emptor* alibi. The critic had mailed the letter to the wrong party, Greeley editorialized. "He should complain to our advertisers themselves, who are not responsible to us for the style or language (if decent) of their advertisements, nor have we any control over them."[22]

So it went. The newspapers continued to accept nostrum advertising, interpreting moral decency as the editors saw fit, and damning their rivals for devising definitions which were unspeakably odious. In 1852 Henry J. Raymond's *New York Times* entered the fray, castigating an unnamed antagonist, probably the *Herald*. A decade later the *Herald* returned the compliment, abusing the *Times*. The next year the *Tribune* had at the *Herald* again.[23]

If newspapers assailed each other's advertising for ulterior motives, there were external critics who blasted the press for puffing patent medicines. In the eyes of physicians, the guilt of the newspaper editor was second only to that of the nostrum maker. "Nothing can be done without the Press—" wrote the physician-author of *Quackery Unmasked*, "enterprise must stop

21 Bleyer, 213; *Tribune*, Apr. 30, 1841.
22 *Ibid.*, Dec. 20, 1841.
23 *Times*, May 28, 1852; *Herald*, Jan. 8, 1862; *Tribune*, Feb. 18, 1863.

here, and the skill of the wizard be hushed in darkness, unless the Press will publish it to the world." The doctors on the Philadelphia committee rebuked newspapers not only for accepting Swaim's preposterous advertising, but also for refusing to print information provided them pointing out the evils of patent medicines. Such slings and arrows were frequent from outraged doctors who were persuaded that the situation amounted to nothing less than the "prostitution of the press."[24]

In the squabbles over patent medicines and the press, the voice of the nostrum maker was rarely heard, publicly, at least. One of the few such battles in the record, happily, was waged between truly noteworthy contestants, those two Napoleons, James Gordon Bennett and Benjamin Brandreth. They had begun their rise to fortune hand in hand, and were personally friendly, even though Bennett had let it be known in the *Herald* that the comradeship was purely a financial one. Should a rival outbid Brandreth, the publisher said, he would restrict or eliminate the pill maker's advertising. On March 17, 1837, Brandreth's status in Bennett's columns remained unchallenged. The champion of purgation devoted several column inches to a defense of his remedy against the "vile allusions" of jealous rivals.[25]

This very day, however, according to Bennett's account, he told his clerk to "expunge" from the *Herald* all of Brandreth's advertising and to return him any money he may have paid in advance. The next day no Brandreth ad appeared. Three days later an editorial heralded an imminent attack on medical quackery "which has of late increased to such an extent in this city as to banish all science and talent from our borders." On March 23 Bennett was ready. He launched his acrimonious rhetoric with a garbled quotation from *Hamlet*:

> I will a tale unfold, whose lightest word
> Will harrow up thy soul.

"For many months past," ran Bennett's tale, "this city has been flooded with medical pills from a certain laboratory, which appear to have spread over the face of the earth with the rapidity

[24] King, 249; *First Report of the Committee of the Philadelphia Medical Society on Quack Medicines*, 26-27; Ticknor, *A Popular Treatise on Medical Philosophy*, 277.
[25] *Times*, Feb. 20, 1880; *Herald*, June 26, 1836. On the squabble, see the *Herald*, Mar. 25 to April 24, 1836, and the *Sun*, Mar. 25.

and virulence of the ten plagues of Egypt. . . . At this moment the great Mokanna of Khorassan, the prophet of the silver veil, the Jannes and Jambres of medical learning, has entirely made every man, and woman, [and] child, so many living pill boxes, wandering over the streets—so many apothecaries' shops teeming with simples and overwhelmed with compounds—so many sickly physical laboratories crawling through human life from time to eternity."

Benjamin Brandreth was the guilty man. He had convinced "his dupes to swallow his pills as fast and as rapidly as they would their dinner." He had deluded them with "the merest twaddle of medical language that ever made the ignorant gape, or the educated cry 'bah!' "

"Since the appearance of Brandreth," the editor asserted, "more medicine has been swallowed in this community in one year than in the ten preceding."

"This is the age of Brandreth pills," Bennett charged. "No—this *has been* the age of Brandreth pills; but a revolution has begun and they will sink more rapidly into oblivion than they ever rose in consequence."

It had ever been his goal, Bennett testified, to keep his paper from becoming "the daily vehicle—the unconscious pander of imposture and humbug—of charlatanism, of impudence, . . . of ignorance pretending to science, or of folly in the habiliments of wisdom and philosophy." Because of this lofty aim, and because of a mountain of complaints against "this prince of charlatans—this master of the science of purging his patients of money and muscle—of cash, comfort, and calmness," the publisher had determined to deprive Brandreth of his right to advertise in the *Herald*.

The prince replied the next day, using the good offices of the rival *Sun*. Having taken such a verbal trouncing, Brandreth, it would seem, might have directed some of the harsh words he customarily bestowed upon his rivals toward the publisher with such a purple pen. Instead he chose to be mild. His strongest epithet for Bennett in the whole countercharge was "the old bachelor." As to the facts, however, Brandreth had a variant version. Bennett had raised the price of his paper from one to two pennies, noted the pill maker, which caused the circulation to decline and limited the readership to a class who paid no heed to advertising. Hence Brandreth had told his agent to take the advertisements for the Vegetable Universal Pills to other journals. "As to Bennett's censure," mocked Brandreth, "I glory in it—his praise I should fear."

The prince of pills had placards made and posted throughout the city teasing Bennett on his unmarried state, but otherwise he seemed not anxious to divert rhetoric from the positive purpose of promoting his nostrums. The editor, however, was loath to let the matter drop. He boasted of his benefactions to public health in exposing Brandreth, slashed at the *Sun* for defending him, and thought up new phrases for excoriating this "medical driveller," this "impudent quack." Bennett harped particularly on Brandreth's alleged pretensions as a writer. This was a huge joke, the editor said. Brandreth did not know how to "write or even spell correctly a sentence of common English," yet he palmed off as his own creations the productions of hired hack writers, who turned out not only advertisements, but literary articles and even a play (at $1.87½ a page). The situation called to Bennett's mind the old epigram:

> For physic and farces
> His equal there scarce is;
> His farce will be physic—
> His physic a farce is.

The publisher's attack on the pill maker was a farce itself. His acid quips at Brandreth's expense and his self-congratulation for defending the public rubbed elbows with advertisements for nostrums not a whit more respectable than the Vegetable Universal Pills. Indeed, a good many of the ads Bennett accepted were downright disgusting. In the venereal category alone, the *Herald* reader could choose from such remedies as Hunter's Red Drop, Mothes' Capsules, Sterling's Oriental Balsamic Compound, Dr. Jordan's Balsam of Rakasiri, Madam Gardion's Specific for Leucorrhoea, and Dr. Goodman's American Anti-Gonorrhoea Pills.

Stormy while it lasted, Bennett's feud with Brandreth, like most newspaper criticism of patent medicines, petered out. The pill maker's ads re-entered the columns of the *Herald* and became bigger than ever.[26] The erstwhile warriors resumed their ascent

[26] *Herald,* Jan. 18, 1840.

hand in hand to loftier levels of fame and fortune in their respective fields of journalism and purgation.

When, a decade later, a select committee of the House of Representatives wanted to show the lengths to which American patent medicine proprietors would go to boost their wares, Brandreth was selected as Exhibit A. His expenditures for advertising, the Congressmen said, had reached the sum of $100,000 a year. That Brandreth's tide had turned and his pills were destined for oblivion, as the committee suggested, proved as poor prophecy as had Bennett's similar prediction thirteen years before. The energetic immigrant continued to pour money into advertising, pioneering in such media as the weekly magazine. Pills rolled from Sing Sing in ever greater numbers. While the Congressmen were studying the nostrum scene, Brandreth bought an interest in a porous plaster plant, thus enlarging his hold on the people's health. In the twenty years from 1862 to 1883, during which proprietary remedies paid a federal excise tax, Brandreth's annual average business surpassed $600,000.[27]

Life in the village on the Hudson was ever busy. Benjamin Brandreth grew into the local squire. He was a solid man, his face round, his gaze direct. His abundant hair was combed straight back; his beard was full. Amiable of manner, Brandreth was esteemed for his wealth, his lack of ostentation, his liberal acts of charity. He took a personal interest in the families of his workers, helping out when crises came. During the summer, when the production of pills was low, he kept his employees on the payroll, paying them half their weekly winter wages. Brandreth became a banker, an Episcopal vestryman, a Knight Templar, a politician. For years he was president of the village. Often he represented his district in state and national Democratic conventions. Twice he was elected to the state Senate. Once he was beaten in a campaign for the national House.[28]

Down in New York City, Brandreth was not forgotten. In 1857 he built on Broadway a massive hotel that bore his name and housed the business offices of his concern. He helped establish the New York Eclectic Medical College, served as one of its

27 *Patent Medicines*, House Report No. 52, 30 Cong., 2 ses. (1849), 31; see ads in *Harper's Wkly.*, Feb. 19, 1859, and *Frank Leslie's Illustrated Newspaper*, Mar. 12, 1859; Holcombe, 164.
28 Engraved portrait of Brandreth in Scharf, ɪɪ, opposite 358; *N.Y. Tribune* and *Times*, Feb. 20, 1880; information provided by Mrs. Redway.

trustees, and contributed to its income. Since aloes and gamboge and colocynth played such vital roles in the Vegetable Universal Pills, it was fitting that Brandreth use some of his wealth to aid a school purveying botanical doctrines.[29]

Despite these widespread interests, Brandreth's Pills remained his primary concern. As it had been on Hudson Street, the making of these pills, and now of plasters, continued largely a family affair. Mrs. Brandreth had died before the move to Sing Sing. In 1837 Brandreth had remarried, and ten more children joined the family circle. Several sons played leading roles in the business, one of them taking the pills for sale back to the country of their origin. Such a homecoming would have delighted his great-grandfather.[30]

In 1880, some forty-five years after his migration to America, Benjamin Brandreth died, in his seventy-second year. He died in harness. That morning he had risen early, reaching the plant, with his eldest son, at six-thirty. He had worked an hour or so in the mixing room. Then came a stroke of apoplexy and death. Thus, at the end as at the launching of his venture in America, Brandreth was mixing the purgative in which he so fervently believed. He bequeathed his large family the factory which annually was marketing some two million boxes of pills. The family carried on.[31]

In the early 20th century, the name of Sing Sing was changed to Ossining. The essential function of Brandreth's Pills remained the same, the same as it had been when Benjamin had learned their potent secret at his grandfather's knee, the same as when James Gordon Bennett had blasted Brandreth for turning people into living pill boxes crawling from time to eternity.[32]

Cavando Tutus.

[29] *Ibid.; Appleton's Cyclopedia of American Biography*, I (1887), 358; *N.Y. Tribune*, Feb. 20, 1880.
[30] *N.Y. Tribune* and *Times*, Feb. 20, 1880.
[31] *Ibid.*; Scharf, II, 361.
[32] *Golden Jubilee Ossining, N.Y., 1901-1951*, pamphlet in the N.-Y. Hist. Soc.; advertising leaflet in folder labeled "Advertisements of medicinal preparations and devices, 1933-7," Records of the Food and Drug Adm., Record Group 88, National Archives, Washington.

PART TWO

HEYDAY

7

"TO ARMS! TO ARMS!!" AND AFTER

To cure Secession *and its ills,*
Take Dr. Scott's Cast Iron Pills;
Well mixed with Powder of Saltpetre,
Apply it to each "Fire Eater."
With Union Bitters, *mix it clever,*
And treason *is warned off forever.*

—VERSE PRINTED ON A PATRIOTIC
ENVELOPE IN 1861[1]

ABRAHAM LINCOLN had scarcely arrived in Washington to await his inauguration when an advertisement appeared on the front page of the *New York Herald.* Using the iteration copy popular at the time, the notice read: PRESIDENT LINCOLN (repeated three times); DID YOU SEE HIM? (repeated four times); DID YOU SEE HIS WHISKERS? (three times); RAISED IN SIX WEEKS BY THE USE OF (only once); BELLINGHAM'S ONGUENT (six times).[2]

Lincoln's new beard was fair game for the advertiser, even if Dr. C. P. Bellingham stretched the truth until it broke in claiming credit for it. It was nothing new, of course, for an American nostrum maker to stretch the truth, nor was there any novelty in an advertisement that linked a patent medicine with the news of the hour. Henry Raymond, the founder of the *Herald's* rival, the *Times,* had in his salad days earned fifty cents a morning by composing little squibs conjoining the day's most titillating headlines with a certain vegetable pill. The vogue had continued, and it was to be one of the Civil War's significant contributions to patent medicine promotion that it provided an abundance of dramatic incidents to tie in to nostrum advertising.[3]

[1] Prints and Photographs Div., Library of Congress.
[2] Feb. 26, 1861.
[3] Francis Brown, *Raymond of the Times* (N.Y., 1951), 22.

[93]

Sometimes, indeed, the incidents were untrue. Two years after Bellingham grew Lincoln's whiskers, Philadelphians who chanced to stroll the streets were startled—and elated—to spy bold headlines on a handbill which a newsboy was distributing. "GREAT EXCITEMENT IN South Carolina!" the massive type read, "BEAUREGARD A PRISONER!" Hurrying to get a copy, the ardent Unionist had his hopes dashed. There was, he discovered, small type hidden amid the large, and when the whole message was perused, the news was of markedly different import: "GREAT EXCITEMENT IN South Carolina! Was being caused before the war by the wonderful cures of Bronchitis, Asthma, Sore Throat, Consumption, &c., &c., effected by Wishart's Pine Tree Tar Cordial, in and around Charleston. BEAUREGARD himself might as well be A PRISONER! as to be confined with a distressing Cough or Sore Throat and not be able to obtain Wishart's . . . Cordial."[4]

Human nature is capricious: people might resent the deception in Wishart's fake poster and still go to the drugstore to buy his medicine.

The Civil War, such an overwhelming event in the total fabric of American life, was certain to have tremendous influence on all the separate threads. Such was the case with that slender—albeit gaudy—thread of medical quackery. There was a gloomy note. Northern nostrum makers did lose their Southern markets. (They were sometimes tardy in admitting it: two months after the firing on Fort Sumter, the J. C. Ayer & Co. was still citing for Union readers the high praise bestowed upon their Sarsaparilla by Confederate mayors, including the chief executive of Montgomery, the first capital of the Confederacy.)[5] Yet there was no excess of grief. The lost markets would in time return, and meanwhile there were new Northern fish to fry.

The Civil War gave nostrum makers a chance to display their patriotism. See's Army Liniment was introduced, and The Union Hair Restorative was marketed, complete with slogan, "Pro Bono Publico!" Holloway's Pills issued a poster showing a blue-clad officer hurrying a box of the remedy to a sergeant who was ministering unto a languishing private.[6]

4 Rare Book Div., Library of Congress.
5 *Frederick* [Md.] *Republican Citizen*, July 12, 1861.
6 See and Holloway posters, Prints and Photographs Div., Library of Congress; Union broadside, National Library of Medicine, Washington.

Brandreth's Pills went swiftly into battle, anxious to cure "THE PREVAILING DIFFICULTY" for "SOLDIERS, SAILORS, AND THE PUBLIC." "Sixty Voices from Army of Potomac" gladly testified that the Pills "protect from the arrows of disease, usually as fatal to Soldiers as the bullets of the foe." This was the major way in which the medicine men enlisted in the ranks, by preventing or curing the many ills that afflicted the brave men who fought the battles. The farther South the armies got, the graver were the hazards, the greater the need of protective medication. "TO ARM! TO ARMS!!—" warned Holloway in 1864, "THE CITIZEN Soldier will find a more deadly foe in the brackish, muddy water and damp night air, than in the most determined enemy." But the Pills would "so purify the blood and strengthen the stomach and bowels that the soldier" could "endure these hardships and still be strong and healthy." Likewise, Hostetter's Bitters were "a positive protective against the fatal maladies of the Southern swamps, and the poisonous tendency of the impure rivers and bayous." The Hostetter firm, indeed, pleaded with the Surgeon-General to give the Bitters a trial in army hospitals.[7]

In advertising aimed at the armies, the constant promise that various remedies could cure diarrhea and dysentery showed that the nostrum makers were in touch with the hard truth. Soldier letters and diaries, as well as official medical records, make it abundantly clear that bowel complaints were the most prevalent ailment among Billy Yanks and caused the most deaths. There was much self-treatment, and it is certain that harsh laxatives must have aggravated many a simple disorder into a health disaster. Nonetheless, many soldiers recovered from their dysenteric ailments, and some naturally assumed that the nostrums they had taken deserved the credit. Thus the patent medicine makers did not lack for military testimonials. An officer in the Shenandoah Valley considered Hostetter's Bitters "The Soldier's Safeguard." Whole battalions, one would guess, praised Brandreth's Pills. Piper's Magical Elixir gathered testimony into a pamphlet so that this remedy for diarrhea might be known to "those noble braves, so many of whom have fallen a prey to disease at the Seat of War." And so it went.[8]

[7] *Harper's Wkly.*, 7 (1863), 270, 414, and 8 (1864), 30; *Vanity Fair*, 6 (Aug. 2, 1862), 50; *Wilkes' Spirit of the Times*, Oct. 29, 1864.
[8] Bell I. Wiley, *The Life of Billy Yank* (Indianapolis, 1951), 136; *Harper's Wkly.*, 7 (1863), 414, and 8 (1864), 30; Piper's pamphlet, Rare Book Div., Library of Congress.

The war theme was used in devious ways by patent medicine promoters. Morse's Indian Root Pills were advertised on the back of facsimile Confederate currency. Drake's Plantation Bitters embossed a message on the mica covering the face of encased postage stamps which, because of the scarcity of metals, were issued in place of small change. Dr. Clarke of Chicago distributed a card containing the woeful ballad of a dying soldier, "Mother, Is the Battle Over?"; on the reverse was a pitch for the doctor's contraceptives and remedy for male weakness. There seemed no limit to which patent medicine men at the North would not go in linking their nostrums to the war.[9]

Confederate patent medicine advertising was much less flamboyant. Many papers continued to run advertisements for Northern remedies long after the firing on Fort Sumter. By 1862 these had largely—though not entirely—disappeared, and the ads for Confederate remedies which replaced them were both less frequent and less patriotic. A Charleston drug concern announced that it had the Memphis-made Cherokee Remedy and other "SOUTHERN PREPARATIONS" for sale at the Sign of the Negro and the Golden Mortar. In Augusta, the makers of Broom's Anti-Hydropic Tincture used bold type to proclaim: "DROPSY CURED! NO YANKEE HUMBUG!" A Nashville-made Ambrosial Oil was marketed which could cure thirty-eight specified human ailments, not to mention ten equine ones. Early in 1865 an Augusta concern reflected the poignant rather than the patriotic side of war by advertising the locally made "Dennis' Compound Dogwood Bitters a Substitute for Quinine." Many Confederate papers in the middle and last years of the war included in their shrunken advertising columns no pills or potions whatever.[10]

When the fighting was over, Hostetter's Bitters—up North— was ready for the new day. "Peace Hath Its Victories" also, an ad announced, and one of them was the Hostetter ability to conquer disease. Demobilization had many aspects, one of them pictured on a poster for T. M. Sharp's Positive Cure for Dys-

[9] Morse and Bicknell items, Bella C. Landauer Collection in the N.-Y. Hist. Soc.; Drake, Holcombe, "Private Die Proprietaries," *Wkly. Philatelic Gossip*, June 13, 1942, 321; Clarke card, Chicago Hist. Soc.

[10] *Athens* [Ga.] *Southern Banner, Augusta* [Ga.] *Daily Constitutionalist, Charleston Daily Courier*, 1861-1863 *passim*; Negro and mortar in *ibid.*, Jan. 18, 1862; Broom's medicine and Ambrosial Oil in *Augusta Daily Chronicle and Sentinel*, Jan. 4, 1862; *Augusta Daily Constitutionalist*, Jan. 1, 1865.

pepsia. A soldier is telling an ailing civilian that Sharp's remedy will work, and the scene is not a military camp but a comfortably furnished living room. Thousands of soldiers were returning to their homes, many of them having used under field conditions the patent medicines which they and their families would henceforth employ. Habit has always been a powerful force in medicine buying.[11]

In addition to acquainting soldiers with various brands of pills and potions, the war helped the remedy manufacturers in another way. Thousands of soldiers returned to civilian life with ruined digestions, malaria, wounds, emotional disturbances, and other ailments that were to cause them trouble for the rest of their lives. Nostrum makers were not unaware of this. Thirty years after Appomattox the Dr. Williams Medicine Company, maker of Pink Pills for Pale People, aimed a pamphlet at the old boys in blue. "Out of the 1,000,000 men mustered out in '65," the message began, "only about 500,000 are now alive." Why this halving of the noble ranks? "Exposure, miasma, bad food, hardships of every description—these and not the bullets are responsible for the extremely rapid death-rate among the veterans." "It is not alone those who were wounded who deserve our sympathy," asserted the Pink Pill pamphleteer, "it is that great majority WHO WERE NOT, but who contracted the seeds of disease in Southern swamps and prisons, and who have as a consequence lost their health before their time."[12]

Not all the illnesses of aging veterans were a legacy of war, but there was enough truth in Dr. Williams' allegations to make his appeal persuasive. Many old soldiers with aches and pains helped nostrum makers maintain their volume of production. One of these was Henry Farrar, who was growing deaf. His "Beloved Bugle," which had led Union troops on many a victorious assault, he could no longer hear, and this distressed him greatly. At last he learned of a certain remedy for deafness. He tried it. His hearing was restored. In gratitude he gave the nostrum company not only a testimonial but a photograph. Farrar's bearded portrait, replete with G.A.R. insignia, medals, and Union army hat,

---

[11] *Harper's Wkly.*, 10 (1866), 415; Presbrey, *The History and Development of Advertising*, 291; Sharp poster, Prints and Photographs Div., Library of Congress.

[12] Williams pamphlet owned by Gerald Carson, Millerton, N.Y.

adorned an advertisement that appeared in papers throughout the Northern states.[13]

But what of the South? Did not aging men grow deaf there as well? From the pages of the Southern press the same Henry Farrar spoke forth. Here he was not "a Civil War veteran" but a "Veteran Musician." His "Beloved Bugle" had been transformed into a "Beloved Cornet," which, rather than leading "troops to many a victory," had merely "helped in his career." He had nonetheless grown deaf, been cured, and gratefully provided a portrait to gaze out at ex-Confederates, still bearded, but deprived of insignia, medals, and hat.

Northern patent medicine merchants were glad to get their Southern markets back. They might wave the bloody shirt at home, but they were not averse to catching a Southern reader's eye with the cut of a man bearing a distinct resemblance to "Stonewall" Jackson. The year 1865 was not yet over before a Charleston druggist was shipping the roots of Southern plants to Massachusetts in payment for the various packaged remedies of J. C. Ayer. The next year a Columbia, South Carolina, editor complained that Southern publishers were giving advertising space at cut rates to "patent blood-suckers" manufactured by Yankee concerns.[14]

The postwar South offered a promising market for patent medicines. Confederate troops had suffered no less than Union troops from the crippling impact of illness, and wartime deprivations had undermined health on the home front. Poverty was well-nigh universal, and with it diseases that come from inadequate diet. The warmer Southern climate caused a higher incidence of malaria and yellow fever, and half the children were afflicted with hookworm. Rural life was often drab, boring, and fraught with anxiety. Circumstances were most propitious for a Southern response to the kind of appeals stridently asserted in nostrum advertising. To be sure, people were sometimes too

[13] The Amer. Med. Assoc. issued three volumes on *Nostrums and Quackery*, all published in Chicago. The first volume appeared in 1911 with a 2nd ed. in 1912; the second volume, edited by Arthur J. Cramp, was published in 1921; the third volume, also edited by Cramp, was published in 1936 and bore the longer title, *Nostrums and Quackery and Pseudo-Medicine*. In references below, the 2nd ed. of the first volume is cited. The Henry Farrar material is at II, 119.

[14] Thomas D. Clark, *The Southern Country Editor* (Indianapolis, 1948), 70; John Bennett, *Apothecaries' Hall, A Unique Exhibit at the Charleston Museum* (Charleston, 1923), 16; *Columbia* [S.C.] *Phoenix*, June 27, 1866.

poor even to afford a bottle of tonic. When cotton prices were low, the volume of nostrum sales fell off. It was at the time that crops were sold and settlement made with wage laborers, white and Negro, that nostrum peddlers chose to invade rural areas.[15]

For decades before the war, Northern nostrums had been advertised to slave owners through the Southern press as being especially efficacious for illnesses common to slaves. The maker of Lee's New-London Pills, for example, at the very start of his career, advised that "Owners of plantations will find them the most useful Domestic Medicine of any extant." The psychology behind an 1844 advertisement for Thomsonian medicines is obvious: "Diseased servants purchased, and a liberal price given for such as are considered incurable." Many a Negro must have carried the nostrum habit from slavery to freedom. The feeling continued that Negroes, because of their poverty and lack of education, afforded an excellent market for the quack.[16]

Ayer's Sarsaparilla continued to flow southward from the North, but the New South did try to shake off colonial subservience. Cathartics are easier to produce than textiles, and numerous nostrum plants sprang up. In Atlanta there were Tanlac, Baby Ease, and Bradfield's Female Regulator; there were S.S.S. and B.B.B.—Swift's Sure Specific and Botanic Blood Balm— Savannah had her P.P.P.: Prickly Ash, Poke Root, and Potassium. Up in Chattanooga, two Union Army veterans bought some antebellum Southern formulas and parlayed them into fortunes still on the rise: Black Draught and Wine of Cardui. Some of these remedies dosed not only the ex-Confederacy but invaded the North. Wine of Cardui fought Lydia Pinkham on her home ground. From New Orleans, Dr. Tichenor's Antiseptic Refrigerant, "for cuts, bruises, sprains, superficial burns, sunburn and mouth wash," carried—still carries—on its label to Yankee drugstores the Stars and Bars.[17]

15 Rupert B. Vance, *Human Factors in Cotton Culture* (Chapel Hill, 1929), 205-94; Harold U. Faulkner, *The Quest for Social Justice* (N.Y., 1931), 233; Thomas D. Clark, *Pills, Petticoats, and Plows, The Southern Country Store* (Indianapolis, 1944), 222; *Amer. Druggist and Pharm. Record*, 24 (1900), 47.
16 *Savannah Columbian Museum*, July 23, 1802, cited in Richard H. Shyrock, ed., *Letters of Richard D. Arnold, M.D.* (Papers of the Trinity College Hist. Soc., Double Series 18-19, Durham, N.C., 1929), 33n.; *Richmond Whig*, cited in Blanton, *Medicine in Virginia in the Nineteenth Century*, 195; *Hearings before the Committee on Interstate and Foreign Commerce of the House of Representatives on H.R. 13086* (Washington, 1906), 10.
17 Presbrey, 297; James H. Thompson, *Bitters Bottles* (Watkins Glen, N.Y.,

The impact of the Civil War on themes for advertising and on the health of soldiers and civilians was of great importance to those who would vend remedies. Of equal significance to the medicine man was the spur which the war gave to the media by which he reached his potential customers. In journalism and advertising, the Civil War launched a revolution. The craving for news from the fighting fronts enlarged the size of daily papers and inflated their circulations. The Sunday edition was born. Pressure for newsprint hastened the discovery of wood pulp paper, introduced in the seventies. Cotton rag newsprint had cost 24 cents a pound in 1862; wood pulp newsprint cost 2 cents a pound in 1900. As the price fell, newspaper size and advertising volume expanded more and more. Wartime shortages of labor and materials affected the rural weekly too. The "patent inside" or readyprint industry was created to furnish small country newspapers with sheets of newsprint already half filled with reading matter and advertising. The war years also saw the real beginning of magazine advertising. During the year 1860, for every person in the United States, there had been issued 29.5 copies of daily, weekly, and monthly periodicals. As a result of the revolution launched by the war, the figure had grown to 107.5 by 1900. In almost every case each separate issue was larger in size.[18]

More and bigger periodicals obviously offered the maker of remedies more chances to confront his potential customers. With more elbow room, he could exercise his creative talents with greater imagination. Small type cramped tightly together began to give way to larger type and more white space. Technical improvements in printing multiplied, including the introduction of photo-engraving. Printing quality improved. Color work was introduced into magazines. In 1900 an expert could remark that never before had the volume of advertising pamphlets been so large and attractive. Two generations earlier, he said, "modest

---

1947), 174; various Atlanta papers; Clark, *Pills*, 248; Tichenor bottle, indicating label was registered in 1883, in author's collection, courtesy of Ben Vincent.

[18] Presbrey, 253; William S. Rossiter, "Printing and Publishing," 12th Census, *Census Reports*, 9 (Wash., 1902), 1,039-1,119; Elmo Scott Watson, *A History of Newspaper Syndicates in the United States, 1865-1935* (Chicago, 1936); Clark, *Southern Country Editor*, 69; George B. Waldron, "What America Spends in Advertising," *Chautauquan*, 38 (Oct. 1903), 156.

and ugly circulars, leaflets, and handbills" had been the rule, but now advertisers were demanding "the most beautiful products of the press."[19]

With the boom in journalism, in the war years and after, the advertising agency, an antebellum infant, passed through a stormy adolescence. Nostrums, as one executive put it, provided the "backbone" of the typical agency's business. At first the sole function of these concerns was to take advertising copy written in the office of the proprietor and place it in newspapers and magazines. Later the nostrum copy came to be drafted by the agency's own staff. In the 1890's, medical advertising "offered the ad.-writer his greatest opportunity," wrote Claude Hopkins, who had been through that mill, and "the greatest advertising men of my day were schooled in the medicine field." The training was rugged but indispensable, he felt. Nostrum copy provided "the supreme test" of a writer's ability, since "Medicines were worthless merchandise until a demand was created." Sometimes medicine proprietors paid a similar tribute to the magic of skillful promotion. "I can advertise *dish water*, and sell it, just as well as an article of merit," one of them boasted. "It is all in the advertising."[20]

Such cocksureness was all very well, but there was chance as well as calculation involved in achieving notable success in the nostrum game. The vigorous George Presbury Rowell, who pioneered many of the rules of advertising agency practice, sought to put all of his special know-how to work in the creation of a patent medicine. He did not belong to the dish-water school, wanting instead a remedy that had some therapeutic merit. Through a medical student, Rowell learned about a mixture which doctors over the years had been prescribing for upset stomachs and whenever a medicine seemed called for on general principles. Since dyspepsia continued at the forefront of American ailments, in climates cold and warm, in summer and winter, such a formula suited Rowell's purpose. The ingredients were capable of being compressed into tablets by machines recently introduced to the pharmaceutical industry, thus assuring other

[19] Rossiter, 1,039-1,119.
[20] Ralph M. Hower, *The History of an Advertising Agency: N. W. Ayer & Son at Work, 1869-1949* (revised ed., Cambridge, Mass., 1949), 44-46, 91-93; Claude C. Hopkins, *My Life in Advertising* (N.Y., 1927), 73; Addison Crabtre, *The Funny Side of Physic* (Hartford, 1874), 80.

qualities Rowell desired in his remedy. The tablets were light and could be shipped cheaply by mail. Since no liquid was involved, there need be no alcohol and no possible encounter with the temperance forces. Also there was no risk of broken bottles, evaporation, or freezing.[21]

Rowell canvassed a variety of possibilities in search of a name for his product, and finally decided to create one from the initial letters of the names of the ingredients. Since these were rhubarb, ipecac, peppermint, aloes, nux vomica, and soda, the result was RIPANS. Instead of terming his pellets tablets, Rowell coined an arbitrary word that was similar but distinctive. The advertising agent set about promoting Ripans Tabules. He had ample advertising space he had contracted for but had not been able to unload, mostly in poorer newspapers. Into this space he crowded messages remarking the merit of the first patent medicine put up in tablet form, the first patent medicine to be sold for a nickel. Rowell's copy emphasized how Ripans Tabules would benefit dyspepsia and illnesses from a disordered stomach. He had determined, so he said, to avoid objectionable or suggestive phrases in his advertising. But he was not above exaggeration. "Wanted—," read one ad, "a case of bad health that R-I-P-A-N-S will not benefit. . . . No matter what's the matter, one will do you good. . . . They banish pain, induce sleep, prolong life."[22]

Ripans did not gain the popularity on which their inventor had counted. The first year, in exchange for $125,000 worth of newspaper space, the tabules netted $976.48, not enough to cover the cost of electrotypes and the postage involved in handling the advertising. Not until the fifth year did sales amount to $2,000 in any single month. At the end of a decade, total retail sales had not yet reached $3,000,000, although 50,000 people were buying a package every day in the year and the venture could be considered a moderate success. "All of which goes to show," Rowell concluded, "that making money in the patent medicine trade is by no means as easy as 'rolling off a log.'"

Those wise in the ways of the nostrum world agreed. Competition was so keen, business methods so complicated in the postwar era, that it was much harder to make a nostrum fortune

21 Rowell, *Forty Years an Advertising Agent, 1865-1905* (N.Y., 1926), 371-80.
22 *Ibid.* The quotations from ads are from the Ripans folder in the Dept. of Investigation, Amer. Med. Assoc., Chicago.

than it once had been. One old hand estimated that only two per cent of the remedies launched on the market in New York won any degree of success at all. A critic was convinced that not more than fifty proprietors in the last two decades of the 19th century had made fortunes exceeding $100,000, and not more than a dozen men had become millionaires. Multitudes of aspiring medicine men never got a firm grip on even the first rung of the ladder of success. Their deplorable, pathetic lot was revealed in the incoming correspondence of the Department of Agriculture in the days following the enactment of the Pure Food and Drugs Act of 1906. From unheard-of villages all over the nation came bewildered letters wondering what the law was all about. Some letters did not have printed letterheads, many were written awkwardly both as to penmanship and grammar, their authors next to illiterate and yet anxious to prescribe for the most serious ailments of mankind.[23]

Even among the more sophisticated patent medicine vendors, a good many bankruptcies occurred, one reason for advertising agencies' acquiring the ownership of nostrums. Indeed, the expense of advertising was a fundamental reason for the failure of many aspiring entrepreneurs. The public seemed unwilling to try a new remedy until after a shrewd and protracted campaign to bring it to their attention. In the eighties, one authority said, it took $50,000 to create a demand. By the beginning of the new century it was several times more costly. The owners of one firm admitted that they had spent $250,000 in advertising charges before the income from sales even paid for the bottles and wrappers.[24]

A miracle did sometimes happen. A man in St. Louis, possessed of $3,000 and a tasteless malaria powder, built up a fortune of $2,000,000 in six years. A comedian with a stock company, which went broke—appropriately—in Peoria, earned his way back to New York selling liver pads of his own devising. He did so well that he put all of his energies into marketing this therapeutic product, and when he next returned to show business it was to finance a dozen minstrel shows. "But, of course," said

[23] Rowell, 399-400; "Pushing Patent Medicine, " *N.Y. Tribune*, Apr. 25, 1886; H. C. Wood, "Nostrums," *Jour. Amer. Med. Assoc.* (hereafter, *JAMA*), 32 (Apr. 29, 1899), 908; Incoming Correspondence, Bureau of Chemistry, RG 97, National Archives.
[24] Hower, 91-92, 98; *Druggists Circular* 45 (Jan. 1901), xi.

the New York nostrum king who was telling the story, "he was one of ten thousand." Rowell, whose promotion of Ripans had been a qualified triumph, agreed. "The chances of success. . . ," he wrote, "are now so remote that he is either a bold or an imprudent man who ventures at the present day upon the introduction of a new remedy by means of advertising."[25]

For those in the big time, advertising budgets became gigantic. In prewar days, Benjamin Brandreth had awed his rivals by achieving a total annual advertising outlay of $100,000. In the closing years of the century, many major proprietors spent double, quadruple, six times this sum. To carry the messages of Scott's Emulsion and Lydia E. Pinkham's Vegetable Compound to the American people required the expenditure in behalf of each remedy of about $1,000,000 a year. Many small newspaper offices possessed no cut of a woman's face except that of Lydia's maternal countenance, which occasionally was shifted from an advertising to a news column to do double duty as Queen Victoria.[26]

To spend sums of this magnitude cost the proprietors and their advertising agents considerable ingenuity. Much of the money went to regular newspapers and to the less high-toned weekly and monthly periodicals. There were scores of journals catering to special interests. Farm papers offered the nostrum advertiser a promising medium. So too did religious journals: nearly 1,000 were published, and comparatively few excluded patent medicine advertising. Some of the more parochial of these organs were so small and so remote that it seems amazing that the advertising agent, even with all his vaunted persistence, was able to ferret them out. Often, of course, the hunting went in the other direction, with editors making advertisers aware of their existence. The results were sometimes amusing, if in a grim sort of way. The *Christian Sun*, selling space to a "doctor" with a "positive cure" for "Nervous Debility, Stricture, . . . diseases of women . . . , and . . . private diseases of men," was published on the campus of a North Carolina sectarian college. In the same column of the Cincinnati *Lookout for Christ and the Church* were notices for the sale of Stuart's Calcium Wafers, a book on the recanta-

[25] A. C. Cantley, "Some Facts about Making Patent Medicines," *Chautauquan*, 27 (1898), 390; "Pushing Patent Medicine"; Rowell, 400.

[26] Presbrey, 337, 364; Hower, 91-92; Hopkins, 75-78; *Scientific American*, 73 (Oct. 5, 1895), 214; Jean Burton, *Lydia Pinkham Is Her Name* (N.Y., 1949), 230; *Printer's Ink*, 121 (Oct. 5, 1922), 44.

tion of Thomas Paine, and preachers' baptismal trousers at $13.50 a pair.[27]

Public attention was assaulted by hundreds of other weapons employed by the nostrum maker. There were the ubiquitous almanacs, and the omnipresent roadside signs.[28] There were joke-books, cook-books, coloring books, song-books, and dream-books. There were handbill ballads, like "Nellie and Her Lover" for Bliss Cough Syrup, and "The Musquitoe's Lament" for Perkins' Infallible Aromatic and Disinfecting Pastile. *The Robber's Roost; or, Last Victim,* boosting Herrick's Sugar Coated Pills, was a rip-roaring paperback tale set west of the Mississippi with lots of gunfire and a gal. In issuing a *Moral Story,* the makers of Hood's Sarsaparilla had perhaps an even better idea, for it was very like a Sunday School paper. At the other extreme was the suggestive pamphlet with titillating title, *Married at Last,* circulated by a consumption cure. There were pill-filled paper weights and decorated porcelain: Mrs. Grover Cleveland appeared on a china platter advertising a kidney and liver cure. Thousands of small cards were brought out in series, and the collector had his choice of dozens of themes, sentimental, athletic, poignant, comic, historical, floral, biographical, or even combinations, like the amusing caricatures of baseball players who "played" for Merchant's Gargling Oil of Brockport, New York. (In nearby Rochester a real baseball club, the Hop Bitters, contested in the National Association.)[29]

Nostrum literature was piled on the counters of drugstores and country general stores. It was delivered to the doorstep of the home. It was sent through the mail, sometimes to special lists of addresses secured from storekeepers and clergymen, sometimes "run through the post office into every man's box." The patent medicine message might be encountered in mail order catalogs and in the back pages of new novels. Perhaps it was only in fiction that the nostrum gospel reached the end sheets and flyleaves of hotel Bibles, but one is tempted to wonder.[30]

[27] Rossiter, 1,045; Presbrey, 458-61; *Sun,* Apr. 26, 1905, and *Lookout,* Jan. 24, 1903, in N.Y. Public Library.
[28] See Chapters 8 and 9.
[29] Items found in the Landauer Coll., except for the Perkins' ballad, in Rare Book Div., Library of Congress; and the Rochester baseball team, mentioned in Samuel Hopkins Adams, "That Was Rochester: To the Greater Glory of Hop Bitters," *New Yorker,* 28 (Aug. 23, 1952), 27-41.
[30] Clark, *Pills,* 106; 1899 Ayer letter to a druggist, in the Landauer Coll.; Crabtre, 86; Presbrey, 259; Boris Emmet and John E. Jeuck, *Catalogues and*

The greater abundance of promotional media in postwar America was accompanied by a greater complexity of marketing. Not only had the advertising agency grown up to specialize in one aspect of the selling function. Prewar distribution patterns also became more elaborate. During the 1850's a drugstore in Springfield, Illinois, at which Lincoln occasionally traded, bought a major share of the medicines it sold directly from the remedy manufacturers, ordering by mail or through the company drummer. There were large jobbers in Chicago and New York who sold the store nostrums of many brands, and for some patent medicines the Springfield house acted as a wholesaler for small country stores within its area. Farther west, where railroads were scarcer, some medicine makers distributed their stock in gaudy wagons, often pulled by four horses, and it was not unusual to find the agents exchanging new stock for old and then tossing the outmoded bottles in the nearest creek.[31]

After the war old methods did not die out completely, but the balance shifted. There was still direct selling by the "gentlemanly agents" of the big manufacturers, "with their little satchels, their regalia cigars, and a bland smile." There was still the practice of placing goods on commission, with accounts to be rendered in six months or a year. There were still instances in which makers set no retail price, letting the local merchant charge what the traffic would bear. But as the postwar years unfolded, the role of the middle man increased in importance. Retail druggists got more and more of their stock from wholesale drug houses. The terms were more often cash. Most retail druggists, complained one of their number in 1881, had about $800 worth of nostrums in stock which they could neither return nor sell. Almost all manufacturers set the price which retailers should charge per box or bottle. The major problem for manufacturer, wholesaler, and most retail druggists seemed to become how a standard price might be safeguarded against the unscrupulous few who set out to cut it.[32]

Indeed, the matter of price was a major factor spurring the drug industry to imitate other branches of the American economy

Counters, A History of Sears, Roebuck and Company (Chicago, 1950), 102-104, 247-50; Maurice Lazar, *The Late Mr. Katterby* (Chicago, 1919), 42.

[31] Birchall and Owen Papers, author's collection; Cantley, 390.

[32] *Amer. Jnl. Pharm.*, 46 (1874), 543; Clark, *Pills*, 232; "Patent Panaceas," *Phila. American*, 2 (1881), 105-106.

in forming combinations for the protection and promotion of common interests. All three levels—retailing, wholesaling, and manufacturing—formed trade associations, and from the early 1880's onward for decades, the leaders of these nationwide organizations strove to perfect a plan by which prices of proprietary remedies could be stabilized. One scheme after another was attempted, only to fail because of inadequate methods of control or adverse court decisions.[33]

The Civil War, once again, lay behind the creation of the trade association among major manufacturers of proprietary remedies. In 1861, faced with the enormous cost of armed conflict, Congress began to consider methods of raising money. Among the host of special taxes suggested was one on patent medicines. From New York City, four leading remedy manufacturers, headed by Frederick H. Humphreys of the Humphreys Homeopathic Medicine Company, went to Washington to protest the imminent action. Their journey was in vain. Thaddeus Stevens, chairman of the House Ways and Means Committee, told them, as Humphreys reported it: "Gentlemen, you must respond. The country is in peril. We must have money. When this exigency is past, your showing will be considered."[34]

Twenty years later the exigency was long since past, but the four per cent tax on the retail price of all proprietary medicines still hung on. Individual protests had been made by medicine manufacturers who felt it unjust to tax the people's right of self-dosage, at least in time of peace. But these had come to nought. To a group of leading proprietors, again including Humphreys, who met informally from time to time in New York, organized pressure seemed to offer greater hope of success. During November 1881, in the office of Charles Crittenton, there was estab-

[33] *National Wholesale Druggists' Association From Its Organization to 1924* (N.Y., 1924); M. N. Kline, "Some Observations on the Price Cutting Problem," *Amer. Druggist*, 36 (1900), 188-89; Herbert B. Harding, "The History of Organization among Manufacturers and Wholesale Dealers in Proprietary Articles," *ibid.*, 190-93. A city-level price-fixing agreement for New Haven, dated June 1, 1887, is to be found in the Yale Medical Library.

[34] Harding, 190-93; Frederick Humphreys, "Origin and History of the Association," *Pharm. Era*, 16 (1896), 900-905; Frank A. Blair, "The Proprietary Association, Its History Since the Founding in 1881," *Standard Remedies*, 19 (June 1932), 4-7, 24-26; Frederick J. Cullen, "The First Twenty-Five Years," mimeographed copy of address delivered in May 1956; interview with Dr. Cullen, then Executive Vice-President, The Proprietary Association, June, 1955. The shorter name was adopted in 1897; the Association had 84 members in 1883, 174 in 1900.

lished The Proprietary Medicine Manufacturers and Dealers Association. Immediately they sent off a memorial to Congress urging repeal of the tax. In March 1883 the deed was done.

Fifteen years later another war brought another tax. Treasury officials wanted the rate set again at four per cent, as in the Civil War. The medicine manufacturers were now in a better organized condition than they then had been to argue the point. Proprietary Association officers suggested that one per cent would be a fairer rate. And "it was through our efforts," the treasurer asserted, "that a compromise [of two-and-a-half per cent] was finally effected." Nor did this revenue measure hang on so long after the cessation of hostilities.[35]

Right from the start the growing trade association had other duties to perform. It represented the manufacturers in the protracted and vain attempts with wholesalers and retailers to stabilize nostrum prices. It vented its wrath on certain drug journals that printed formulas purporting to be those of remedies made by Association members. It sought to restrict the infringement of trade-marks and the counterfeiting of labels. It lobbied against a tax on grain alcohol used in manufacturing and the arts. It took quick and decisive action whenever any measure restrictive of patent medicines was even hinted at in the corridors of state legislatures or the national Congress.[36]

The assembling of the major remedy manufacturers into the Proprietary Association was one form of consolidation that achieved one kind of bigness. Another sort of bigness through consolidation was also evident in the patent medicine industry, as it was in most of the American economy, during the postwar world. Not all the nostrum fortunes made during the late 19th century were a pot of gold at the end of a rainbow that began with a poor man and his recipe. Many of the leaders of the Proprietary Association had never mixed a formula. They were promoters who bought and sold medicines as other men might buy and sell mills or railroads. One of the earliest of these entrepreneurs, who also dabbled in gold mines of a more literal kind, was Demas Barnes. Among the remedies in which he was

[35] Harding, 192.

[36] *Amer. Druggist*, 36 (1900), 306; Harding, 190-93; *Standard Remedies*, 1 (Feb. 1915), 3-4, and 2 (Mar. 1916), 17-18; Blair, 4-6. On the Proprietary Association and restrictive legislation, see Chapters 13 and 14.

interested were Castoria and Plantation Bitters. A St. Louis entrepreneur, James Ballard, not only produced patent medicines under his own name—including a remedy named Campho-Phenique—but he acquired the rights to other nostrums which had established themselves in public favor under different proprietorship. One was that hardy veteran, Swaim's Panacea. The first president of the Proprietary Association, Charles Crittenton, in whose New York office the organization had been born, was a merchant-manufacturer of similar stamp. Indeed, he was the largest dealer in the country for a while, keeping 12,000 proprietary articles in stock, and constantly acquiring and launching new brands of his own. It was he who had given Lydia Pinkham her first major boost.[37]

In the new day of ever bigger business, the small-time operator found the going hard. Yet the would-be maker of medicines was better off than the beginner in petroleum or steel. Costs of raw products were scarcely higher than before the war, even if promotion was both more expensive and more complex. Certainly recipes were as cheap as ever. Hundreds of hopeful men and women kept coming to the market with their wares. The number of nostrums, it seemed, was almost as "formidable . . . as were the frogs of Egypt." In 1905 a leading drug trade journal listed the names of over 28,000, and the next year a witness before a Congressional committee estimated that there were 50,000 patent medicines made and sold in the United States. If the giants were few, the pygmies still were many. Although only an infinitesimal percentage of this staggering effort to dose the American public ever got into any one drugstore, the problem was enough to make a druggist groan. As early as 1872 one apothecary felt assailed by an "epidemic" of patent medicines, and a decade later a fellow-spirit tore his hair and wailed: "Oh, for the return to the good old days of past years, when 'patent medicines' comprised less than a dozen articles."[38]

[37] Rowell, 269, 403; Demas Barnes, *From the Atlantic to the Pacific, Overland* (N.Y., 1866), 5; George H. Simmons, "Works of the Council on Pharmacy and Chemistry," *Southern Med. Jnl.*, 8 (1915), 259-65; Swaim's bottle wrapper in author's collection; *Pharm. Era*, 16 (1896), 968-70; Burton, 123-25.
[38] William Brewer, "Reminiscences of an Old Pharmacist," *Pharm. Record*, 4 (1884), 326; Philip L. Allen, "Dosing the Public as a Business," *Leslie's Monthly Mag.*, cited in *Druggists Circular*, 49 (1905), 124; *Hearings before the Committee on Interstate and Foreign Commerce . . . on H.R. 13086*, 7; *Amer. Jnl. Pharm.*, 44 (1872), 535, and 51 (1884), 651.

All in all, the skillful patent medicine proprietor, ever agile at turning environmental currents to his advantage, floated to a new prosperity on the great flood loosed by the war. He even managed, indeed, as we shall see, to turn contrary medical developments to his account. Wrapped in the flag—in time, in both flags—he catered to the troops, followed them home, and stayed for years. Lest they forget him, lest anyone forget him, the nostrum maker stepped up his advertising in the war-swollen press and turned to that new specialist, the advertising agent, to help him write and place his copy. He combined with his fellows to eliminate a hampering wartime tax and to take other crucial steps for the benefit of the trade. He opened up an export market that carried American nostrums over the seven seas and dwarfed in volume the English sales of Perkins' tractors a million-fold.[39]

On the eve of the war, in 1859, the proprietary medicine industry had an output valued in census figures at $3,500,000. By 1904 the sum had multiplied by more than twenty times. An observer reckoned that the value of cocoa and chocolate, blacking and bluing, flavoring extracts and axle grease, beet sugar and glue, castor oil and lard, kindling wood and cosmetics, could all be added together, and still the total sum would not bulk so large as the $74,500,000 which was the manufactured value of American patent medicines. At retail prices, the nostrum-taking American public paid many millions more.[40]

Abraham Lincoln's beard had grown a long way.

[39] Files of drug journals like the *Amer. Druggist* and *Pharm. Record* frequently report foreign opportunities.
[40] 13th Census, 8 (*Manufactures*, 1909), 452; Allen, 123.

THE GREAT OUTDOORS

"I say the landscape was made for man, and not man for the landscape."

—WILLIAM DEAN HOWELLS, *The Rise of Silas Lapham*[1]

MARK TWAIN was but one of many Americans who, during the post-Civil War expansion of the nostrum traffic, objected to a particular type of effrontery on the part of patent medicine men. Among the "blessings" of 19th-century civilization which Twain's Connecticut Yankee carried back to King Arthur's England was outdoor advertising. Knights went about sandwiched between tabards emblazoned with slogans for prophylactic toothbrushes. Other knights wielded paint-pot and stencil-plate to such good effect "that there was not a cliff or a boulder or a dead wall in England but you could read on it at a mile distance" an urgent appeal to purchase shirts "which were regarded as a perfect protection against sin."[2]

Colonial America had been rather like King Arthur's Court before the Yankee came. The amount of advertising was meager. The English custom of hanging signboards from shops denoting the wares sold within was in use. Apothecaries in every colonial town advertised their location with the Sign of the Unicorn and Mortar, or the Sign of Galen's Head, or some other therapeutic symbol. Pamphlets and broadsides were imported proclaiming the efficacy of the old English patent medicines. American printers set type for some promotional literature, reprinting British items. Of local initiative there was almost none at all.[3]

[1] (Boston, 1884), 18.
[2] Samuel L. Clemens, *A Connecticut Yankee in King Arthur's Court* (N.Y., 1917), 127-28, 167-68, 206.
[3] Presbrey, *The History and Development of Advertising*, 113-17; Young and Griffenhagen, "Old English Patent Medicines in America," *Chemist and Druggist*, 167 (June 29, 1957), 714-22. Examples of broadsides for old English nostrums may be found, among other places, in the Div. of Medical Sciences, Smithsonian Institution; the Hist. Soc. of Penna.; the Folger Shakespeare Library; the College of Physicians of Philadelphia Library.

When Americans began to promote their own nostrums during the Revolutionary generation, these wares were advertised not only in the columns of newspapers but also in broadsides and handbills and on the exposed surfaces of rocks, rills, woods, and templed hills. Aetherial Oil of Tar, for example, was an American-made product announced in an American-printed broadside of the Revolutionary decade. Compounded by a New Jersey "Chymist" named Isaac Bartram, the oil was said to possess a "warming and stimulating Property" and, taken internally or applied externally, it was professedly good for palsies, trembling, convulsions, low spirits, dropsies, sand and gravel, and the king's evil. These fearsome ailments were set forth in attractive typography, and the broadside contained a cut of a unicorn's head. Other nostrum promoters paid printers to devise handbills and posters. A New Yorker named Ransome testified on the broadside to his patriotism since his remedy was christened the American Pills. As time went on, woodcut artists like Alexander Anderson were called upon to carve cupids and lions and American eagles for the adornment of patent medicine posters. Illustrations tended to be small. From Houston during the days of the Texas Republic came a broadside advertising Texas Universal Pills; the sole illustration was fittingly a lone star. Up in the United States, McAlister's Ointment's husky Hercules was dwarfed by gigantic letters in a woodblock poster printed in black, red, blue, green, and yellow.[4]

By the 1840's a Philadelphian could complain of nostrum posters flaunting themselves from "the walls of our inns—the corners of our streets, and our pumps thereof—the wrecks of burnt, dilapidated buildings, with their standing abutments—the fences enclosing vacant lots in all our cities, if not our small villages, and the decks and cabins of our steamboats." A Bostonian could condemn the men who walked the streets ringing doorbells for no other purpose than to thrust inside "blazing handbill[s]" touting various patent medicines.[5]

[4] Aetherial Oil broadside in Amer. Antiquarian Soc.; American Pills broadside in Rare Book Div., Library of Congress; Anderson's proof books in Prints Div., N.Y. Public Library; James B. Gilman's Texas poster, 1838, in Rare Book Div., Library of Congress, and Landauer Coll., N.-Y. Hist. Soc.; McAlister poster, 1845, Prints and Photographs Div., Library of Congress.

[5] Euen, *An Essay in the Form of a Lecture, on Political and Medical Quackery*, 28; Morgan, *A Warning against Quackery*, 4.

By this time, too, other forms of outdoor advertising were well beyond the pioneering stage. About 1800, painted advertisements began to appear on rocks and walls. Two decades later the sandwich man, wearing his signboard fore and aft, first tramped the sidewalks of New York. Next came the advertising wagon, rumbling through the streets its sides ablaze with signs. Outdoor advertising was becoming ubiquitous. By the sixties, asserted a man who did not admire the art, there was "no relief" from its constant bombardment "in all the earth."[6]

One of the most energetic of the outdoor advertisers was a self-styled "doctor" named Henry T. Helmbold. In 1850 he had been a young man in Philadelphia looking for the big chance. He determined to hitch his wagon to the leaves of a plant growing among the Hottentots near the Cape of Good Hope. Buchu was its name, and it carried Helmbold far.[7]

Helmbold's choice of buchu was shrewd, for in selecting it he seemed to acquire not only the blessing of orthodox medicine but also the novelty of an exotic newcomer to the materia medica. The natives of South Africa had long used the plant as medicine and as cosmetic, since rubbing the powdered leaves upon their greased skins imparted an odor akin to peppermint. English and Dutch physicians, in the 1820's, had introduced the shrub into European practice. By 1840 it had reached America and become official in the *Pharmacopoeia*. The *Dispensatory of the United States*, while Helmbold was launching his version, termed buchu "gently stimulant, with a peculiar tendency to the urinary organs, producing diuresis," and listed among the illnesses for which regular physicians were prescribing it, "gravel, chronic catarrh of the bladder, morbid irritation of the bladder and urethra, disease of the prostate, and retention or incontinence of urine from a loss of tone in the parts concerned in its evacuation."[8]

Helmbold did not feel bound to follow orthodox medicine too strictly. The Extract of Buchu which he prepared was much weaker than the official formula, and contained, besides buchu,

[6] Presbrey, 210; George Wakeman, "Advertising," *Galaxy*, 3 (1867), 203.
[7] Historian, "Who Helmbold Really Was," *Druggists Circular*, 56 (1912), 654-57. This incorporates "A Birdseye View of His Career," by "An Old Friend" of Helmbold; "An Intimate View of Him as Drug Store Proprietor," by a former employee, John W. Ferrier; and "Helmbold as a Proprietary Medicine Man," by "An Ex-Manager."
[8] *Dispensatory of the United States* (11th ed., 1858), 155-56; *ibid*. (25th ed., 1955), 196-97.

cubebs, licorice, caramel, molasses, and some peppermint to simulate the native flavor diminished as a result of Helmbold's watering down. Moreover, while seeking to associate his product with official medicine, he went far beyond orthodox practitioners in his claims. In circulars Helmbold referred readers to discussions of buchu in the *Dispensatory* and in standard medical texts. Like these volumes, Helmbold, in discussing therapeutic uses, stayed below the belt. He put his emphasis, however, on secret diseases.[9]

Helmbold launched a vast advertising campaign of a surreptitious sort. He shouted loud about things one was wont to mention in a whisper. He had his minions quietly deposit pamphlets in hotels and public toilets. Bound in pink paper, they bore the title *The Patient's Guide, A Treatise on Diseases of the Sexual Organs*, and the back-cover promise, "The Human Constitution Saved from Wreck." They were frightening documents. Grim adjectives and grimmer cuts depicted the horrors of venereal diseases, caused by "excesses in married life, early indiscretion, or self-abuse." Symptoms were listed to permit each reader to ascertain his own state of health. Danger signals included heaviness of the eyelids, black spots before the eyes, restlessness, great mobility, the inability to contemplate disease without a feeling of horror. Worse was to follow, for if such symptoms went unchecked by healing draughts of Helmbold's Buchu, the patient faced "*Loss of Power, Fatuity, and Epileptic Fits,*" "*Insanity and Consumption.*"[10]

Frightening American mid-Victorians proved for Helmbold a means to both wealth and acclaim. Not that he abandoned his shady pamphlets—a new edition entitled *The Dime Physician* was issued in 1871.[11] But Helmbold also began to cry his Buchu in a manner more decorous, if even louder, than before. During the Civil War, the "doctor" took on other diseases and new media. Instead of syphilis and self-abuse, he stressed diabetes and rheumatism. Instead of sneaky pink paper, he sought the advertising pages of the best magazines and the many flat surfaces of the great outdoors.

9 Historian, 656.

10 "Our Quack Doctors and Their Performances," *Ntl. Quarterly Rev.,* 8 (1864), 331-32; George W. Morton, *The Patient's Guide* (Phila., 1860), in the Toner Collection, Rare Book Div., Library of Congress.

11 "Our Quack Doctors and How They Thrive," *Ntl. Quarterly Rev.,* 24 (Dec. 1871), 79-80.

Helmbold's new role called for a new stage, and he built the most elaborate one his profits could buy. Moving from Philadelphia to New York, Helmbold constructed a "Temple of Pharmacy" that gained renown as the most "buchuful" structure on Broadway. Costing over $250,000, it featured sarcophagus soda fountains, floor-to-ceiling mirrors, monogrammed gas globes, marble floors with the doctor's initials inlaid in brass, fountains for dispensing perfume, and canary birds tweeting in their cages. Amid such splendor, Helmbold had his own "Sanctum Sanctorum"—so read the letters on the glass door—in which the main feature was a bust carved from some rare wood representing Helmbold himself. The labels for the doctor's proprietary preparations showed a full-rigged ship resting atop the Temple roof. This was purportedly Helmbold's own yacht which had been taken apart, carried aloft, and reassembled. In truth the ship was a dummy, consisting of masts, spars, and rigging. The engraving on the label was real, at any rate. On this point Helmbold was a stickler for the genuine.[12]

Temple attendants wore elaborate uniforms, and paid formal deference whenever the high priest appeared. They stood at attention at their counters on either side of the long store. Helmbold passed between them, first between the drug clerks, then through the soda men, next past the Negro parlor attendants, finally through the bookkeepers and managers to the Sanctum Sanctorum. Every lesser member of the hierarchy intoned a respectful "Good morning."

Such a ritual in such a Temple made for notoriety, and notoriety brought customers and sold Buchu. Among the metropolitan worthies who might be seen making a purchase at the Temple were "Boss" William Tweed, Jay Gould, Jim Fisk, Commodore Vanderbilt, John Jacob Astor, and James Gordon Bennett. Sightseers from the provinces put Helmbold's emporium on their list of big city sights to see. If they managed to catch a glimpse of the doctor himself, so much the better. He was as much worth looking at as was his elaborate store.

Helmbold was a small intense man. Just over five feet in height, he made up for lack of stature with unaccustomed vigor. He walked with a brisk step, gestured nervously, spoke in a penetrating metallic voice. His manners were punctilious, grandly

12 Historian, 654-57.

courteous. His clothes were stylish. His forehead was broad, his nose straight, his eyes dark. Helmbold's most prominent feature was his intensely black hair. This engulfed his face: thick and wavy atop his head, it flowed down and around his ears, covering his upper lip, hiding his chin, and cascading over his cravat. The same jet hue marked his heavy brows.[13]

As in his Temple, so when he went abroad, Helmbold surrounded himself with lavish grandeur. His state conveyance was an open barouche ornamented in gold and drawn by three horses in tandem, their heads adorned with violets. The Negro driver, "big Dave," could make his charges dance and could doom a fly on the ear of the leader with a dexterous flick of his long whip. Helmbold was fond of speed. He had a stable of Kentucky-bred carriage and saddle horses, and he liked to take the reins and drive daringly through Central Park. The doctor gave his own name to a race horse, and it was good enough to win the Grand Union Hotel stakes at Saratoga.[14]

Helmbold's whole mode of life was on the same conspicuous scale. He entertained the drug trade with banquets at Delmonico's. He had a summer house at Long Branch, where he was seen at times with President Grant. The doctor went abroad. In Paris, on one Independence Day, he invited all the Americans in the city to a celebration that cost $20,000. It was so regal that even the Shah of Persia came by to pay his respects.[15]

Like many other titans in the nostrum trade Helmbold had an instinctive awareness that his own gaudy career sold medicine. His Temple, his equipage, his champion race-horse—all carried the message of Buchu. Endorsements were provided, if in an unwitting way, by Boss Tweed, the Shah of Persia, and President Grant. It certainly pleased the vibrant little man when a group of actors on the variety stage put on a skit showing the Hottentots gathering healing leaves for Helmbold. It must have amused him to hear that, when a statue of the German naturalist von Humboldt was dedicated in Central Park, there was a young lady who asked, "Was the Doctor present?" These were blessings indeed.[16]

---

13 *Ibid.*; Holcombe, "Private Die Proprietary Stamp Notes," *Scott's Monthly Jnl.*, April 1938, 65-67, and May 1938, 97-99.
14 *Rowell's American Newspaper Directory, 1870,* 42; Historian, 654-57.
15 *Ibid.*
16 *Ibid.*; Rowell, *Forty Years an Advertising Agent,* 401.

Yet while dramatizing himself, Helmbold did not forsake the tried and true methods of reaching the public. He continued to circulate the pink-paper pamphlets aimed at readers who, although perhaps aware of the President, might never have heard of the Shah. He bought whole pages in such respectable papers as the *New York Tribune* and announced that he intended to do likewise in every newspaper in the land. He must have come close to fulfilling this boast. Men were hired whose sole job was to check papers for the Helmbold message, and huge bins in the Temple were so jammed with the results of their perusal that discarded papers had to be carried off in cartload lots.[17]

Helmbold advertising became a feature of *Godey's Lady's Book* and *Harper's Weekly*. One ad, in which the doctor called himself a "Practical and Analytical Chemist," quoted at length from the *Dispensatory* and depicted the Hottentots—looking like American Indians—gathering buchu leaves at the Cape of Good Hope and wrapping them in huge bundles addressed to Helmbold in New York. Another advertisement sought to place the doctor's extract within the architecture of scientific medicine which, "like the Doric column, stands simple, pure, and majestic, having fact for its basis, induction for its pillar, and truth alone for its capital." Yet there was a touch of the baroque in a list of illnesses which Buchu could cure: "General Debility, Mental and Physical Depression, Imbecility, Determination of Blood to the Head, Confused Ideas, Hysteria, General Irritability, Restlessness and Sleeplessness at Night, Absence of Muscular Efficiency, Loss of Appetite, Dyspepsia, Emaciation, Low Spirits, Disorganization or Paralysis of the Organs of Generation, Palpitation of the Heart, And, in fact, all the concomitants of a Nervous and Debilitated state of the system."[18]

In addition to all this, the chief priest of the Temple became an ardent convert to the gospel of outdoor advertising. The war years witnessed a new upsurge in the amount and ingenuity of the appeals spread across the urban and the rural landscape. Such advertising, one man felt, was the "monomania" of the time. "We breakfast on aloes," another observer noted, "dine on quassia, sup on logwood and myrrh, and sleep on morphine and

[17] *Tribune*, Sep. 22, 1865, Sep. 24, 1870; Historian, 656.
[18] *Harper's Wkly.*, 7 (1863), 688; 10 (1866), 16; 12 (1868) 207; 15 (1871), 703 [the Hottentots]; *Godey's* 76 (May 1868), inside front cover; *N.Y. Tribune*, Sep. 8, 1865.

prussic acid!" That buchu was omitted would have grieved Helmbold sorely.[19]

One reason for the boom was that the federal government during the war went in heavily for outdoor appeals. Such an example was not sufficient to persuade the most reputable business concerns to adopt the more extreme forms of the technique; until the mid-1890's they frowned on massive signs as unsightly and undignified. The pioneers, here as elsewhere in advertising, were the patent medicine men, with circuses and tobacco vendors close behind. That consummate showman P. T. Barnum unquestionably contributed to the boom. If he gave lessons to those of his contemporaries who were selling pills and potions, it must be remembered that he had gone to school by observing how earlier nostrum makers had heralded their wares. Promotional genius though he was, Barnum had failed at marketing a grease to grow hair on bald heads.[20]

In the city, wherever one's eyes turned, they encountered advertising. "On the buildings are blazing signs," a critic noted, "on the curb-stones are posters, and banners with inscriptions pendant between the lettered fronts of six-story buildings shut out the view of the sky. Never a brick pile rises in any part of the city but it is covered almost in a night with the fungus and mould of hot notoriety-hunting." Other forms and techniques also abounded. Nostrum ads stared down at riders from panels in the horse-cars, and these same cars had piles of handbills on rods to be pulled off by curious customers. Even the uncurious had throwaways thrust into their hands by small boys standing at busy intersections. In the theater, stage comedians mentioned nostrums by name to audiences who had seen other brands advertised on the asbestos curtain before it went up. Nostrum ads were pasted to mirrors in public waiting rooms. Outdoors again, the billboard men continued to stalk the streets. (Now and then, perhaps, things might fall out, as suggested in a *Harper's Weekly* cartoon, that the man whose sign advertised Dr. Popinjay's Malarium should have the shakes, whereas the poor fellow who bragged about Stubs' Rough on Colds should suffer with a cough and runny nose.) The prewar single stroller became a

[19] Wakeman, 203; Crabtre, *The Funny Side of Physic*, 86.

[20] Presbrey, 211-16, 501; Hower, *The History of an Advertising Agency: N. W. Ayer & Son at Work*, 81.

"line of men who walk[ed] down Broadway, each with a huge letter on his shoulder, all spelling a word." Whether such troops ever donned official army uniform is not known: in England Parliament prohibited human advertisements for pills from wearing the queen's scarlet. A harbinger appeared on Broadway in 1875: at night, high on a roof, a huge green circle of light was flashed upon a screen, and within its circumference one advertisement after another came and went.[21]

Despite such novel techniques, it was the simple poster which predominated. Lithography in color made its appearance shortly before the Civil War, and patent medicine promoters were quick to seize upon its novelty for store-window display. Poster size was small, but most of the area could be used for picture. Three posters copyrighted in 1860, for example, reveal a dainty miss dosing her doll with Viner's Vermifuge, a buckskin guide saving a forlorn frontiersman with Dr. Girard's Ginger Brandy, and Molly Pitcher loading a cannon amid the battle for—so it would seem—Dalley's Magical Pain Extractor. Not until the 1880's, however, were lithographic techniques developed to permit such feats to be shown in massive size for outdoor display. Until then the woodcut emphasizing lettering remained king of the urban landscape.[22]

Billposting was not so much a business as a battle. The desire to monopolize the most advantageous surfaces was understandably strong. But it was hard to do. No flat surface was sacred, and the next man might stick the laudation of his bitters squarely on top of the praise of your pills, even though you had obliterated a puff for plasters not ten minutes before. It was enough to give nightmares to the conscientious journeyman at the trade. "The Billposters Dream," indeed, was a favorite theme for lithographic humorists, who liked to show what might happen to advertising slogans on a well-plastered board. It might be: "People's Candidate for Mayor / The Hippopotamus at Barnum's Museum." Or "Spaulding Prepared Glue / Will Extract Corns in 2 Minutes." In 1869 the first blow was struck against guerrilla posting when

[21] Wakeman, 203-204; Presbrey, 258-59; David L. Dykstra, "Patent and Proprietary Medicine: Regulation and Control Prior to 1906" (unpublished dissertation, Univ. of Wis., 1951), 27; "Art and Advertising," *Nation*, 20 (1875), 342; *Harper's Wkly.*, 29 (1885), 31; E. S. Turner, *The Shocking History of Advertising!* (N.Y., 1953), 164.

[22] Presbrey, 502; the 1860 lithographs in Prints and Photographs Div., Library of Congress.

billboard space was leased on the fence around the site where a new post office was being built in New York City. This trend was to curb the confusion, although it did not reduce the quantity of posters blanketing American cities.[23]

Rural walls and trees played host to woodblock posters, too, but the scourge of the countryside came not so much from printer's ink as paint. The three decades after the war came to be called "The Age of Disfigurement." Defilement of scenery for advertising purposes displayed the same greedy exploitation of nature's bounty that marked other aspects of the Gilded Age. In 1876 an editorialist for the *New York Tribune* could sum up and condemn: "There is an ancient nuisance now bursting into a development so glaring that it calls for a universal protest. . . . It is not enough that fences and sheds are painted over with the names of nostrums; enormous signs are erected in the fields, not a rock is left without disfigurement. . . . The agents of these nostrums range the whole country, painting rocks, fences, and sheds in violation of the owner's will—oftentimes by night—and disposing in the same manner of the bridges belonging to counties and municipalities. They take especial pains to visit all places of Summer resort, violating the beauty of mountain scenery, and the seclusion of the remotest valleys. They have long since crossed the continent, and laid their unclean paws on the Rocky Mountains and the Sierra Nevada."[24]

Among those with the longest grasp in this gilding of the scenic lily was Henry T. Helmbold. "Who has not heard of 'Buchu'?" inquired a prominent advertising agent in 1870. "Why, this magic word adorns every dead wall, fence, rock, and telegraph pole from the Atlantic to the Pacific." It was truly a transcontinental reach. Capitalizing on public excitement in the newly completed Union Pacific Railroad, Helmbold had his agents smear Buchu's name along the route until it outnumbered the painted appeals of all competing nostrums. Some of the results were awesome. "The bare spaces available on the sides of the Rocky Mountains," a friend of the "doctor" noted, "which

23 "Bill-Poster's Dream" lithographs of 1862, 1864, and 1871 are found respectively in the Eno Collection of Prints, N.Y. Public Library; reproduced as plate 58 in Harry T. Peters, *America on Stone* (Garden City, 1931); and in Prints and Photographs Div., Library of Congress. Presbrey in his plates reproduces the post office site from *Harper's Wkly.*, 13 (1869), 676.

24 Arthur P. Kimball, "The Age of Disfigurement," *Outlook*, 57 (Oct. 30, 1897), 521-24; *Tribune*, May 13, 1876.

seemed to the Western traveler as almost inaccessible and un-
surmountable for the sign painter, displayed the irrepressible
advertisement of 'Helmbold's buchu.' "[25] That Helmbold still
had some stretch left is revealed by a passing reference to a Buchu
advertisement and the Egyptian pyramids.[26]

Despite such audacity, Helmbold was not to fulfill his early
promise throughout a long career. It was not that buchu gave out
on him: even officially it lasted a long time, remaining in the
Pharmacopoeia until relegated in 1940 to the *National Formulary*, although in truth the medical profession had long since
abandoned the African plant. Helmbold's failure was a personal
one. There was a darker side to his penchant for speed, his high-
strung self-dramatization. Pressures were too great. The doctor
drank to excess. As an associate put it, he was "often crazy
drunk." At length things snapped. Helmbold was confined in an
asylum. Although he improved and resumed his business, he
suffered a relapse. Seven times, according to a former manager,
he was incarcerated in a mental hospital. The Temple of Pharmacy was closed, and the canaries died in their cages. There
were lawsuits, one between Helmbold and a brother, over the
right to make Extract of Buchu. In 1892 the "doctor" died at
Long Branch, where he had played host to President Grant.[27]

Despite his misfortunes, Helmbold at the height of his career
could well step into the gallery of self-made men with which the
postwar world abounded to represent the patent medicine industry. Shrewd, venturesome, long on vanity and short on
scruple, Helmbold and his Buchu deserve their glittering niche in
the Gilded Age.

Painting the landscape with patent medicine slogans went on
apace. James Whitcomb Riley spent a season traveling about
Indiana daubing signs on roadside boards and barns to spur the
sale of Oriental Liniment. He paid the farmers for the space he
used, but other brushmen were less scrupulous. In the 1870's
single operatives like the Hoosier poet, hired by the medicine
maker, gave way to professional painting and billposting concerns
ready to make the whole nation their sphere of action. They

[25] *Rowell's American Newspaper Directory, 1870*, 42; John C. Dent, "Quacks
and Quackery in America," *Once a Week*, 27 (1872), 236; Historian, 654.
[26] *Ibid.*
[27] *Ibid.*; 654, 657; *Dispensatory* (25th ed.), 197; *National Formulary*
(10th ed., 1955), 102-103.

shocked travelers from Europe with the extent of their success. An Englishman named Marshall, writing of his tour across America in the late seventies, referred to the theme again and again.[28]

Patent medicine advertising, this traveler said, "is one of the first things that strike the stranger as soon as he has landed in the New World: he cannot step a mile into the open country, whether into the fields or along the high roads, without meeting the disfigurement." In the sparsely settled sections of New York City above 80th Street, there were "huge notices of aperients, liniments, pills, plasters, powders, hair-dyes, etc., completely cover[ing] rocks and palings, and the blank walls of houses." The rocks along the Hudson were similarly covered, and "staring white-paint" pill puffs on the Palisades near West Point evoked from Marshall another protest: "It really makes one feel indignant when one sees the beauties of Nature so dishonoured by such nauseous embellishments from the paint-pot." At Niagara, the visitor found both the American and the Canadian sides of the falls disfigured with huge ads for Herrick's Pills and Lightning Oil. There was worse to come: "the nuisance culminates at Chicago," Marshall noted, "for here is the paradise of white-paintism." Yet the railroad routes to the farther West were almost as bad, with a certain variation introduced by Merchant's Gargling Oil, for which the outdoor lettering, like the medicine itself, was yellow. Echo Canyon on the Union Pacific had garish ads "daubed up against the red sandstone precipices just in the most striking part of the whole gorge." Nearing San Francisco, the English traveler noted down that "VINEGAR BITTERS IS ALL THE GO FOR LOVE!" and "YOSEMITE BITTERS GOOD FOR BELLY AKE."

Other visitors—like Robert Louis Stevenson—moaned about the same condition. There was so much space in America, there were so many medicines. The urge to spread therapeutic messages far and wide seemed irresistible. Indeed, a vigorous competition developed among practitioners of this craft, who sought to outdo each other at conquering the unconquerable. The minions of P. H. Drake chopped down an entire mountain-side forest

28 Marcus Dickey, *The Youth of James Whitcomb Riley* (Indianapolis, 1919), 105-14, 137; Presbrey, 500-501; W. G. Marshall, *Through America* (London, 1881), 32, 59, 77-78, 111-13, 143, 284-85.

Plate 1

CONTAINERS for four old English patent medicines, of the type much in vogue in America especially during the several decades preceding the Revolution (ch. 1). Godfrey's Cordial and Hooper's Female Pills from the Samuel Aker, David and George Kass Collection, Albany, N.Y.; the Opodeldoc bottle from the collection of Mrs. Leo F. Redden, Kenmore, N.Y.; the Turlington Balsam bottle, found in an Indian grave in South Dakota, in the U.S. National Museum. All photographs courtesy of the Smithsonian Institution.

The Seal of each Bottle.

Plate 2

JOHN PETER ZENGER reprinted in 1731 a British promotional man pamphlet is in the New York Academy of Medicine Library,

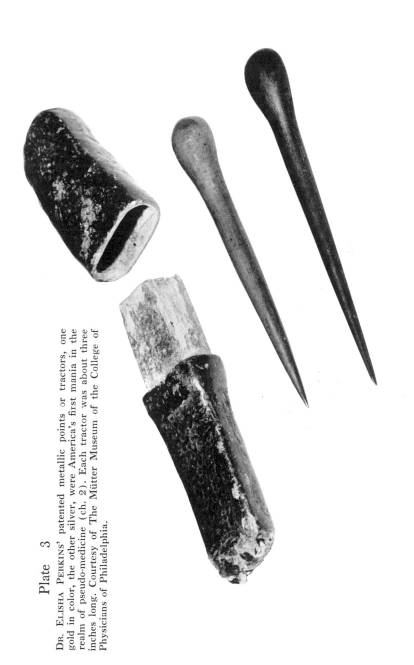

Plate 3

Dr. Elisha Perkins' patented metallic points or tractors, one gold in color, the other silver, were America's first mania in the realm of pseudo-medicine (ch. 2). Each tractor was about three inches long. Courtesy of The Mütter Museum of the College of Physicians of Philadelphia.

T. W. DYOTT,

Wholesale and Retail Druggist, &c.

Nos. 137 & 139, NORTH-EAST CORNER OF SECOND AND RACE STREETS,

PHILADELPHIA,

Offers for Sale or Barter, at very reduced prices, a large and general assortment of choice and well selected *Drugs and Medicines, Patent Medicines, Chemicals, Dye Stuffs, Colours, Window Glass, Vials, Bottles, &c.* with a variety of other articles usually called for.

His extensive Stock, consisting chiefly of his own manufacture, or of goods purchased at the very lowest prices, for *Cash*, enables him to sell to Country Merchants, Druggists, Physicians, and Manufacturers, on the most advantageous terms, or take in *Barter* any of the following articles, *for which he will always give the highest market prices:* viz. Bright Rosin, Turpentine, Lampblack, Pink Root, Rice, Cotton, Tobacco, Sugar, Molasses, Coffee, Rum, Gin, Brandy, Bees-wax, Wheat Flour, Rye and Buckwheat Meal, Hams, Pork, Bacon, Butter. Lard, Cheese, Rye and Apple Whiskey, Peach Brandy, Mackerel, Shad, Pearl and Pot Ashes, Flaxseed, Flaxseed Oil, Logwood, Firewood, Castor Oil, Castor Oil Beans, Soap, Candles, Glass, Lead, Nails, Glue, Furs, Feathers, Rags, Paper, Bristles, Brushes, Shoes, Hats, Saddlery, Domestic Goods generally, Real Estate, in or near the city of Philadelphia, U.S. Bank Stock, &c. &c. &c.

From the extensive and general assortment of articles offered for sale by T. W. DYOTT, and the favourable terms on which he conducts business at his establishment for the accommodation of purchasers, he presumes that country merchants, manufacturers, and dealers in general (whom he solicits to give him a call,) will find it their interest to supply themselves as above.

N. B. Each article is warranted to be of the most pure and genuine quality of its kind.

☞ JAMES BEDFORD, New-Orleans, General Agent for T. W. DYOTT.

Plate 4

DYOTT was one of America's first merchandisers to develop a national market for his patent medicines, and barter was involved (ch. 3). From *Whitely's Philadelphia Annual Advertiser Directory* for 1820, courtesy of the Library of Congress.

Plate 5

PRESUMABLY the face and signature of Samuel H. P. Lee, one of two Connecticut Lees to patent Bilious Pills in the 1790's, and Dyott's portrait in glass as made during the 1820's in his own glassworks; on the other side is a portrait of Benjamin Franklin (ch. 3). The Dyott photograph courtesy of the Smithsonian Institution, where the flask is housed; Lee's Lithontriptic in the author's collection.

Plate 6

PORTRAITS of four 19th-century medicine proprietors: Samuel Thomson (upper left), who patented his botanical system (ch. 4); H. T. Helmbold (upper right), who painted advertisements on the Rockies (ch. 8); Benjamin Brandreth (lower left), who fought James Gordon Bennett in the pages of the penny press (ch. 6); David Hostetter (lower right), who helped make the patent medicine almanac a textbook for the nation (ch. 9). Thomson from his *Guide to Health*, 1835 ed.; Helmbold from a woodcut, circa 1871, reproduced in *Druggists Circular*, Nov. 1912, used by permission of Topic Publishing Co., New York City; Brandreth from J. Thomas Scharf, *History of Westchester County, New York*, II, opposite 358; Hostetter from Erasmus Wilson, *Standard History of Pittsburg, Pennsylvania*, opposite 880. Brandreth and Hostetter photographs courtesy of the Library of Congress.

Plate 7

As HERCULES slew the Hydra, so Swaim's Panacea conquered a multitude of horrible diseases (ch. 5); Radam's Hercules wore a business suit (ch. 10). The Swaim device from a proof book of Alexander Anderson, courtesy of Prints Division, The New York Public Library; the Radam device gold-stamped on the cover of his *Microbes and the Microbe Killer*, in the author's possession.

Plate 8

THE INDIAN theme was perennially popular in patent medicine promotion (ch. 11). The Old
[...] about 1850, courtesy of the Library of Congress; the Indian Compound lithograph,

Plate 9

PILL promotion and patriotism during the Civil War, 1863 (ch. 7).
Courtesy of the Library of Congress.

Plate 10

THE PRETTY face, as of 1867, served as a bitters lure.
Courtesy of the Library of Congress.

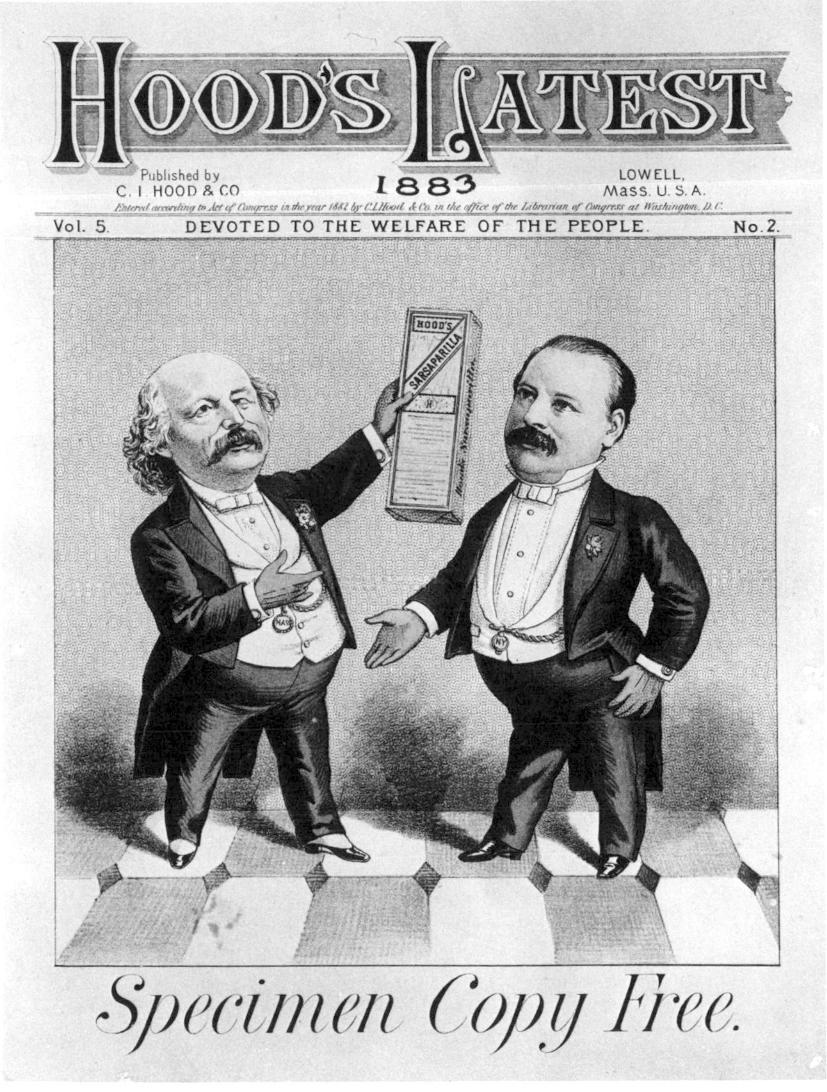

Plate 11

A MEDICINE with political appeal:
Benjamin Butler and Grover Cleveland appear on the cover of a sarsaparilla magazine.
Courtesy of the Bella C. Landauer Collection
in The New-York Historical Society.

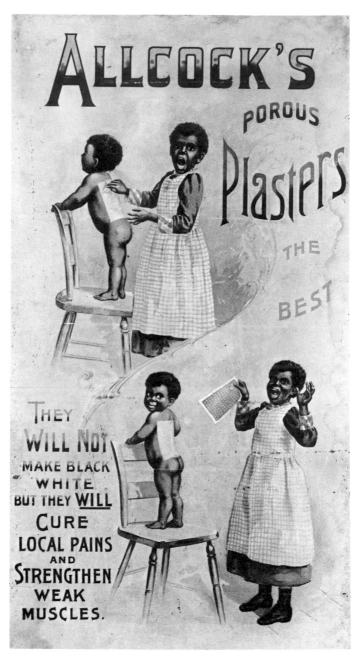

Plate 12

AN 1893 effort to be humorous in the cause of a healing plaster.
Courtesy of the Bella C. Landauer Collection
in The New-York Historical Society.

Plate 13
ONE pure maiden against a whole host of evils (ch. 11).
Courtesy of the Bella C. Landauer Collection
in The New-York Historical Society.

Plate 14

THE COVERS of a pamphlet promoting The Mormon Elders Damiana Wafers, one of countless nostrums promoted with a sex pitch. Courtesy of the Bella C. Landauer Collection in The New-York Historical Society.

HAMLIN'S
WIZARD OIL

THE GREAT MEDICAL WONDER.

There is no Sore it will Not Heal, No Pain it will not Subdue.

HAMLIN'S COUGH BALSAM

PLEASANT TO TAKE
MAGICAL IN ITS EFFECTS.

HAMLIN'S
BLOOD AND LIVER PILLS
For Liver Complaint, Constipation,
AND ALL
Disorders of the Stomach and Digestive Organs.

PREPARED AT THE LABORATORY OF
HAMLINS WIZARD OIL COMPANY, CHICAGO, ILL.

Plate 15

A MUSICAL medicine show, one of many such aggregations sent forth by John A. Hamlin to sing the praises of Wizard Oil (ch. 12). Courtesy of the Bella C. Landauer Collection in The New-York Historical Society.

Plate 16   Two heroes of the battle against patent medicine abuses. "The Great American Fraud" series which Adams (left) wrote for *Collier's* during 1905 and 1906 was an outstanding and timely journalistic critique (ch. 13). Harvey Washington Wiley (right), Chief of the Bureau of Chemistry in the Department of Agriculture, spearheaded the drive for a national food and drug law (ch. 14). The Adams portrait reproduced from the *Bookman*, Aug. 1905; the Wiley photograph courtesy of the Library of Congress.

so Pennsylvania Railroad passengers could read about Plantation Bitters in letters four hundred feet high. Yellowstone Park and the California redwood forests were likewise invaded. One promoter bought a Mississippi stern-wheeler, painted it bright red, added the name of his nostrum in letters twelve feet tall, and ran it up and down the river. Another medicine man got himself a steamship, bedecked it with advertising for a liniment, and let it float to destruction over Niagara Falls. Still another offered to pay for the pedestal of the Statue of Liberty if he could use it as a base for his advertising posters. Others besides Helmbold looked abroad for new worlds to conquer. Drake of the Plantation Bitters is said to have sent men to paint a sign on Mount Ararat.[29]

It did not take the criticism of visitors from overseas to upset many Americans at what was happening to the landscape. The exploits of the advertisers, charged the *New York Tribune* editor in 1876, were changing "scenery" into "obscenery." There had been protests before, and even an occasional law. The desecration of the most famous and awesome of American natural wonders, like Niagara Falls and Yellowstone Park, aroused the whole nation. Civic groups, art associations, women's clubs, legislators, and editorial writers combined in a crusade to save American beauty. Ordinances were enacted, laws were passed, administrative decisions were made, and the tide of white paint receded. New York City forced advertisers to paint over and thus obliterate their slogans on scenic rocks. By the new century, both the United States and Canada forbade advertising on governmental property at Niagara, although a huge sign still loomed from private ground on Canadian soil. Many advertisers withdrew from the wonders of nature on their own account, not wishing to risk the odium of being thought unpatriotic. Even the Associated Billposters of the United States and Canada, organized in 1890, soon joined most other Americans and officially condemned the painting of signs on rocks and other natural objects in scenic settings.[30]

[29] Stevenson, *The Travels and Essays of Robert Louis Stevenson* (N.Y., 1909), 108; Lewis Atherton, *Main Street on the Middle Border* (Bloomington, Ind., 1954), 223; Presbrey, 389-90; WPA, *New York, A Guide to the Empire State* (N.Y., 1947), 674; *Druggists Circular*, 49 (1905), 123; Kimball, "The Fight against Advertising Disfigurement," *Scribner's Mag.*, 29 (1901), 104.

[30] *Tribune*, May 13, 1876; Presbrey, 500, 504; "The Future of Scenery," *Scribner's Mag.*, 24 (1898), 378; Charles M. Robinson, "Abuses of Public Advertising," *Atlantic Monthly*, 93 (1904), 289-99.

So much effort went into saving the national shrines, however, that little energy was left to fight for everyday scenery. There were a few hardy souls who took the law into their own hands. A Peekskill woman and her friends went about tearing down all paper and cloth advertising signs they could reach. In a Southern city, posters for a certain nostrum were ripped off by male citizens as soon as discovered—out of respect for womanhood. The superintendent of the New York state asylum in Utica organized his own personal war to eliminate roadside advertising along the route he traveled between his home and work. Several railroads forbade sign-posting on property they owned along their tracks. More local legislation was passed, often nullified in the courts. Despite all this, however, many critics felt that the American landscape was in greater jeopardy than ever before in history.[31]

There was, indeed, as the 20th century approached, a new boom in outdoor advertising. The Associated Billposters could afford to look down their noses at painted patent medicine notices on the rocks of Niagara Falls and Yellowstone. New lithographing techniques were outmoding paint and achieving such striking results that the most respectable firms were joining nostrums and tobacco in crying their wares in the great outdoors. "Shall we hold nothing sacred," inquired a friend of nature in 1904, "—sky or ocean, rock or tree, public building, church, or monument?"[32]

It was the echo of an old cry. Helmbold had heard it when he spread the name of Buchu across the continent, and it was destined for countless more repeatings. For in 1904 the automobile was barely born, and the biggest boom of all in outdoor advertising was just getting under way.

[31] *Ibid.*; "The Future of Scenery"; Kimball, "A Chance for Scenery," *Outlook*, 60 (Nov. 26, 1898), 772-74; editorial, *Outlook* (Jan. 23, 1904), 197-98.
[32] Presbrey, 502-504; Hower, 81; Robinson, 290.

ST. GEORGE AND THE DRAGON

"They can talk about Shakespeare, but in my opinion old Hostetter—and Ayer—had more influence on the national life than any of 'em."

—UNCLE HENRY, in *Collier's Weekly*

". . . to draw the line nicely, and fix definitely where the medicine may end and the alcoholic beverage begin, is a task which has often perplexed and still greatly perplexes revenue officers, and especially where a preparation contains so large proportion of alcoholic spirits as your does."

—COMMISSIONER OF INTERNAL REVENUE TO HOSTETTER & SMITH, August 22, 1883[1]

A MODERN-DAY student of history and a modern-day man of business, each interested in his own particular way in the century-old traditions of Hostetter's Bitters, met in Pittsburgh on a spring afternoon.[2] They sat for a while in the Hostetter outer offices, where the paper work was done, chatting about the past. Then the businessman said: "Would you like to taste the Tonic we make today?"

The student agreed, and the businessman led the way through a locked door to a large back room. The air was fragrant with the sweet odor of spices. A huge silvery mixing tank stood near a shelf on which were tumbled a score of volumes concerning pharmacy. Close at hand in a rack were several large glass bottles, each filled with a mixture of herbs resembling rough-cut tobacco. The herbs were slowly yielding up their essences to a small quantity of alcohol, which had been poured over them. In

[1] Cited in Walsh, *Cures, The Story of Cures That Fail*, 48, and in *JAMA*, 1 (1883), 283.

[2] The businessman was Ben Hyde, an important stockholder, and the episode occurred during April 1956. In 1959 the Hostetter name was bought by Lanolin Plus. *FDC Reports*, "The Pink Sheet," *Drugs and Cosmetics*, 21 (June 29, 1959), 20.

due time this pungent liquid would be drained away through spigots in the bottoms of the bottles and mixed in the silvery tank with the proper proportions of distilled water and cane alcohol. In another corner of the room there rested an aging vat beside a table upon which the small bottles were placed when filled with the final product. On the table were a number of bottles made of amber glass, bearing white labels front and rear. A bright red and dark green message proclaimed the contents, Doctor Hostetter Celebrated Stomachic Bitters Tonic.

The student, surveying the scene, expected the businessman to pick up one of the bottles, procure a spoon, and pour out and present for sampling a prescribed dose of the aromatic stomachic. Not so, however. The businessman got instead a shot glass. After rinsing it at a sink, he filled it to the brim from the spigot on the vat. Then he handed it to the student, who proceeded to taste the warm, mellow, bitter-sweet potency of the liquid it contained. In similar fashion many before him had sampled the various versions bearing Dr. Jacob Hostetter's name since the first bottles appeared on the market more than a hundred years before.

It was not Dr. Hostetter who had introduced the bitters into commerce, even though this Lancaster County, Pennsylvania, physician had worked out the formula for use in his practice. The business venture was launched by Dr. Jacob's eldest son. David Hostetter was to become a self-made man with a vengeance, but when he first marketed the bitters, he was thirty-four, with a record of nothing but false starts. He had grown up on the family farm. At sixteen he had taken a job as chore boy for a drygoods store, rising during seven years to the status of manager. Then, in partnership with another man, he had opened a drygoods store for himself. Hardly was this venture under way when David succumbed to a violent attack of Gold Rush fever. In April 1850 he went to California, traveling by way of Panama. David did not find a fortune in the gold fields. After a few weeks he returned to San Francisco, feeling that a man with mercantile experience might get more gold by setting up a business in the booming town. He became a grocer. Within a month one of the fires that swept so frequently across the young and flimsy city burned the aspiring grocer out. David went back to Pennsylvania.[3]

3 C. Robinson, ed., *The Biographical Encyclopaedia of Pennsylvania of the Nineteenth Century* (Phila., 1874), 618-19; Charles E. Warren, "Pittsburgh,"

At home, too, the news was bad. His partner had absconded, leaving the drygoods store deeply in debt. David went to work for some railroad builders, serving as paymaster for the crew installing the Pennsylvania lines around Horseshoe Bend. On this job he met another former resident of Lancaster, a man named George W. Smith. Smith had some capital and the willingness to venture it in marketing a proprietary version of David's father's remedy. So it was that, in 1853, the first bottles of the Celebrated Stomach Bitters were made at Pittsburgh, a city close to the sources of Monongahela rye.

The plant at first was small, the employees few. Some half dozen people concocted the bitters in part of a building that rented for the modest sum of $175 a year. But David was an energetic salesman, and he traveled far and wide. Within the first year he brought home not only many orders, but also a bride, Rosetta, the daughter of a Cincinnati businessman. Domestic bliss and commercial success came hand in hand. By 1857 the bitters partnership was happily forced to move into larger quarters all its own, and by the beginning of the sixties it had become a nationwide advertiser with a trade-mark known from coast to coast. As Hercules had clubbed the Hydra for the Panacea of William Swaim, so now St. George slew the Dragon for the Bitters of David Hostetter. Astride a rearing horse, the helmeted but otherwise naked knight plunged his sharp spear down toward the open jaws of the fearsome monster.[4]

Hostetter's dragon was a symbol for countless evils. Some of them were once summed up by a rhymester in the partnership's employ.

> Dyspepsia's pangs, that rack and grind
> The body, and depress the mind;
> Agues, that, as they go and come,
> Make life a constant martyrdom;
> Colics and dysenteric pains,
> 'Neath which the strong man's vigor wanes;

Mag. of Western Hist., 3 (Jan. 1886), 26-66; *Pitts. Commercial Gaz.*, Nov. 6 and 7, 1888; Erasmus Wilson, ed., *Standard History of Pittsburg, Pennsylvania* (Chicago, 1898), 1,005-1,008.

4 *Industries of Pittsburgh, Trade, Commerce and Manufactures* (Pitts., 1879), 127; genealogical information furnished by William P. Ortale, General Manager of the Hostetter Corporation in 1956, whose association with the Hostetter fortunes dated from 1949.

Bilious complaints,—those tedious ills,
Ne'er conquered yet by drastic pills;
Dread Diarrhea, that cannot be
Cured by destructive Mercury;
Slow constitutional decay,
That brings death nearer, day by day;
Nervous prostration, mental gloom,
Heralds of madness or the tomb;
For these, though Mineral nostrums fail,
Means of relief at last we hail,
HOSTETTER'S BITTERS—medicine sure,
Not to *prevent*, alone, but *cure*.[5]

It was not often that St. George charged forth in such poetic mood; he more often confronted the dragon in plain prose. In one guise or the other, however, the anti-mineral doctrine appeared in Hostetter advertising year after year. The Bible itself furnished texts. "That compend of Divine Wisdom and messenger of glad tidings to the human race," ran one appeal, "says nothing about mercury, antimony, and other mineral irritants as remedies for diseases: but it refers with great emphasis and in at least one hundred passages, to the use of *vegetable curatives*, and more especially *vegetable invigorants*." Jeremiah, David, John, and Paul were called upon to testify. This herbal gospel on the part of botanical promoters, of course, was decades old. By the mid-19th century, in the wake of the therapeutic nihilism preached by some regular physicians, there was room for a broader vision. Any rigorous medication, the Hostetter seers asserted, vegetable as well as mineral, was bad. Especially should one eschew "the drenching class of purgatives."[6]

Sweet are the uses of analogy. "Dynamite and giant-powder might answer admirably to remove obstructions from Hell Gate in East River, New York," one Hostetter advertisement suggested, "but explosive measures in medication are ever attended with dangerous consequences." Medical violence was not only risky, it was old-fashioned, one of the "follies" persisting in the face of new knowledge. "There are hosts of people who, because

[5] *Hostetter's United States Almanac, 1867.*
[6] *Ibid.*, 1861; 1887 advertisement from the advertising proof file in the Corporation's archives, which the author was permitted to examine, as he was much other surviving material, through the generosity of Mr. Ortale.

they have adopted certain principles, continue to swallow them to their dying day in defiance of the laws of common-sense." Such bullheadedness was stupid. Purging, bleeding, and blistering were on the wane, and a more humane therapeutic day was dawning. Tonics, cordials, and restoratives were receiving enhanced prestige from regular practitioners. The bitters, therefore, were up to date. They had been compounded by a doctor. No other remedy could match their mildness. They were "as harmless as water from the mountain spring." So ran the therapeutic argument.[7]

If there was anything mild about the bitters, it would appear, it was their herbal content. Running an analysis in 1883, a Department of Agriculture chemist found that the herbal oils and extracts, all in all, amounted to some four per cent of the total product. David Hostetter was not revealing the secret of his formula, but the chemist made a guess. The mixture contained various essential oils, he said, such as those of anise and coriander, and some vegetable bitters, such as cinchona and gentian. Later probers were to name these and suggest other botanical possibilities: orange peel, cloves, cinnamon, rhubarb, calamus, columbo, centaury, serpenteria. Aromatics, tonics, and laxatives such as these, Dr. Hostetter had been able to find in the official pharmaceutical tomes of his day. Countless doctors were prescribing them, often in mixtures, to excite the appetite, to invigorate the digestion, to rid the stomach and bowels of gas, to relieve dyspepsia, to "exalt the energies of all parts of the frame." But the customary tonic dose dispensed by the regular physician was considerably more generous in its proportion of herbal ingredients. Hostetter's four per cent seemed a bit on the stingy side. "An article containing so little that is even nominally medicinal," the Commissioner of Internal Revenue wrote, put him on his guard, especially when he considered what was in the other ninety-six per cent.[8]

Sixty-four per cent of Hostetter's Bitters, the chemist had reported, was water, but the other thirty-two per cent was absolute alcohol. Herein lay the reason for the Commissioner's

[7] 1887 and 1888 ads, advertising proof file; *Harper's Wkly.*, 10 (1866), 687.
[8] *JAMA*, 1 (1883), 281-85; Oleson, *Secret Nostrums and Systems of Medicine*, 95; Amer. Med. Assoc., *Nostrums and Quackery*, II, 740-43; *Dispensatory of the United States of America* (10th ed., Phila., 1854), *passim*, with quotation as to tonic powers from p. 2.

perplexity. For if this high a proportion of alcohol turned the bitters into a beverage, those who sold it would be forced to buy a federal license. And there was evidence that the bitters was, at least occasionally, dispensed in just this way. Up in Sitka, Alaska, Hostetter's potent liquid had been served in saloons by the drink. Bars and stores in the States now and then followed the same practice.[9]

Despite "an almost irresistible tendency of the mind to conclude that no genuine medicine needs so much whiskey and so few drugs in it," the Commissioner of Internal Revenue, in 1883, resolved his dilemma by letting the nature of the sale determine the status of the bitters. If it was sold across the counter as a drink, the dispenser would have to pay for a liquor license. If sold in the bottle as a medicine, no alcoholic beverage tax applied. What happened after the bottle was bought was no concern of the Commissioner. "Us kids heard," Carl Sandburg was to remember, "that you could get drunk on one bottle of Hostetter's." Officially, at least, the Commissioner did not listen to such tales.[10]

The Commissioner's decision was eminently satisfactory to the proprietor. He had denied fervently, year in and year out, that the bitters was a drink, at the same time, with equal fervency, extolling the quality of its alcoholic content. While insisting that the remedy received "its extraordinary and unequalled potency" from its herbal ingredients, Hostetter advertising stressed the presence of the alcoholic "vehicle." Indeed, the compounder was willing to admit to a higher proportion of alcohol—thirty-nine per cent—than the Department of Agriculture chemist had discovered in the samples he had analyzed. Nor was this "stimulating basis" the sort of bad liquor which competitors poured into their products. Hostetter's Bitters contained "the pure Essence of Rye." After the proprietor received the spirits from the still, he put them through a complicated process to remove the "acrid and corrosive oils" which tainted other bitters. And there certainly were scores of other bitters with which David Hostetter's product had to compete.[11]

9 *JAMA*, 1 (1883), 281-85; Hostetter v. Sommers, 84 Fed. 333.

10 *JAMA*, 1 (1883), 281-85; Sandburg, *Always the Young Strangers* (N.Y., 1952), 228.

11 Hostetter's almanacs, 1861 and 1864; 1909 President's report, in Minute Book of the Hostetter Company, in the Corporation's archives. Independent analyses sometimes showed an amount of alcohol greater than 39%. See John

During the second half of the 19th century, indeed, America developed a mighty thirst for bitters. The intensity of that thirst unquestionably owed much to the temperance movement. 1851 was a red-letter year for opponents of alcohol, for in that year the legislature of Maine, the first in the Union to take the step, had voted the state completely dry. This was the initial major triumph in a new tack taken by temperance crusaders, the substitution of legislation for persuasion as the main method of their efforts. They would not let up on their campaigning to convince the drinker of the iniquity of his sin, but they would help bolster his resolve with laws forbidding the sale of liquor. As Maine went, so went other New England states, and before the end of the decade all Northern states but one and two states in the South had enacted prohibition laws of greater or less stringency. These laws were badly enforced, but they placed liquor under an additional handicap: drinking could be condemned not only as immoral; it was illegal as well. The price of alcoholic beverages rose, quality declined. On such a battleground, evasionary tactics might be expected. Two years after the enactment of the Maine law, amid the continuing agitation, Hostetter's Bitters had been born.[12]

The Hostetter promoters avowed their hearty approval of temperance. During the Civil War they considered it a shame that Union commanders provided troops with common whiskey and quinine as an "invigorant" on the eve of a hard march or dangerous battle. This did "more harm than good," albeit admittedly it was less damaging than the dastardly Rebel practice of prescribing alcohol and gunpowder, which resulted in "delirium for the time being, and the most terrible after-effects." The bitters would be much superior, and the proprietor was sure that the time was not far off when "a humane government" would recognize this fact and "sanction and adopt" them for military use.[13]

The chaos of wartime brought a retreat from prohibition, but the temperance forces returned to the attack with redoubled zeal in the postwar world. Hostetter marched with the crusaders.

Phillips Street, compiler, *The Composition of Certain Patent and Proprietary Medicines* (Chicago, 1917), 32-35.

[12] Ernest H. Cherrington, *The Evolution of Prohibition in the United States of America* (Westerville, O., 1920), 135-162; Arthur C. Cole, *The Irrepressible Conflict, 1850-1865* (N.Y., 1934), 160-63.

[13] Hostetter's almanac, 1864.

[131]

Distilled liquors, he asserted in his almanac for 1869, "richly deserve the stigma that has been cast upon them by the friends of Health and Temperance." This did not mean, of course, that medicines should abandon alcohol. Science did not permit it. Only alcohol could preserve the medicinal properties of vegetable extracts in a fluid state. "Only by a *diffusible stimulant* [could] the medicinal constituents . . . be conveyed directly to their destination." This was a truth established by the "most eminent Lights of Medical Science" and admitted by the "leading champions of Temperance," the noble editor Horace Greeley among them.

Most of Hostetter's competitors employed a similar pitch. There were others among the bitters crowd, however, who grabbed even more tightly the coattails of temperance advocates and boasted that there was no alcohol at all within their bottles. In an extremely rare instance this was true. Walker's California Vinegar Bitters was almost devoid of alcohol, containing, at least, no higher a proportion than did beer. Walker's laxative liquid, according to a manufacturing pharmacist, was "a villainous, turbid, disgusting sour swill." Such a genuinely temperance bitters angered the proprietors who admitted to having alcohol in their own. The non-alcoholic brands, charged a competitor whose product was largely rum, were "teetotal humbugs," promoted by "unphilosophical balderdash," and about as therapeutically "effective as bilge water." Most bitters parading under the temperance label, however, though their promoters fervently denied that they contained alcohol, actually did so in substantial amounts. Some half-dozen concoctions advertised as absolutely non-alcoholic— indeed, claiming that they were a specific treatment for inebriates —were in fact forty to eighty proof.[14]

"Let me advise you as a friend," wrote Josh Billings in a mock letter to a bitters proprietor, "if it is indispensably necessary to cheat a little in the manufaktur ov the 'Salvashun Bitters' let it bi all means be in the rutes; don't lower the basis."[15]

[14] *Dr. Walker's California Bitters Almanac*, 1872, in N.Y. Public Library; Walker's handbill, Landauer Coll., N.-Y. Hist. Soc.; Street, 33, 35; Oleson, 186; P. H. Drake & Co., *Morning, Noon, and Night, 1872*, Landauer Coll.; *Druggists Circular and Chemical Gazette*, 49 (1905), 124; *Family Health Almanac, 1876*, N.Y. Public Library.

[15] Gallatin, Mo., *North Missourian*, May 25, 1865, cited in Atherton, *Main Street on the Middle Border*, 223.

Many Americans, beset with temperance pressures, agreed with Josh's counsel. Whether they knew it or not, they were interested in the "basis." They took their doses from square bottles, from round bottles, from bottles shaped like cabins, pigs, drums, fish, globes, lighthouses, Indian maidens, and even the bust of President Washington. But the basis was the same. To judge by store ledgers from one state, Mississippi, some families replenished their stock of alcoholic nostrums every day.[16]

Doubtless there were many naive and gullible who did not know what they drank. They found themselves afflicted with some of the numerous symptoms listed in the bitters advertising. They sought relief. The warm feeling, the sense of elation following an ample dose, proved that the medicine was seeking out the source of the infirmity. Particularly might this genuine ignorance prevail in the case of temperance devotees purchasing the non-alcoholic bitters, so-called. Other ailing Americans drank Hostetter's and similar bitters, avowedly alcoholic, in a like spirit, seeking health and being convinced by advertising that no herbal essences were really safe unless preserved in Monongahela rye or rum.

For some thirsty Americans the alcoholic bitters were sheer subterfuge. The renewed temperance campaign was taking hold. In 1872 the Prohibition Party first put a national ticket in the field. In 1874 the WCTU began its doughty work. The decade of the eighties witnessed terrific agitation, some statewide legislation, and the drying up of many American communities by local option. In the nineties the pace quickened. The Anti-Saloon League entered the fray. Countless school systems introduced the study of temperance textbooks which used a "scare" psychology not unlike that employed in patent medicine advertising. Areas dry by local option spread. For many who liked their liquor, the opportunity to buy was legally gone. For others, in regions not yet arid, family pressure or neighborhood opinion bore down heavily. For those deprived, one legal and almost respectable recourse was open: the steady pursuit of health through high-proof bitters.[17]

[16] Thompson, *Bitters Bottles*, 75-77; Clark, *Pills, Petticoats and Plows, The Southern Country Store*, 223.
[17] Cherrington, 165-82, 254-58; Allan Nevins, *The Emergence of Modern America, 1865-1878* (N.Y., 1927), 336-38; Arthur M. Schlesinger, *The Rise of the City, 1878-1898* (N.Y., 1933), 354.

Even this effort, however salubrious it may have been, often pricked the conscience. This conclusion may be deduced, perhaps, by an argument from silence. Bitters bottles were sold by the millions, many fabricated in decorative forms with the expectation that they might adorn the mantelpiece and serve as a perennial advertisement. Yet the number of bottles that survive, compared with the vast quantity put upon the market, is amazingly small. A bitters-bottle collector suggests the reason: "The same conscience that was deluded to a belief that bitter tasting stimulants could be imbibed innocently in the guise of medicine turned more honest in a fear of discovery of its peccadilloes, and was impelled to destruction of the evidence of its secret tippling." The proprietor who sought to market a bitters displayed shrewd business sense; in expecting his fancy bottle to end up on the parlor what-not, his judgment was less sound.[18]

David Hostetter stuck to a plain square bottle with high sloping shoulders and a stubby neck. But its contents were potent and palatable, and its sales were very good. In 1859 some 432,000 bottles went out upon the market; three decades later, just after David's death, sales exceeded 930,000. Truly golden years lay in between. To judge from excise stamps purchased from the government between 1862 and 1883, Hostetter's Bitters had an annual average retail sale surpassing $1,000,000.[19]

During these years St. George was indeed a busy knight, but David Hostetter found time to diversify his interests. As his fortunes rose, he became one of the most substantial citizens in Pittsburgh's business community. He helped establish a bank. He played a role in promoting the building of railroads. He was much excited when the first natural gas well was struck not far from Pittsburgh, and he hurried to bring back rubber bags filled with the gas for chemical analysis. David was interested in petroleum also, and he took part in the battling which beset this new and turbulent industry.[20]

In his mature years, David Hostetter had a rough-hewn sort of face. He was almost entirely bald, but wore a full and scraggly beard that reached down to his chest. His forehead was high, an

18 Thompson, 11, 13.
19 Hostetter's almanac, 1861; "A Summary of the operations of . . . The Hostetter Company," in the Corporation's archives; Holcombe, "Private Die Proprietary Stamp Notes," *Wkly. Philatelic Gossip*, Aug. 19, 1939, 621.
20 Warren, 261-66; Wilson, 1,005-1,008; *Pitts. Commercial Gaz.*, Nov. 7, 1888.

impression exaggerated by his lack of hair. His nose was long and straight. His eyes were dark, topped by quizzical brows. He and his family lived in a three-story mansion, ornate with stained glass windows, a circular staircase, and elaborate wood-carved mantelpieces. David was a thoroughly devoted family man. He and Rosetta were parents of five children, one daughter and four sons. Three of the four boys died while still young men.[21]

It was David Herbert, the second son, who inherited not only his father's name but also his diligence and capability. He had been taught by private tutors before going to the small local university that later was to bear the city's name. Then, like two of his brothers before him, Herbert had gone abroad to study at Heidelberg. Back in Pittsburgh, he had taken courses at a business college. After a year on a ranch in the West for health and pleasure, he came home to work.[22]

The young man had a round face, dark eyes, prominent ears, and thin black hair. He did not imitate his father's long and ragged beard. Instead he wore a large and bushy mustache with curling ends. He was fond of hunting, riding, and yachting, but these pursuits did not detract from an earnest concentration upon business. The first job in his apprenticeship was that of purchasing agent for one of the railroads his father had helped establish. Advancement came quickly. Other tasks were added to Herbert's duties. He was trained well as heir apparent.[23]

David Hostetter succumbed to kidney trouble in November 1888. George Smith, his partner, had died four years before. Hostetter left a fortune of some $18,000,000. It had all begun with Dr. Jacob's formula. As a legacy the bitters was to prove equally lucrative. D. Herbert took the helm. In 1889 he formed a corporation with himself as president. All but a fraction of the stock was held by members of the family. There were 900 shares, each worth $100 at par. This sum of $90,000 was larger than the total tangible assets of the new corporation, including the manufacturing and printing plants and all unsold bitters on hand.

[21] Portrait bound as frontispiece to 1887 Hostetter's almanacs in Corporation's archives; genealogical material in archives; *Pitts. Press*, Feb. 6, 1955; *Pitts. Commercial Gaz.*, Nov. 7, 1888; Warren, 261-66.

[22] Genealogical material in Corporation's archives; *N.Y. Times*, Aug. 4, 1902; *American Weekly*, Aug. 20, 1950; *The Book of Prominent Pennsylvanians* (Pitts., 1913), 181; Charles A. Rook, ed., *Western Pennsylvanians* (Pitts., 1923), 138.

[23] Portrait in *Book of Prominent Pennsylvanians*, 181; Rook, 138.

These assets amounted to $75,510.57. Yet the value of the Hostetter name was worth much more. Few concerns with so small an investment in plant, so modest a capitalization, were selling a product which grossed $500,000 a year. It is hardly any wonder that in the decade that remained before the new century began, the dividends paid by the Hostetter Company, despite a sag caused by the panic of 1893, totaled 850 per cent. Both St. George and Herbert could well be proud.[24]

Herbert ran the company much as his father had run the partnership. Large sums were spent for advertising, some to pay for "readers" which printer's devils set in type for insertion in newspapers to the confusion of the public. Looking like news, the "readers" bore such tantalizing heads as "The Devil Fish Described by Hugo," "Which Was It? Bacon or Shakespeare?" and "Put Not Your Faith in Princes," to lure the curious on to the point at which they learned that Hostetter's Bitters were indispensable to health. This was one way of conveying an advertising message. There was another way, one upon which Herbert spent nearly $100,000 a year, almost half the total advertising budget. This too was a legacy from David's day, and it constituted the main Hostetter contribution to patent medicine promotion. Late in 1860 there had appeared the first edition of *Hostetter's United States Almanac for the Use of Merchants, Mechanics, Farmers and Planters, and All Families.*[25]

Patent medicine almanacs were not new in America when David Hostetter entered the field. When they did begin, they joined forces with a long tradition that ran back into the colonial period. The almanac, with its calendar, its amazingly long-range weather predictions, its counsel on when to plant and when to reap, its household hints, its witticisms and its proverbs, antedated even Poor Richard. The editors of many of these annual documents were, like Franklin, sound and sober men who looked with disfavor upon quackery. One of them offered this prayer in 1813: "From quack lawyers, quack doctors, quack preachers, mad dogs and yellow fever, good Lord, deliver us!" A policy of antagonism to patent medicines also was evident in certain medi-

[24] *Pitts. Commercial Gaz.*, Oct. 31, 1884, Nov. 6, 1888; Minute Book; Rowell, *Forty Years an Advertising Agent, 1865-1905*, 390.

[25] Earnest Elmo Calkins, *And Hearing Not—* (N.Y., 1946), 93; 1888 and 1892 ads, advertising proof file; "A Summary of the operations of . . . The Hostetter Company."

cal and health almanacs, often edited by doctors, that began to appear in the second decade of the 19th century. If only to defend themselves, one would think, the patent medicine proprietors should have resorted to the same medium. Adept as they usually were at pioneering techniques of appeal to the populace, the nostrum makers were tardy in adopting the almanac. Once started, however, they soon outdistanced the field. Over their predecessors and their non-nostrum competitors, the distributors of patent medicine almanacs had one great advantage. The almanacs were free.[26]

Who wins the palm for priority is, as with the story of most origins, hard to tell. Some patent medicine men, in the late 1820's, bought space in commercial almanacs to tout their wares. In the 1832 edition of the *Farmers and Mechanics Almanac*, William Swaim paid for six whole pages to boost his Panacea. A decade was to pass, however, before proprietors began to send forth cover-to-cover almanacs all their own. One of the very first was *Bristol's Free Almanac: for 1844*, issued from Batavia, New York, in behalf of a sarsaparilla. On the cover stood a naked man, the skin of his abdomen folded back exposing his bowels. Encircling the man were the twelve signs of the zodiac. This feature appeared somewhere in the pages of all almanacs. Few of Bristol's successors, however, were to be so ingenious as he in linking their remedies with diseases prevalent during the passing months. "And now the Dog Star rages," began the text for August. "The fierce heat boils in the veins and channels of life, and turns the ruddy currents of health to poisonous streams that course through the system, and, if not speedily expelled, engender a hundred forms of sickness and decay."[27]

Once pioneers like Bristol had paved the way, other nostrum promoters followed the trail. Americans were in for an annual dosage of millions of threatening words and frightening pictures. Before the forties were over, Dr. David Jayne had launched his *Medical Almanac and Guide to Health* in behalf of an assortment

[26] Clarence S. Brigham, *An Account of American Almanacs and Their Value for Historical Study* (reprinted from *Proceedings of the Amer. Antiquarian Soc.*, Oct. 1925); George L. Kittredge, *The Old Farmer and His Almanack* (Boston, 1904), 100-103.

[27] Brigham, 7-8. On the question of origins, I have been helped by a letter from Milton Drake of Riverdale, N.Y., citing his Check-List and Census of American Almanacs. The Bristol's almanac is in the Rare Book Div., Library of Congress.

[137]

of family medicines, two of which were vermifuges. Staring out at readers with big round eyes was a horrendous tapeworm. Some time during the fifties, the worm turned, assuming a different pose, and presumably a more comfortable one, for he was to hold it unchanged for more than half a century.[28] Long almanac runs were certainly not rare. One of the hardiest, begun in the early fifties, called the world's attention to the Cherry Pectoral and other remedies made by James C. Ayer. Ayer's *American Almanacs* traveled farther and confronted more ailing folks than any other, even Hostetter's. Full production had not yet been achieved in 1855 when Ayer's copywriters took to parody in order to convey their message, securing a reader impact approximating that of Jayne's worm.[29]

> Once upon a midnight dreary, while I languished sick
> and weary,
> With a cough that still returning, lungs and stomach
> rendered sore,
> While I groaned, nor thought of napping, suddenly
> there came a tapping,
> As of someone gently rapping, rapping at my chamber
> door:
> Only this, and nothing more.

The knocker, it developed in ensuing verses, was "an ancient lady . . . whom the neighbors called Aunt Shore," and she besought the sufferer to try that "wondrous balsam," Ayer's Cherry Pectoral.

> At the word I drew the stopple, to my lips I pressed
> the bottle,
> And adown my ulcered throttle did a swallow smoothly
> pour,
> When straightway a pleasant feeling of repose went
> softly stealing
> Through my worn and weary vitals, which I have not
> felt before
> For full half a year or more.

[28] Jayne later dated his almanacs from 1843, but Drake has found no copy earlier than 1847. The early worm appears in the 1850 edition in the Landauer Coll.; the later worm was seen in the 1859 edition, in the N.Y. Public Library, *passim* to 1911 edition in the Landauer Coll.

[29] Ayer's almanac, 1855, in N.Y. Public Library.

Then each day I kept imbibing, spite of sceptic's slurs
  and gibing,
From a Cherry Pectoral bottle, which I kept behind
  my door;
And my lungs forgot their ailing, and my cheek,
  which fast was paling,
Soon resumed the pristine lustre, which long before it
  wore,
  In the jolly days of yore.

Toward the end of the century, though there was less poetry in them, there were more Ayer almanacs. The concern was averaging $120,000 a year printing some 16,000,000 copies of its various editions. During one year the total may have soared past 25,000,000. In 1889, with the peak not yet reached, the company's own publishing plant had equipment to print, fold, and send to the bindery 100,000 almanacs a day, their presses consuming some 25 miles of paper in the process. That year Ayer issued almanacs or pamphlets in 21 languages, intended not only to persuade most immigrant groups in the United States but to ship literally around the world. The same medical exhortations appeared in Spanish, Portuguese, French, German, Dutch, Swedish, Norwegian-Danish, Bohemian, Welsh, Italian, Finnish, Turkish, Armenian, Greek, Bulgarian, Polish, Hawaiian, Burmese, Chinese, and the Gujarati dialect of India.[30]

All the major patent medicine proprietors, and many with a more modest ranking, got in the almanac game. Some strove for attention through novelty—producing a pamphlet the size of a postage stamp, laying heavy emphasis on Shakespeare, hiring the leading humorists of the day to do original pieces. But most followed a fairly traditional format. There were the usual astronomical data, the rising and setting of the sun, the phases of the moon, the position of the planets, which many proprietors bought year after year from an obliging astronomer in Massachusetts for thirty dollars. There was often advice to the farmer and housewife, sometimes cartoons, and nearly always jokes, clipped from the daily and comic papers by members of the office force. The

---

[30] *Amer. Druggist and Pharm. Record*, 36 (1900), 228; Sidney A. Sherman, "Advertising in the United States," *Amer. Statistical Soc. Publications*, ns 7 (Dec. 1900), 5. A bound collection of Ayer's almanacs for 1889, with a two-page foreword, is located in the Peabody Institute Library, Baltimore.

reader would not go far without encountering a message from the sponsor. For the nostrum proprietors did not forget that the purpose of the whole venture was to sell their products, and each small raft of wisdom or amusement was floated in a vast therapeutic sea.[31]

Each year just before the Christmas season, local druggists and general storekeepers all over the nation received supplies of almanacs, for which their only payment was a small charge for freight. Each year between Christmas and New Year, these almanacs were placed upon thousands of counters for millions of families to carry home, or were distributed to doorsteps by youngsters willing to peddle all day for a quarter. Hung from a nail in a kitchen corner, laid on the top of a bureau, each almanac was a calendar, a reference work, a source of entertainment—in some cases, indeed, a family's complete library—for twelve long months. Many copies surviving in archives testify to the hard and constant use to which almanacs were put; the pages are dog-eared and finger-smeared, the margins crammed with pencilled notations of income and outgo.[32]

In the Pennsylvania farm home of Mark Sullivan, the family library consisted of several schoolbooks, a local weekly paper, and an incomplete copy of *Uncle Tom's Cabin*. To young Mark the annual arrival of the nostrum almanac was a literary event. The same was true for Carl Sandburg out in Illinois. He and a brother and sister read the Hostetter issues aloud to each other, discussing the points of the jokes. Thousands of youngsters across the nation, destined for futures much less literary, must have done likewise. The patent medicine almanac was a sort of informal textbook for educating the American people.[33]

Quantitatively, indeed, the almanacs were a mighty important textbook. No other printed sources were issued in such large editions. Perhaps the Bible was an exception, one taken account of by the Ayer company in drafting its boastful slogan: "Second

[31] *Hazeltines Pocket-Book Almanac for 1885* and *Dr. O. Phelps Brown 1872 Shakespeare Almanac*, in the Landauer Coll.; *St. Jacobs Oil Family Calendar 1883-84* [with selections by Bill Nye and Joel Chandler Harris], in N.Y. Public Library; A. C. Cantley, "Some Facts about Making Patent Medicines," *Chautauquan*, 27 (1898), 389; Ayer's almanac, 1885, in the author's collection.
[32] Ayer almanac order form, 1864, in Landauer Coll.; McLaughry & Tyler, Fountain Green, Ill., Invoice Book, 1860 . . . 1877, Ill. State Hist. Library; Gerald Carson, *The Old Country Store* (N.Y., 1954), 247-48; Sandburg, 118, 148-49, 227-29.
[33] *Ibid.*, 227-29; Sullivan, *The Education of an American* (N.Y., 1938), 67.

only to the Bible in circulation—is Ayer's Almanac." Close behind the product of the Ayer printshop came the almanacs which David and then Herbert Hostetter issued from 1861 through 1910. By the early 1870's the Hostetter publishing division, begun in 1866, was turning out a "United States" almanac, another English edition for California, and eight foreign language versions. During the last quarter of the century, the annual printings ranged from 10,000,000 to 13,000,000 copies. When these almanacs were added to those of Ayer, and when the millions issued by other competitors were heaped on the pile, there must have been printed each year from the 1870's through the 1890's at least one patent medicine almanac for every two Americans, not to mention those that went overseas.[34]

That many of the nostrum proprietors made or added to fortunes is doubtless one token of the educational effectiveness of these textbooks they issued year by year. Perhaps there was a wider impact. The almanacs may have helped form social attitudes in the American grass-roots mind of the late 19th century. Or, at any rate, the points of view revealed in almanac humor may reflect the judgments and prejudices of the common men toward whom the almanacs were aimed. For certainly the patent medicine proprietors, even in an age in which the art of public relations lacked sophistication, would hardly have repeated in issue after issue stereotypes offensive to the main body of their potential customers. If this be so, minority groups were held in low esteem by the native Americans in village and on farm to whom the almanacs were primarily directed. Granting that there were conventions in humor that may have softened the blow, the Irishman, the Jew, and the Negro were treated with derision and scorn.[35]

The sons of Erin, in quip and cartoon, show up as pugnacious, stupid, dishonest, and cowardly. Often the facial features were drawn with a simian cast, but with hardly the bitterness displayed in the sketching of the Jew. Tramps, peddlers, or pawnbrokers, Jews were always after money and slow to yield it up.

[34] Holcombe, "Private Die Proprietary Stamp Notes," *Scott's Monthly Jnl.*, Jan. 1938, 396; *Industries of Pittsburgh*, 127; Hostetter's almanac, 1900; "A Summary of the operations of . . . The Hostetter Company."

[35] The Hostetter Corporation retains an almost complete file of the almanacs; the N.Y. Public Library also has a good file; Richard Hofstadter, in *The Age of Reform From Bryan to F.D.R.* (N.Y., 1955), 77-81, comments on the anti-Semitism of the Populist movement of the 1890's.

The Negro too was portrayed in unkindly fashion, with kinky hair, huge lips, and monstrous feet, a simpleton who was shiftless, unkempt, and untrustworthy. Year after year, beginning in the mid-eighties, one change after another was rung on the theme that Negroes steal chickens.

Other nostrum almanacs besides those issued by the Hostetters followed a similar line with these minority groups. Millions of Americans may well have had their social attitudes influenced, or their prejudices confirmed, by such a steady diet of unflattering caricatures. Occasionally, even while printing editions for earlier immigrant groups in their own languages, almanac editors seemed to wonder if continued immigration was desirable. One 1897 Hostetter cartoon depicted "The White Man" following the Indian up to the land of the Great Spirit, and calling: "Make room for me. I am the last real American. Emigration has put me in the same fix with yourself."

Whatever may be said of Hostetter as educator, as salesman Herbert was successful. In his first ten years as president of the corporation, with a capital stock of $90,000, Herbert paid out over $810,000 in dividends. The new century opened optimistically, though problems aplenty soon were to appear.

One of the difficulties stemmed from success itself, as Herbert's father had discovered before him. Hostetter's Bitters was so popular that unscrupulous competitors sought to cut in on its market. Once an employee who knew the formula ran off to start a rival plant. Many advertisements over the years sought to warn the public to be on guard against impostors. Frequent lawsuits sought to run counterfeiters out of business. Especially aggravating was the empty-bottle racket. By techniques harking back to the heyday of the old English patent medicines, real Hostetter bottles, the labels still intact, were refilled with a cheap substitute brew and retailed as the real thing. Such cases Hostetter's usually won, but victory was hard to keep. "Despite our most earnest efforts," Herbert reported to his stockholders, "the counterfeiting and imitating of our Bitters grows on apace, and today are being manufactured extensively in New York City, New Orleans, San Francisco, Denver, St. Louis, & Cincinnati: our net loss from this source must be very great, but not only have we difficulty in apprehending these numerous compounders, but in the event of our being successful the damages awarded are simply absurd, and the firm after being convicted changes its name, moves to another cellar, and resumes business."[36]

This was aggravating, but more threatening was the increased tempo of the temperance movement. The dry forces had fully wakened to the possibilities inherent in a bitters bottle. In 1883 the WCTU had organized a Department of Non-Alcoholic Medication to do battle, and "in their zeal for reforming things," according to a drug trade periodical, "their fervor doth often get the better of their judgement." Worse than this, from Hostetter's point of view, was the way in which the growing number of prohibition states, or areas dry by local option, classed bitters of high alcoholic content as a drink. "The acute stage appeared first in Georgia," Herbert reported, "where nothing that will intoxicate or that contains Alcohol can be sold or given away." In a dozen other states, mostly in the South and West, similar hazards confronted St. George, and druggists were asking help in defending themselves when arrested for selling the bitters in violation of the laws. Court victories were won in some cases when aid was given, but the future appeared grim.[37]

Out of the same arid atmosphere arose a ghost to haunt the company, a ghost Herbert doubtless hoped his father had put to rest. A new Commissioner of Internal Revenue, in 1905, reversed the stand of his 1883 predecessor and ruled that high-alcoholic nostrums, even when sold in bottles, were liquors, that their manufacturers required a rectifier's license, and that retailers must pay a federal fee. The name of Hostetter's Bitters appeared on the first list. This was, Herbert told his stockholders, a "hard blow," and one that seriously hurt prestige and curtailed sales. Worse was yet to come. For the prohibition forces were on the march, and no mere bitters manufacturer could hope to stop them.[38]

[36] Minute Book, 1899, 1908; law cases include: Hostetter v. Adams, 10 Fed. 838; Hostetter v. Fries, 17 Fed. 620; Hostetter v. Sommers, 84 Fed. 333; Hostetter v. William Schneider Co., 107 Fed. 705; Hostetter v. Martinoni, 110 Fed. 524.

[37] Dykstra, "Patent and Proprietary Medicine: Regulation and Control Prior to 1906," 182; *Amer. Druggist and Pharm. Record*, 26 (1900), 93; Minute Book, 1908, 1909.

[38] *Ibid.*, 1908-1911; Dykstra, 117-19; *Bull. of Pharmacy*, 19 (1905), 400, 488; 20 (1906), 181-82. Herbert Hostetter died in 1924, and, according to the Minute Book, the bitters passed from the hands of the Hostetter family in 1935.

10

"A MICROBE IS A MICROBE"

"To delay for the sake of diagnosis is simply to waste valuable time. It is one of the errors of so-called scientific medicine, and should have nothing to do with the cure."

—WILLIAM RADAM, 1890[1]

MANY Americans got their first inkling of the germ theory of disease from patent medicine advertising. Always among the first by which the new is tried, nostrum promoters were quick to sense the dramatic implications inherent in the researches of Pasteur and Koch and their fellow-scientists. Even before most American physicians had become persuaded that bacilli could cause disease and that weakened bacilli introduced by inoculation could promote immunity,[2] a rash of germ-eradicating nostrums had assailed the mass market. Among the first and boldest was a pink liquid called the Microbe Killer. It was made by William Radam, a Prussian who had emigrated to the vast state of Texas.

This contemporary of Pasteur—and Radam was wont both to cite the French bacteriologist and to berate him for limited vision—had once been a soldier in the Prussian army. His real occupation, however, was that of gardener. "Circumstances of my early life," he wrote, "placed me in close commune with Nature." Settling in Austin, Texas, Radam devoted himself to raising fruits and flowers. For nearly two decades he improved his thirty acres of soil and operated a nursery and seed-store. Then disaster closed in upon him. Radam for years had suffered with malaria, trying in vain the remedies prescribed by a whole host of physicians and proprietary advertisers. At length his condition worsened, complicated by sciatica and rheumatism. To physical suffering was added overwhelming grief, for two of

[1] Radam, *Microbes and the Microbe Killer* (N.Y., 1890), 58.
[2] Phyllis Allen Richmond, "American Attitudes toward the Germ Theory of Disease (1860-1880)," *Jnl. Hist. Med. and Allied Sciences* 9 (1954), 428-54.

Radam's children died. Desperate and despondent, the gardener set out to find his own cure.[3]

Radam turned to nature to show him the path to truth. "All my early life," he wrote, "was passed amid flowers." Radam had been no mere dirt gardener. He had sought to keep himself informed of horticultural advances. "I was an earnest subscriber," he asserted, "to every floral magazine that came within my knowledge." In the pages of these periodicals Radam discovered clues that aided him with his experiments. He turned to medical journals too, but they proved no more helpful to his inquiry than physicians had been to his health. Indeed, he said, "whenever I took one up it diverted me from the line of my researches, disturbed the tenor of my investigations, and confused my ideas."

The medical journals, nonetheless, seem to have provided Radam with a key clue, the microbe. He became convinced that his body was filled with these minute but evil creatures. "When I drove to my seed-store," he wrote, "I knew that I could sit only on the edge of my buggy, because the microbes would not let me sit any other way, and when I stepped to the ground I knew that it took me several minutes before I could move, the microbes that produced sciatica and rheumatism being disturbed and so preventing me." The gardener was a living barometer. His "collection of microbes" could anticipate an imminent cold snap by two days, and "when the storm came, they would freeze, and force" him "to take refuge by a red-hot stove to get them quieted."

In his dire extremity, Radam was dazzled by the blinding light of revelation. Killing microbes in the human body, he decided, was the same as killing bugs on plants. With this latter task he had long been concerned. Radam recalled all the pest poisons he had read about. He thought back over all the chemicals he had used. He remembered offering a $1,000 prize for something that would destroy cabbage blight without hurting cabbages. Two military men had tried for it. They placed an old kerosene can over an ailing cabbage plant and ignited a spoonful of sulphur inside the can. The fumes did indeed kill the blight, "but the cabbage, too, was dead as a door-nail." This experiment had failed but, thinking back upon it, Radam became persuaded that "if I could discover any thing that would kill blight, fungi,

[3] Radam, iii, 39-41, 69-101, 287-98.

and microbes on plants without injuring them, I should also be in possession of something that would cure me."

Aided by his garden books and a small microscope, Radam set forth to save his life. He began to perform experiments on the diseases that afflicted grapes, strawberries, and geraniums, treating them with poisons suggested by the Department of Agriculture, dosing them with drugs and medicines left over from his own vain quest for health. The gardener was horrified that so many of the chemicals prescribed by doctors for man's ills were lethal both to fungi and to plant. But he gathered a few hopeful hints from his toilsome greenhouse hours.

Another of nature's purifying mechanisms, Radam believed, was lightning, which during a thunderstorm cleared the air. At such times, he asserted, "no fungi were formed, and I too felt better, breathing more easily and being more free from pain." Meat and milk kept longer, also, and plants were "more full of life." Radam asked himself the question: "What is air? Is it nothing more than oxygen, nitrogen, carbonic acid, ammonia, and water, with electricity pervading all? And if there be any thing more, what is it? and how can we make it?" The persistent gardener devised an apparatus which, he thought, might duplicate nature's beneficial action. It failed, but he tried again and again. "I must either succeed or die," he wrote, "so I put all my energies into it, and persevered." After a year of effort, he found what he was after, and he christened it the Microbe Killer.

The miraculous potion that flowed forth from Radam's experiments was, he held, a universal non-poisonous antiseptic. As the germs of decay in houses were destroyed by paint, in railroad ties by creosote, in meat by wood smoke, and in corpses by embalming fluid, so the microbes of decay in the living body were annihilated by his marvelous discovery. The concoction could be taken in such huge amounts that it would saturate all the tissues and permeate all the blood of the human frame, and this with safety to the person, with destruction to the microbes. The remedy was therefore sovereign: it could bring all disease under absolute control.

What made Radam so sure was that he had tried his invention on himself and it had saved his life. He had drunk copious draughts. The microbes had fought back. His blood teemed with them, and he could feel them moving about in anguished protest against the action of the medicine. The battle almost destroyed the battleground. Radam felt weak and low. But on he went. The microbes gave grudging ground. In three months the gardener felt like a new man. In six the last microbe was dead and Radam was cured.

The physician had cured himself and, according to his theory, he could cure all men. Yet he wanted further proof. The Microbe Killer, Radam realized, might make the basis of a profitable business. But he had no medical training. In what was basically important, Radam felt, this made no difference: to cut down weeds, need a farmer be a botanist? Nonetheless, there were hazards. The doctors were tightly organized and jealous of competition from without their ranks. Radam knew he ran the risk of a charge of manslaughter should he give his helpful medicine to a patient who might die from the poisons being simultaneously administered by a regular physician. For the next stage of his tests, the gardener determined to find hopeless cases not under other treatment. He learned from his Negro workers of a man dying of consumption and of a woman suffering from a growth in her breast. Even yet, Radam was cautious. He did not prescribe his remedy for the woman, nor put a jug of it into the hands of a man who came to report her sad plight. Radam told him that if he wanted to take a gallon there was one in the next room. "The gallon soon disappeared," Radam recorded, "and I consoled myself with the thought that if the woman died I could conscientiously swear that I did not give her the water."

But the woman did not die, nor did the consumptive man. Both were restored to health. Other people heard the news. Many were mystified, finding it hard to believe that Radam, "a nurseryman and florist . . . a plain man, from a so-called backwoods country," could have made such a revolutionary discovery. But they begged tearfully for Microbe Killer to treat their ailments. Radam gave it to them. Cures mounted. Soon Radam was so busy making medicine that his gardens went to weeds. With some reluctance, for among his flowers Radam "felt like a father among his children," the medical pioneer determined to let both himself and the world profit by his discovery.

In 1886 Radam patented his invention, "a new and Improved Fumigating Composition for Preserving and Purifying Purposes." The text of his specifications was singularly silent about the medical purposes the gardener had in mind. He did avow that his invention would "kill all fungus, germs, parasites, and other matter producing fermentation or decay," but Radam stressed the value of this, not for preserving health, but for preserving fruits and meats. The patent revealed how he managed to ape nature's lightning. Inside a large closed tank the inventor built an oven. Into the bottom of the tank he poured water, and into the oven he placed a mixture of chemicals: four ounces of powdered sulphur, two ounces of nitrate of soda, an ounce of black oxide of manganese, an ounce of sandalwood, half an ounce of chloride of potash. The chemicals were burned, the products of their combustion mingling with the vapor of the heated water and being absorbed by the water remaining in the tank. When the combustion was over, the water was allowed to cool. Sediment and floating particles which had spilled over from the violent burning were removed. The water was drawn off and tinted a pale pink by the addition of wine. The sovereign remedy was ready for bottling.[4]

Such a process of manufacture was so haphazard that no two Microbe Killer batches would contain the same proportion among the ingredients. Yet on one thing all future analysts were to agree, that the lion's share of Radam's remedy was water. A Department of Agriculture chemist was to place the percentage at 99.381. As for the rest—what rest there was—a doctor was shortly to suggest that a product identical with a batch of the Microbe Killer which he had analyzed might be produced for less than five cents a gallon by adding to a gallon of well water about an ounce of red wine, a dram of impure muriatic (hydrochloric) acid, and four drams of impure oil of vitriol (sulphuric acid). Such was Radam's man-made pink lightning.[5]

If Radam's patent was vague on the relationship of his process to therapeutics, the same could not be said for his trade-mark, secured the next year. This symbol was reminiscent of the design which William Swaim had devised for his Panacea seven decades earlier. In both, a husky male wielded a mighty club, but Radam's hero was a 19th-century Hercules, clad not in shaggy

4 U.S. Patent Office, Specification forming part of Letters Patent No. 349,900, Sep. 28, 1886.
5 Eccles, "Radam's Microbe Killer," *Druggists Circular and Chemical Gaz.*, 33 (1889), 195-96; Amer. Med. Assoc., *Nostrums and Quackery*, I, 447.

pelt but in neat business suit. Instead of swinging at a multi-headed Hydra, this athlete wielded his gleaming bludgeon at a tall skeleton, its bony arms raised to ward off the inevitable blow. Thus would the Microbe Killer conquer death itself.[6]

Radam began to advertise his "solution of gases." "My life at this period," he wrote, "became very exciting, very different from the peaceful times I had among my flowers." Demands from the ailing, reading testimonials of Radam's early patients, grew so great that he was hard put to keep up the supply. The medical profession was critical, but during the early boom their verbal attacks seemed only to publicize the Microbe Killer more. Radam took pleasure in the rumor that some of his most severe critics from within the medical profession were surreptitiously using his medicine themselves. "I killed nobody," Radam explained, "and of course any man may cure another with water if he likes."[7]

What exasperated the gardener more than criticism were efforts to steal his lightning. Eight or ten presumptuous souls sought to trespass on Radam's prerogative as the sole maker of the sole universal destroyer of all microbes. The first had the audacity to paint an advertisement on Radam's own fence. All the old tricks were used. His jugs were simulated; his wrappers, circulars, and advertising were copied; his price was undercut. Driven to distraction, Radam went to court. "I soon discovered," he wrote, "the joy and delight which lawyers feel when they are engaged in plucking a fat goose." Radam learned something about geese from the experience. He found that it helped to pluck them if he used in his promotion judiciously selected quotations from a judge's decision, even though that decision had been against him, both in the original court and on appeal. Radam was lucky that there was advertising value in his suits against competitors. He got nothing else. In one case he did win a verdict against a rival Microbe Destroyer, but the damages amounted to only a single cent and in the Texas Supreme Court the decision was reversed.[8]

---

[6] A copy of the trade-mark is stamped in gold on the front cover of *Microbes and the Microbe Killer*.

[7] Radam, 99-103, 145.

[8] *Ibid.*, 113-18; Alff et al. v. Radam, 77 Texas 530 (1890), cited in *Southwestern Reporter*, vol. 14, p. 164; Radam v. Capital Microbe Destroyer Co. et al., 81 Texas 122 (1891), cited *ibid.*, vol. 16, p. 990.

Notwithstanding his troubles, by 1890 the ex-gardener from Texas was really in clover. He had seventeen widely scattered factories producing gallon jugs of Microbe Killer, which now was manufactured in three strengths. He owned a store on Broadway where an agent stood ready to offer a free glass of the remedy to any passerby who wandered in. He had exchanged his Austin acres for a mansion on Fifth Avenue overlooking Central Park. There William Radam sat, according to the frontispiece of a treatise he published in 1890, a stocky, bearded man with frock coat, striped pants, and a heavy watch chain, peering through a compound microscope at the bacilli he had conquered.[9]

Microbes and the Microbe Killer contained many other plates besides the portrait of the author. Most of them, Radam asserted, were so far as he knew the first photographs ever reproduced of bacteria. Whatever their authenticity, they were enough to give the average layman a nasty shock. Evil-looking dots and blobs, they bore such titles as "Microbes in a Stale Egg," "Fungus on a Ripe Strawberry," and the germs of cancer, piles, and uterine catarrh.

Any John Doe with an ache or pain who looked at the magnified portraits of these terrifying little monsters, even if he could not read Radam's equally disturbing prose, might well consider three dollars a jug for Microbe Killer an overwhelming bargain. For the literate, Radam's volume, which was loaned by his agents to all comers, had other facets of fascination no less grim.

The microbes so vividly pictured in the plates, so the text explained, abounded everywhere. A baby drew them in with his first breath, even if he had not already inherited them from his mother. The sea was full of them. They ran rampant in barns and museums. They congregated in homes. They crowded into hospitals. A quarter of a million of the tiny demons could cluster on an inch of surface. There was absolutely no escape.[10]

Slowly and laboriously the titans of natural science, like Pasteur, had learned that a few diseases were caused by bacteria. But these inquirers had been halting and shortsighted. They had

9 Radam, 104; Food and Drug Administration records, Interstate Office Seizure File No. 1628, Record Group 88, Ntl. Archives. A pince-nez appears in a "revised and abridged" 1912 edition of *Microbes and the Microbe Killer* in *ibid.*

10 This and the following paragraphs from Radam, vi, 24, 54-60, 107-108, 120-29, 140-43, 150, 178, 198-203.

been more intent on theories than on facts. They had been more concerned with classifications than with cures. It had been left for a simple gardener to discover the full truth.

"My proposition is simple," Radam told his readers, "but it comes from study and observation of Nature. I have found that all disease may be concentrated under one head. It may assume different forms in different persons. It may be known, for instance, as fever in one, pneumonia in another, diphtheria in a third, cholera or diarrhoea in a fourth, and so on. But the differences which give rise to the necessity for using such names are merely details. There is, in truth, but one disease. . . . And just as there is actually but one disease, so there is but one cause of disease, and that may be limited in the common acceptation of the one word 'decay.' But what is decay? The visible result of fermentation. And what is fermentation. The phenomena produced in organic matter by the action of microbes."

To a person who was sick, it made no difference whatever which infinitesimal body had laid him low. The farmer did not worry about the name of the weed which was choking his corn. "A microbe is a microbe"—this was William Radam's basic theme. It was a fundamental fact of blessed promise, for "The same treatment affects them, the same curative agent kills them, whatever their form or whatever be the effects which they produce."

In the light of this gospel, how futile, how brutal, the procedures of regular medicine! What will the physician do when a new patient is admitted to the hospital? "He will stop at the bedside of that patient, and although the poor fellow may be too sick to rise or turn, he will spend half an hour pounding and thumping him, listening to his heart and lungs, and going through a tedious ceremony, simply to try to diagnose some minute points which have nothing whatever to do with the cure or with the mode of treatment that the disease calls for. It looks scientific. It tends to surround the doctor's calling with a halo of mystery. It deceives the patient and the public. It keeps them in ignorance. . . . Diagnosing disease is simply blindfolding the public."

But after diagnosis comes something much worse: the pouring of poisons down the patient's gullet, the chopping him apart with knives. "The instruments of the surgeon," Radam charged, "are the means of destroying more lives in our hospitals and colleges than are the weapons of all our desperadoes and law-breakers."

Don't send for a doctor, the ex-gardener warned his readers: to delay for diagnosis is to waste valuable time. "Suffice it to know that there is trouble of any kind, and the microbe killer will reach it."

It must be the Microbe Killer. For patent medicines were as dangerous as doctors. Countless blood-purifiers went forth onto the market accompanied by glowing claims, but not one of them could destroy a single micro-organism. Yet gullible people bought them in huge amounts. Truth to tell, Radam confided to his readers, "The public likes to be humbugged." Both in the country and in the city, thousands of men and women had fallen victim to well-worded promises and had even borrowed money to buy worthless nostrums. "This city of New York abounds with men," Radam reported (in straightfaced goose-plucking prose), "who live entirely, and live well, on the money they squeeze out of the pockets of individuals who are silly enough to trust them." This was sad but it was true. "People should not be led away by every charlatan who jumps up before them and talks; but as long as the world lasts there will probably be fools in it, and fools are a godsend to rogues."

In the pages of Radam's red-bound volume, there sounds an antiphony between the grim and the glad. The author did not play the gloomy strain for too many measures at a time. Quickly he trumpeted the note of cheer. He gave case histories of marvelous recoveries. He expatiated on the Microbe Killer's harmlessness. He argued that drinking the sovereign water for the prevention of disease was better than being forced to take it as a cure. He boasted that a severe yellow fever epidemic in Key West could have been stopped short if the Collector of Customs, to whom Radam had hurried two free gallons, had seen fit to use the remedy. He bragged that the Microbe Killer could have saved the German Emperor's life had not jealous physicians intercepted seven letters which his former subject had sent to Frederick containing the good news about the healing potion.

A certain amount of blind or selfish opposition to any new discovery is always to be expected. The Kaiser's doctors, the Texas doctors, did not bother him, Radam asserted, with their indifference or criticism. Gratuitous condemnation was a different thing. At that a man had a right to be incensed. In the closing pages of *Microbes and the Microbe Killer*, Radam expressed his sense of outrage at a "most uncalled-for act of injustice." A physician and pharmacist named R. G. Eccles, on the staff of the Long Island College Hospital, had published an analysis of the Microbe Killer in a drug trade journal that was ridiculous and false. Instead of testing Radam's remedy as a self-respecting doctor should, by noting its effects upon human beings, Eccles had contented himself with sitting down in his own laboratory and examining it. He had boldly charged that Radam was putting sulphuric and hydrochloric acids into his medicine. Now Radam was willing to "cordially endorse" the judgment Eccles had expressed that these acids were poisonous. But the former gardener stoutly denied putting them into his remedy. Indeed, he had gone before a notary public and sworn a solemn oath: "I have never bought nor used one dollar's worth of sulphuric or muriatic acid to make my Microbe Killer."[11]

Dr. Eccles had also penned a "funny sermon" on microbes, Radam asserted, which proved only that he had misinterpreted Microbe Killer advertising and needed to read Radam's book. The whole attack, in fact, was "wanton and unwarranted," and probably never would have occurred at all had Radam seen fit to purchase advertising space in the *Druggists Circular and Chemical Gazette*.

Despite some sharp words, there was in Radam's reply to the critique a tone of lofty indulgence, a holier-than-thou air he really did not feel. The attack was in earnest, the blow was telling, and the ex-gardener was turning again to lawyers to get them to help him launch a libel suit.

Eccles had called a spade a spade. Radam, said the doctor, was a "misguided crank" intent on "out-quacking the worst quacks of this or any other age," by engaging in "the business of universal poisoning" while earning profits of 6,000 per cent. Sulphuric acid ruined the teeth, enfeebled the digestion, and injured the kidneys. Radam did not even use pure ingredients, for analysis revealed traces of chemicals denoting the cheapest commercial grades. Radam's theories, said Eccles, were fantastic. To maintain that microbes caused all diseases was "downright humbuggery." To suggest that a fungus was an animal was to

11 *Ibid.*, 358-66.

mistake a locomotive for a cabbage. To use "microbe" as a word for one common thing—here Eccles was preaching his "funny sermon"—was like asserting that lions, tigers, dogs, horses, hyenas, rabbits, deer, and camels were identical because each was a "beast." Anything potent enough to kill all these animals was pretty sure to kill a human being in the bargain. "A universal microbe killer," Eccles insisted, "would necessarily be a universal life destroyer." But Radam's Microbe Killer could not cure anything. His hyperbolic claims were "simply laughable."[12]

As Eccles and Radam had traded verbal blows, so they were to exchange court suits. The master of the Microbe Killer had not postponed until the pages of his treatise a public reply to the Brooklyn physician's charges. Radam had defended himself in newspaper advertising and brochure. At times he came very close to losing his temper in print, accusing "those little parasites" of "slandering" him "by falsely putting forward poisonous formulas as mine" and "by attempts at blackmail." He challenged Eccles to give him fifty incurable patients for three months, and—except for those who were too far gone, like rotten potatoes, or too drugged down—the ex-gardener promised to cure them all. As he got set to hail Eccles into a Manhattan court for libeling the Microbe Killer, so Eccles prepared to return the compliment in Brooklyn for the language Radam used in countercharging. The Brooklyn case came first to trial. The doctor sought $20,000 damages because Radam had called him a charlatan and a quack. The maker of the Microbe Killer went to great pains to defend himself. He employed as chemical expert a man soon to manage the Farben interests in America. He secured as attorney the eloquent agnostic, Robert Ingersoll. And he presented a case that caught Eccles completely by surprise.[13]

Up to this point, Radam had stoutly denied that the Microbe Killer formula published in the *Druggists Circular* during 1889 was even close to a good guess. There was neither sulphuric nor hydrochloric acid in his healing potion, he had said, both of

12 Eccles, *Druggists Circular*, 33 (1889), 195-96.
13 "Radam's Libel Suit," *ibid.*, 37 (1893), 121-22; Eccles, *ibid.*, 148-49; Eccles, "Fifty Years of Battling for Pharmaceutical Reform," *ibid.*, 51 (1907), 18; *N.Y. World*, Sep. 29, 1889. The Brooklyn trial took place on March 9, 1893, in the New York Supreme Court of Kings County. For information about the trial I am indebted to James A. Kelly, Brooklyn Borough Historian and Deputy County Clerk.

which, indeed—in this he had concurred with Eccles—were poisons. In the Brooklyn court Radam spun round. His own expert witness presented an analysis that differed from that of Eccles only in details. Radam vigorously insisted that both the Microbe Killer and the formula Eccles had printed were of tremendous therapeutic value. He lauded his own originality in finding a method of putting the two acids into a remedy of such demonstrated blessing to mankind.

Dr. Eccles was startled but not routed by Radam's amazing about-face. Presenting to the jury medical evidence concerning the risk of imbibing the acids over long periods, the lawyers for the Brooklyn physician also cross-examined Radam. They got him to admit himself to be "the most learned and profound of living American naturalists." Then they plied him with questions on the elementary facts of botany. The ex-gardener could not define an anther. He could not place potatoes, calla lilies, or poppies in their proper botanical orders. When asked to explain his ignorance, Radam blithely asserted that since discovering his Microbe Killer he had forgotten these inconsequential facts. Now all he knew about was the cause and cure of all disease.

The Brooklyn jury were not persuaded that this was true. They awarded Dr. Eccles the sum of $6,000.

Radam appealed the verdict and then in Manhattan sought revenge. The lawyers for the Microbe Killer—Ingersoll had been replaced—outpointed the attorneys for Eccles and the *Druggists Circular*. They kept their learned American naturalist off the witness stand. They prevented the Brooklyn physician from presenting to the jury a well-rounded case. The matter hung on a legal technicality. The defense pleadings had been drawn up in general terms, asserting that Dr. Eccles' article was true in every particular, without stating in detail each point. Radam's lawyers cited precedent wherein a decision regarding libel had been reversed because the pleadings had been so drawn. The judge agreed. He forbade the defense to prove that the statements in the Brooklyn doctor's article were justifiable because true, and he charged the jury to bring in a decision against Eccles and the drug magazine. The members of the jury deliberated on the sum to be awarded Radam. Ten wanted to give him six cents, but two held out for a larger amount, in order to take back from

Dr. Eccles part of the money he had been given in Brooklyn. The compromise sum was $500.[14]

For the moment Radam was $5,500 short on the exchange, but he did not care. "I am gratified," he said, "for it is a complete vindication of the unjust charges and libelous attack on the microbe killer." His witnesses had tried to show that the attack by Eccles had hurt his business. Now he sought to use the verdict to recoup his losses. In newspaper and pamphlet Radam proclaimed that the therapeutic value of the Microbe Killer had been proved in court. He cited the judge. He quoted testimony from his many witnesses—a sewing machine executive, the inventor of a typewriter, a Baptist clergyman, a music teacher, the president of the Mount Holly and Bedford Railroad. All told the same tale: how they had undergone years of suffering caused by catarrh, or consumption, or ulcerated legs; how they had found the Microbe Killer and been cured. On the average, according to the court testimony, cures had required from fifteen to thirty gallons of the potent potion, at a cost of three dollars the jug.[15]

At the time of the trial, Radam sent a warning to Dr. Eccles. Refrain from any further attacks upon the Microbe Killer, the ex-gardener threatened, or you will be "challenged to mortal combat." But the Brooklyn physician weighed the issue and took the risk. He reported in detail the outcome of the trial and continued to label Radam as an utter humbug. Yet no duel ever took place. What, after all, had Radam to gain? He had one court victory to publicize, and in time a court of appeal reversed his Brooklyn defeat. Why worry about a few more vitriolic paragraphs in a drug trade journal?[16]

For, after all, who read the *Druggists Circular and Chemical Gazette*? The masses of mankind were learning about the miracles which bacteriologists were indeed beginning to work through the pages of newspapers, the same papers in which William

14 Eccles, *Druggists Circular*, 37 (1893), 148-49, and 51 (1907), 18; "Radam's Libel Suit," *ibid.*, 37 (1893), 121-22; *N.Y. Tribune*, May 3 and 10, 1893; *Pharm. Era*, 9 (1893), 477, 510. The trial took place during May 1893 in the New York Supreme Court of New York County. I am indebted to Dr. Ethel K. Ware of New York City for examining the surviving records for me.

15 *Ibid.*, 477; court extracts used as an advertisement in the *N.Y. Press* were reprinted in a pamphlet, *Radam's Microbe Killer in Court*, found in Food and Drug case no. 603, Office of the Solicitor of the Department of Agriculture, Record Group 16, Ntl. Archives.

16 *Pharm. Era*, 9 (1893), 510; Eccles, *Druggists Circular*, 51 (1907), 18. The higher court ordered the Brooklyn case retried, but the action was discontinued in 1895.

Radam was advertising. How many men and women, among the millions who saw the dramatic news stories and the astounding advertisements, could differentiate between the credentials of microbe-hunter Pasteur and those of microbe-hunter Radam?

The inability of the general public to discriminate between a French scientist and a Texas quack is one important factor that helps to explain a disturbing paradox: the age in which major discoveries were made for the first time explaining much disease in a genuinely scientific way was the very age in which patent medicines reached their apogee. The period in which the medical profession acquired the knowledge to demonstrate beyond question the folly of quackery was the very period in which the nostrum business achieved the largest sales and the most unscrupulous promotion America had yet seen.

Behind the paradox lie many factors besides man's continuing credulity. One is the complexity of the medical problems. It was to take time for the separate details of the new medical knowledge to be comprehended, evaluated, coordinated, and applied. The old killers were still the big killers in 1900. Influenza and pneumonia headed the list, for which there were no "well-defined and generally accepted plan of treatment." Tuberculosis was second. Serums could not prevent the white plague (though many had already been tried), nor could drugs cure it. The best thing to do was to avoid infection, but the public was indifferent and anti-spitting ordinances went largely unenforced.[17]

Man still suffered grievously from diseases commonly transmitted by water, milk, and food. Gastrointestinal ailments ranked third in the mortality table. Summer diarrhea was ubiquitous, especially hard on infants and children. No serum had yet succeeded in preventing typhoid fever, and cities like Cleveland and Pittsburgh had major outbreaks early in the new century.[18]

In due time medical science and its practitioners were to acquire a prestige among the general public which they never enjoyed during the 19th century. But in the closing third of that century, many Americans continued skeptical of regular doctors, and with some reason. Despite improvements that were under way, most American physicians, in their knowledge and dedication, were no Pasteurs. At the worst, the situation was very bad.

[17] *JAMA*, 34 (1900), 112-13, 501-502, 564; National Office of Vital Statistics, *Vital Statistics of the United States, 1950* (Wash., 1954), I, 169-70.
[18] *Ibid.*

One "doctor" acquired his diploma by marrying the widow of a colleague and putting his own name on the dead doctor's diploma. Another got licensed by showing a Chinese napkin to a county clerk and saying it was a diploma from a Chinese medical school. Countless more attended shoddy proprietary schools that were little more than diploma mills. Even at Harvard, the head of the medical school explained in 1870, written examinations could not be given because "a majority of the students cannot write well enough."[19]

Many American physicians, during the years in which the germ theory was being established by European research, had not yet adopted the last major medical doctrine to pass westward across the Atlantic. Dr. Oliver Wendell Holmes and others had brought home the French attack on "heroic" medication, and, although therapeutic nihilism won many converts, its triumph was not complete. One problem was the medicine-taking habit instilled by long usage in the American people. People wanted to take something and many doctors prescribed to fill the demand. The correspondence of a busy village doctor in Illinois, who practiced from the mid-1850's into the nineties, is typical. He received many letters, penciled by humble people, filled with bad grammar, wretched spelling, and fervent pleas to send more medicine. One woman tersely revealed an oft-repeated cycle— from home remedy to nostrum to physician—evidence that the promises in patent medicine advertising often fell short. "I am troubled with worms," she wrote. "2 months ago I took turpentine[.] A week after I took A whole bottle of virmifuge[.] still no relief. I am worried all but to death so please fix something so I will get relies[.]"[20]

Insofar as therapeutic nihilism did take hold with the medical profession, its reign helped the nostrum promoter. Indeed, here was a situation in which the patent medicine man could have it both ways. The excesses of heroic medication had driven people to nostrums. Now the excess of caution in prescribing on the part of doctors who adhered to nihilistic tenets worried people who

---

[19] Shryock, *The Development of Modern Medicine*, 314, 353-54, 388; Arthur D. Little, "A Leaf Out of Medical History," *Jnl. Med. Assoc. Ga.*, 32 (1943), 5; Robert S. and Helen M. Lynd, *Middletown* (N.Y., 1929), 442; Nevins, *The Emergence of Modern America*, 267, 276-78; Schlesinger, *The Rise of the City*, 216-17.

[20] Papers of Dr. John Francis Snyder of Virginia, Ill., in Ill. State Hist. Soc.; the letter cited is from Lizzie Bierhause, Mar. 1, 1887.

had the medicine habit and tempted them to resort to proprietary brands.

The impact of nihilism in high places had another effect. It weakened the emphasis in medical education upon pharmacology and the materia medica. Doctors trained in even the best schools got scant grounding in therapeutics. "If surgery were taught in the same dilettante way that materia medica is in too many of our medical colleges," one physician noted, "surgical cases would be to a great extent in the hands of the instrument makers, who would be instructing the surgeon through their commercial travelers as the medicine houses are attempting to do with the general practitioner." The lack of adequate training regarding drugs made doctors easy prey for a clever new dodge developed by the manufacturer of patent medicines, by which pseudo-science assumed not only the mantle of science, but also its coat, pants, shirt, tie, and drawers.[21]

Nostrum makers began to simulate the methods by which medical and pharmaceutical science kept the profession informed of new developments. Articles appeared in medical periodicals—some journals created for the purpose and others fairly reputable but careless in editorial policy—reporting exciting new therapeutic advances. The names of the new remedies were not blatantly suspect, like Radam's Microbe Killer, but had a scientific lilt—Syrup of the Hypophosphites, Extract of Pinus Canadensis, Lithiated Hydrangea. Formulas were given and also were printed upon the package, but frequently "in such a way," so noted an organ of the American Pharmaceutical Association, "that no pharmacist can put it up." Besides citing a formula, these journal articles described complicated chemical procedures relating to the process of manufacture and numerous details from exhaustive clinical tests. All this was drafted with consummate skill: the phraseology was properly esoteric, the illustrations impressive, and the great good news in the conclusion presented with dignified restraint.[22]

[21] Frank Billings, "The Secret Nostrum Evil," *Ill. Med. Jnl.*, 8 (1905), 489-90; W. S. Fullerton, "The Objectionable Influence of Proprietary Medicines upon the Young Practitioner," *Jnl. Minn. State Med. Assoc.* 26 (1906), 447.

[22] On this technique see Amer. Pharm. Assoc., *Proceedings*, 38 (1890), 68-69; Solomon Solis Cohen, "Shall Physicians Become Sales-Agents for Patent Medicines?" Phila. County Med. Soc., *Proceedings*, 13 (1892), 213-16; George H. Simmons, "Work of the Council on Pharmacy and Chemistry," *Southern Med. Jnl.*, 8 (1915), 259-65; a collection of pamphlets and brochures in the Toner Coll., Rare Book Div., Library of Congress.

After the journal article—sometimes without one—came the reprint. It was mailed to the desk of the busy doctor, who was informed that this latest advance of science was being presented to the medical profession as a prescription item to be employed or not as doctors saw fit. Soon there appeared in the waiting room of the physician a detailman, equipped with more literature and free samples, who looked the same and talked as knowingly as did the agents of reputable pharmaceutical manufacturers presenting their "ethical specialties."

The truth was that the first prescription which the doctor wrote out directing a druggist to provide any given patient with a bottle of Fellows' Syrup of Hypophosphites was apt to be the last. When the sufferer looked at the printing on the carton, the label, and the pamphlets which came with his prescribed remedy, he found enough medical counsel, in vigorous, down-to-earth, and frightening language, to let him dispense with a doctor. The patient took this course with a feeling of security, for it had been a doctor who had pointed the way. As late as 1915 Fellows' proprietary syrup was not spending a cent in advertising direct to the public, but ninety per cent of its sales were over the counter without a prescription.[23]

The nostrum makers were using doctors to get at their patients. Surveying his mail for 1899, a medical professor at Yale found that 424 circulars concerning medicine and its uses had come to his desk. Only fifty-four of them, he said, could he designate as "respectable." But the unrespectable were accomplishing what their promoters had hoped to achieve. Some ninety per cent of American doctors, another critic estimated sadly, were prescribing proprietary preparations.[24]

Patent medicines of secret composition advertised direct to the public, an observer suggested, might be likened unto "*the wolf in his own clothing.*" The Microbe Killer was of this kind, though even Radam put advertisements in medical journals. On the other hand, proprietary pharmaceutical specialties made up of old drugs claiming to be new, promoted only to doctors although labeled so that a patient could dose himself, were "*the wolf in*

[23] Simmons, 261.
[24] Henry L. Swain, "The Attitude of the Profession toward Patent Medicines and Appliances," *Yale Med. Jnl.*, 8 (1901), 169; C. C. Fite, "Solution of the Proprietary-Medicine Question," *Phila. Med. Jnl.*, 1 (1898), 431.

sheep's clothing." Both sorts fooled many American sheep, some of them possessing medical degrees.[25]

Agile quacks managed to profit from yet another development of modern medicine. Specialization among physicians was slow in coming, partly because in earlier days only the charlatan had confined his practice to one part of the body. It was one of this breed, an eye doctor, whom the physician-novelist S. Weir Mitchell had met in the lobby of a small-town hotel. Made curious by advertising which claimed that the charlatan could restore sight to the blind by removing the eye, scraping its back, and restoring it to the socket, Dr. Mitchell, incognito, accosted the man. "May I ask," he said, "what anesthetic you used?"

"I can hardly explain that to you," the quack replied, "you wouldn't understand; but I can tell you that it's shaped something like a spoon."[26]

The same French school that taught therapeutic nihilism shifted the emphasis away from the sick man as a single entity and stressed a necessary concern with the pathology of individual parts. To this type of medical inquiry, specialization in medical practice was a natural sequel. The trend went on most rapidly in the ever-larger cities where there were enough cases of any given malady or malfunction to keep a specialist busy. Medical specialization permitted improved treatment, but it was more expensive, and inherent in the point of view was a possible hazard to diagnostic judgment.[27]

Specialists sometimes tended to forget that illness can be more than the sum of a patient's diseased organs. The crowded bustling cities where specialists held sway were the very sort of environment to produce or aggravate psychosomatic disorders. Many a man with localized pains got no satisfaction from the seemingly mechanical ministrations of brusque specialists. He turned elsewhere. Either he resorted to a quack who at least would listen sympathetically to his complaints, or he perused the long list of symptoms in nostrum advertising and prescribed for himself. The desire to be cured, not piece-meal but all at once, is natural and strong. William Radam could find a sympathetic

[25] Parke, Davis & Co., *Open Pharmacy and Scientific Substitutes for Proprietary Preparations* (Detroit, 1884), 7-8.
[26] M. G. Selig, "Quacks and Quackery," *Jnl. Mount Sinai Hospital,* 4 (1938), 673.
[27] Shryock, 187-89, 382-83.

audience to hear his attack on specialization in medicine and the concept it implied, "that nobody can cure all ailments."[28]

There was another facet still. A bottle of tonic seemed cheaper than a visit to an internist or an orthopedist or a gynecologist with all his fancy equipment. Many patients who were willing to admit that specialization meant better medical care objected to the cost. As the 19th century came to a close, the medical profession was rising in public esteem as to its science, but it was falling with respect to its economic practices. Nor would the nostrum promoters let the American public forget this growing grievance. In almost every tirade against the regulars, the patent medicine men raised anew the old, old cry of greed, greed, greed.[29]

With all the difficulties that still beset the science and art of medicine as the 19th century waned, there never before had been so firm a foundation in science on which to build a critique of quackery. William Radam could make and sell his Microbe Killer, but Dr. Eccles could attack him with sounder medical and chemical understanding than earlier critics had possessed. One thing that might be helpful would be to get Dr. Eccles' message to the same public who were reading Mr. Radam's advertising. During the first decade of the 20th century giant strides were to be taken in this direction.

[28] Matthias Nicoll, Jr., "On Quackery and Causes for Its Growth," *N.Y. State Jnl. of Med.*, 22 (1922), 572-73; Radam, *Microbes and the Microbe Killer*, 206.
[29] Shryock, 382-83.

PART THREE

THEMES

44

THE PATTERN OF
PATENT MEDICINE APPEALS

*"The advertising quack . . . is the black wolf, aye, the
Bengal tiger of the profession. . . . He is full of shrewdness
and cunning, and knows poor, weak human nature like a
book."*—DR. WILLIS P. KING, 1882[1]

THE next stage in the narrative of patent medicines in America
concerns an expanding criticism that leads to restrictive laws.
Before turning to these events, let us pause for some analysis.
The psychology of patent medicine advertising is important because of both its priority and its variety.

Nostrum manufacturers turned to ingenious advertising before
other manufacturers did because they had to. So long as the
demand for a product exceeded the supply, as David Potter has
pointed out, the role of advertising could be simple and unso-
phisticated.[2] Retailers could insert into newspapers the simple
message: "Here it is. Come and get it." Customers would hurry
to the store. Manufacturers, disposing of their output easily, had
no need to go to the expense of advertising and of differentiating
their products from those of other producers making the same
things. Not until the amazing development of manufacturing
capacity brought supply abreast of demand, in the decades following the Civil War, were most American producers really
confronted with the problem of competitive selling in an economy
of abundance. Then those who processed food and made soap and
manufactured bicycles began to take lessons from the remedy
vendor.

The medicine man had something to teach because he had
operated in an economy of abundance almost from the start.
Since sickness was well-nigh universal, the demand for his wares

---

[1] King, *Quacks and Quackery in Missouri* (St. Louis, 1882), 6.
[2] Potter, *People of Plenty, Economic Abundance and the American Character*
(Chicago, 1954), 166-88.

was potentially inexhaustible. But then, so also was the supply. At least from the days of the four Lees and Thomas Dyott, American production of proprietary remedies was off to a fast start. There was no end to the variety and quantity of ingredients available, and there were soon more pills and potions than Americans could swallow conveniently. The medicine man's key task quickly became not production but sales, the job of persuading ailing citizens to buy his particular brand from among the hundreds offered. Whether unscrupulous or self-deluded, nostrum makers set about this task with cleverness and zeal.

Another reason for pioneering by patent medicine promoters in the psychology of advertising lay in the goal of the customers. They wanted to regain or to preserve their health. Problems relating to disease are complex, and the thinking about them in the 19th century was extremely confused. There was more to the matter than whether a hat fit or an axe cut. These circumstances gave the remedy maker plenty of elbow room for subtlety.

Many examples of the remedy promoter's ingenuity have been cited in the preceding pages. Here the purpose is to present in a systematic way the pattern of appeals made to would-be customers, as that pattern emerges from a study of the nostrum advertising of more than a century. There were fads and vogues in the presentation of packaged remedies to the public, as earlier chapters reveal, yet these were often changes rung on basic themes. Certain fundamental appeals appeared over and over again.

The first requirement for success in a competitive world, as Dyott and Swaim, Brandreth and Helmbold, were quick to realize, was: Be known. Unless the identity of the product was firmly fixed in the minds of those who might buy, there was no hope. This called for lavish advertising. Patent medicine men confronted the American citizen as he read his mail, as he perused the paper, as he strolled the streets, as he traversed the countryside. They devised schemes to slip up on him unaware— the plain envelope, the fake news story. They struck not only slyly but often. One pill was advertised thirty-seven times in the same issue of a paper. Dr. Donald Kennedy's Medical Discovery and Dr. T. Felix Gourard's complexion cure were promoted, year in and year out, without the slightest change in copy, for over forty years.[3]

---

[3] Ticknor, *A Popular Treatise on Medical Philosophy*, 277; Rowell, *Forty*

The impact of repetition was strengthened if the product name was memorable. Some proprietors turned to alliteration, and the sick could dose themselves well-nigh through the alphabet, from Burdock Blood Bitters to Swift's Sure Specific. That the names of medicines, year after year, were printed in the same distinctive type induced a feeling of familiarity. Pictorial symbols served the same function. The trade-mark, indeed, was a fixed star in a universe of flux. The ownership of medicines might change again and again, and so might the formula. The diseases for which medicines were advertised might vary over time, and sometimes even names were altered. Trade-marks, however, protected first by common law and then by federal statute, endured forever. Radway's ministering angel and Lydia Pinkham's maternal countenance were known to generations.[4]

The would-be purchaser of any product wants assurance that it will serve the purpose for which intended. Would a remedy cure? The proprietor answered, of course, with a resounding yes. And he often added that the cure was sure, swift, and safe. In the very names of nostrums these basic traits were underlined: Dr. Sweet's Infallible Liniment, Comstock's Dead Shot Pellets, Pronto, Warner's Safe Cure.[5] Many lines of copy were devoted to reiterating the same assurances. Merely to state, no matter how emphatically, that a remedy could cure, was not enough. The reader was a cagey customer, and he wanted proof.

The manufacturer was called upon, in one way or another, to trot out his credentials. Flamboyance of personality could be a sales asset, as the antics of Henry T. Helmbold reveal. Yet no matter how lively the promoter or how lavish his headquarters, persuasiveness has seemed to require that he stand with at least one foot planted somewhere within the broad domain of medicine.

This remedy is worthy, countless advertisements have claimed, because its proprietor is a member of one of the healing professions, a doctor, a druggist, a nurse. Many patent medicines, in truth, were made by physicians and pharmacists—to the despair of their colleagues—and other proprietary formulas did not vary

Years an Advertising Agent, 387; Hower, *The History of an Advertising Agency*, 296, 298.

[4] Rowell, 390; Paul, *The Law of Trade-Marks*.

[5] Advertising materials in the Landauer Coll., N.-Y. Hist. Soc.; Pronto listed in Amer. Med. Assoc., *Nostrums and Quackery*, III, 140. In this chapter the three volumes in this set are cited as N&Q with the appropriate volume number.

significantly from formulas in official volumes. By no means all, however, of the packaged remedies seeking shelter under reputable medicine's tent have had even these slim excuses for being there. The title of doctor has been appropriated, time and time again, with no justification whatever. The name and fame of noted scientists have been stolen to give the posture of greatness to the quack. Soon after Paul Ehrlich announced the discovery of salversan for treating venereal disease, a New York charlatan marketed a blood poison cure, usurping not only the German bacteriologist's name, but even his famous formula number, "606."[6]

By many ruses have quacks sought to convince the public of their medical respectability. "The common method of supporting barefaced imposture at the present day. . . ," wrote Oliver Wendell Holmes in the 1840's, "consists in trumping up 'Dispensaries,' 'Colleges of Health,' and other advertising charitable clap-traps, which use the poor as decoy-ducks for the rich." James Morison, in selling his Vegetable Universal Medicines in America, boasted of his British College of Health. Even if no son of Uncle Sam could equal the London grocer who swore in court that he had taken 18,000 of Morison's pills, still the American market was flourishing. American nostrum makers, imitating Morison, institutionalized themselves into medical dignity. In Philadelphia William Wright had a North American College of Health, and in Cleveland W. H. Libby had an Indian Medical Infirmary.[7]

Another practice widespread among quacks was the distribution of books and pamphlets giving medical advice. Since colonial days Americans had been accustomed to consult home treatment volumes compiled by doctors and sold by apothecaries. Early in the 19th century, nostrum makers began to trespass on this field. Selling the booklets cheaply, or giving them away, proprietors followed the familiar format, listing health hazards from ague to wounds. When it came to suggested therapy, of course, something besides the customary simples was prescribed. Moffat's

6 Daniel Drake, a letter on quackery, Sep. 15, 1846, printed in an unidentified journal, 1858, clipping in Toner Coll., Rare Book Div., Library of Congress; N&Q, II, 114-16.
7 Holmes, *Medical Essays*, 87; Morison, *Practical Proofs of the Soundness of the Hygeian System* (3rd ed., N.Y., 1832), in N.Y. Academy of Med.; *N.Y. Sun*, Mar. 30, 1837; Wright brochure in Rare Book Div., Library of Congress; Libby, *The Indian Hygiena* (Cleveland, 1865).

Medical Manual and Haas' *Every Man His Own Physician* are examples of the art, and in 1875 came *The People's Common Sense Medical Adviser in Plain English*. Published by Ray Vaughn Pierce of Buffalo, a doctor who had a Favorite Prescription and was responsible for a Golden Medical Discovery, this compilation of "common sense" was to go through a hundred editions in the course of sixty years.[8]

Nostrum makers donned the medical mantle in other ways. They larded their advertising with quotations—or misquotations—from medical authorities. They simulated "The Doctor's Advice" columns in the newspapers. They buried in what appeared to be straightforward counsel on health a purportedly innocent formula, although one of the ingredients, with a high-sounding pharmacopoeial name, was really a proprietary article. They stood with the angels and shouted, in tones of loftiest medical rectitude, anathemas at the devilish quacks. In 1890 the makers of Vin Mariani mailed to doctors a pamphlet entitled "The Effrontery of Proprietary Medicine Advertisers." What at first glance looked like another professional blast at the enemy turned out to be an ingenious self-bestowed blessing upon an alcoholic concoction containing coca leaves.[9]

Yet, in their concern for medical science, the nostrum makers displayed a curious ambivalence. While seeking to ally with it, they must at the same time condemn. While borrowing the prestige of the physician, the patent medicine men must also traduce him. While appropriating the merits of medical knowledge, they need not feel responsible for its shortcomings. Quackery, as usual, could have things both ways.

Year after year nostrum advertisers told the layman about the failings of the doctors. Wherever regular physicians were weak, lo, there the nostrum maker was strong. Their therapy was brutal, his was mild. Their treatment was costly, his was cheap. Their procedures were mysterious, his were open. Their prescriptions were in Latin, his label could be read by all. Their attack on illness was temporizing, his was quick. Their approaches were cumbersome, his were simple. Their techniques led to the grave, his never failed. Most nostrums were like

[8] Moffat (N.Y., 1839); Haas (N.Y., 1853); Pierce, 1st ed. in N.Y. Academy of Med. and 100th in Ntl. Library of Med.
[9] N&Q, I, 628; II, 186, 203; the Vin Mariani pamphlet in Toner Coll.

Louis Goelicke's Matchless Sanative, the very "Conqueror of Physicians."[10]

Why, if a nostrum was as sure and swift at curing as its maker kept asserting, did not regular physicians quickly adopt it? Because doctors—at least some of them—did not want to cure people. They got more profit from keeping the patient sick. "Most doctors prescribe BAD-EM SALZ," its manufacturer told the public, "but some of them don't. One doctor, more honest than the rest, explained it this way: 'BAD-EM SALZ? Yes, I used to prescribe it a great deal, but I stopped. Why? Simply because the patients didn't come back to me. If I had kept on they would all have been taking BAD-EM SALZ and getting well without my assistance!' "[11]

Thus many regular physicians, as the quacks would have it, were deliberately selfish in opposing patent medicines. Others were enmeshed in the tangled coils of their stodgy profession, practicing by rote what they had learned, unable to detect a new idea when they saw one. Hence they were blind to the one dazzling new discovery that was destined to end forever the pain and suffering of disease.

Over and over again, throughout the history of patent medicines, promoters have pierced through the darkness yet enshrouding illness and come up with the perfect remedy. They have done so, often, by conceiving a completely new theory of disease, a monistic theory with a one-shot therapy, and the panacea is the medicine advertised. Benjamin Brandreth had found the root of all illness in constipation, and he sought to purge mankind to health. Dr. Donald Kennedy advanced a bloodhound theory of medicine. "My Medical Discovery," he advertised, "seldom takes hold of two people alike! Why? Because no two people have the same weak spot. Beginning at the stomach, it goes searching through the body for any hidden humor. . . . Perhaps it's only a little sediment left on a nerve or in a gland; the Medical Discovery slides it right along, and you find quick happiness from the first bottle. Perhaps it's a big sediment or open sore, well settled somewhere, ready to fight. The Medical Discovery begins this fight, and you think it pretty hard; but soon you thank me for making something that has reached your weak spot."[12]

10 Goelicke poster in Landauer Coll.   11 N&Q, II, 185.
12 *Frank Leslie's Popular Monthly*, 43 (1897), back cover.

Hundreds of similar theories have bestrewn the pathway of American pseudo-medicine, each of them a discovery "of far more reaching importance than those obtained by Koch or Pasteur"[13] or whatever genuine scientist held highest public esteem at the moment of bottling. The springboard for the leap to truth has not always been located within the human body, in bowel or kidney or blood. Science is a broad domain, and the nostrum man has been quick to base his monistic concept on an exciting event occurring in any of science's provinces. He has dogged the botanist's footsteps, grabbing a new plant or seeing new virtue in an old one. Tobacco and coffee, maple sugar and pineapple, asparagus and celery, are among the bounties from nature exploited by the patent medicine man. Dr. Miles' Compound Extract of Tomato, a big seller in the 1830's, made catsup a sovereign remedy for mankind's ills.[14]

The mineral realm, too, provided the nostrum maker with happy inspirations. "So deep was the faith in iron" during the early Industrial Revolution, Lewis Mumford has written, "that it was . . . a favorite form of medicine, chosen as much for its magical association with strength as for any tangible benefits." In this spirit American males were urged to overcome sexual weakness by swallowing Aromatic Lozenges of Steel. Creosote had earlier been exploited as a cure for cancer, but as a panacea it did not rank with petroleum. In the 1840's when the dark greasy liquid began to foul his salt wells, Samuel M. Kier hauled it twenty miles to Pittsburgh, poured it into bottles, and called it "THE MOST WONDERFUL REMEDY EVER DISCOVERED!" "The lame . . . were made to walk—the blind to see." Kier soon had more oil than he could handle medicinally, and he succeeded in refining some so that it would burn and cast a light. Thus he became a pioneer in an industry much greater than he could have imagined when he issued a circular praising petroleum in verse:

The healthful balm from Nature's secret spring,
The bloom of health, and life, to man will bring;

13 N&Q, II, 145.
14 Wyndham B. Blanton, *Medicine in Virginia in the Seventeenth Century* (Richmond, 1930), 111; Turner, *The Shocking History of Advertising!* 24, 54-55, 282-83; Shryock, *The Development of Modern Medicine*, 20; Dr. Talbot's Concentrated Medical Pineapple Cider, *Harper's Wkly.*, 8 (1864), 687; Dr. Butler's Asparagus Bitters, Thompson, *Bitters Bottles*, 21; Celery Compound handbill, Landauer Coll.; Pickard and Buley, *The Midwest Pioneer*, 282-83.

As from her depths the magic liquid flows,
To calm our sufferings, and assuage our woes.[15]

Elisha Perkins' metallic tractors had many heirs. The advertising pages of American history abound with Magnetic Fluids and Galvanic Belts, Electric Insoles and Electro-Magnetic Wrist-Bands, plus an infinite variety of cravats, pillows, anklets, elbow pads, necklaces, head-caps, corsets, combs, and infernal machines by which magnetic entrepreneurs have tried to transmit healing potency to the ailing human frame. The young lady suffering from sick headache who sought help in the late 19th century from the Electrikure, put the shiny silver cylinder in a crock of water, moved the switch to position six, attached coin-sized discs to her wet ankle with elastic bands, and leaned back in a chair. She did not know that the green wires carried no current, that the metal cylinder was heavy from crushed rock.[16]

The apparatus of the chemist, with its bubbling retorts and test tubes filled with bright and foaming liquids, has brought to nostrum advertising the awesome authority of the laboratory. Not only complicated formulas of the chemist's compounding, but also simplified essences of his analysis, have poured into patent medicine bottles. The basic elements of the universe itself have gone to the aid of suffering humanity. Dr. Judge's Oxy-Hydrogenated Air cured catarrh, deafness, and consumption when sucked or sniffed through a tube from the bottle in which it was confined. The National Ozone Company prepared twenty-four different remedies ranging from an ozone specific for cholera to an ozone tonic for the uterus.[17]

15 Mumford, *Technics and Civilization* (N.Y., 1934), 164; Wootton, *Chronicles of Pharmacy*, II, 367; *N.Y. Eve. Post*, Jan. 5, 1804; Pickard and Buley, 282; *Carpenter's Annual Medical Advertiser* (Phila., 1836); John F. Fulton, "The Impact of Science on American History," *Isis*, 42 (1951), 187-88; *Dictionary of American Biography*, X, 371-72; Paul H. Giddens, *Early Days of Oil* (Princeton, 1948), 3; Giddens, *Pennsylvania Petroleum, 1750-1872* (Titusville, 1947), xi, xii, 17; *Frederick* [Md.] *Examiner*, Jan. 19, 1853; circular reproduced in Giddens, *Early Days*, 3.

16 *A Treatise on the Application of John H. Tesch & Co.'s Electro-Magnetic Remedies* (Milwaukee, 1866), in the Rare Book Div., Library of Congress; Boston Electro-Pathy Institute broadside, 1859, in Amer. Antiquarian Soc.; Dr. Wm. O. Parmenter's Magnetic Oil poster from the 1840's in the Landauer Coll. The Electrikure No. 2 was made in New York City, rediscovered in Mississippi, and given to the author by Eugene B. Antley.

17 Dr. Cullen's Vegetable Remedy poster, Rare Book Div., Library of Congress; Judge pamphlet (Boston, 1878), in Ntl. Library of Med.; Oxydonor ad, *Frank Leslie's Popular Monthly*, 43 (1897), 630; *Ozone Era, and Family Physician* (Chicago, 1885), in Chicago Hist. Soc.

Oxygen has had its tens, but radium has had its hundreds. Quick to exploit the discovery of the Curies was Dr. Rupert Wells, and even his name was fake. He called his medicine Radol, labeled it as "radium impregnated," and advertised it as a "marvelous radiotized fluid" which would cure cancer in all forms, locations, and stages. Samuel Hopkins Adams, writing in *Collier's*, demurred. "Radol," he said, "contains exactly as much radium as dishwater does, and is about as efficacious in cancer or consumption." The liquid was an acid solution of quinine sulphate with alcohol added, and such a product could be expected to exhibit the bluish fluorescent glow which Wells attributed to radium. Radol was eventually put out of business. But the mysterious and potent new element continued to shed its emanations into the well-filled ranks of quackery. The radium nostrums are a case example of a broader phenomenon in quackery. "For each step forward which science makes, cautiously and limited," wrote Haven Emerson, "there is a curiously distorted shadow of pseudo-science, claiming blindly that now at last the goal is reached, warping out of all proportion the added bit of knowledge."[18]

Botany, chemistry, and electricity have all served their turn. Yet, to the nostrum maker, science has been an even more elastic word. It has encompassed not only the genuinely new but also the old newly rediscovered. The whole realm of the exotic has been a happy hunting ground in which the adventuresome promoter has trapped alluring lore. Millions of medicine bottles have been vended on the authority of faraway places and ancient times.

The itinerant mountebank of the 1740's who persuaded colonists to buy his Chinese Stones was the honored ancestor of a host of oriental descendants. Especially in the mid-19th century, when the European powers were opening up the ancient country, did nostrums flourish bearing such names as Dr. Lin's Celestial Balm of China, Dr. Drake's Canton Chinese Hair Cream, and Carey's Chinese Catarrh Cure. The advertising and labels caught the strangeness of it all. Dr. Lin presented an exquisite engraving of

18 N&Q, I, 68-75; typed ms. entitled "Drug Inspection and Correlated Studies," in folder "Drug Lab (243)," Bur. of Chem., General Correspondence, 1909, Record Group 97, Ntl. Archives; Samuel Hopkins Adams, *The Great American Fraud* (Chicago, 1906), 91. For other versions see N&Q, II, 616; *Radium Water* (East Orange, N.J., 1926), in Yale Med. Library. Emerson cited in Harry H. Moore, *Public Health in the United States* (N.Y., 1923), 167.

a Chinese sage sitting in an elaborate chair; one servant held a
parasol over his worthy head while another brought a bottle of
the Balm. Dr. Drake also pictured an oriental scene, bolstered,
however, with American verse:

> Our distant brothers, the *Chinese*,
> Long fam'd for their refreshing Teas,
> Produce a *Cream*, so rich and full,
> That clothes with hair the baldest skull.[19]

(The Consul General in Shanghai gave this advice some
decades later to would-be American exporters of proprietary
remedies: "The favorite design for calendars [advertising patent
medicines] used to be an illustration of an old classic tale, but
now the Chinese prefer a girl picture either in semi-Western or
Chinese dress.")[20]

In the meantime, however, Americans continued to be fasci-
nated by the remote. While excitement was high over the depreda-
tions of the Barbary pirates, Ibraham Adam Ben Ali, a Turk or
(as an editor thought more likely) "some crafty native, who has
assumed a Turkish name" went about selling the Incomparable
Algerine Medicine for the scurvy. On the heels of the Mexican
War, the Mexican Mustang Liniment became a popular product.
At the same time a patent medicine man discovered the exoticism
of that distant spoil of war called California. In the same year
that gold was discovered in Sutter's stream, Frederick Fay sought
gold through marketing a proprietary version of a California
plant called Canchalagua. Soon after Commodore Perry had
ended Japan's feudal isolation, an American named Grindle
began to sell Japanese Life Pills, a blood purifier made from a
recipe discovered—so he said—by a common sailor who had
been cast away "upon the *mysterious shores of Japan*" eight
years before the Commodore arrived. The Japanese Emperor
was shortly to be one of the recipients of ornate boxes of Cherry
Pectoral especially prepared for donation to foreign sovereigns
by James C. Ayer. Other dignitaries so honored included the
Sultan of Turkey, the Queen of Spain, the King of Siam, the

[19] *S.C. Gaz.*, Nov. 21, 1743; *Pa. Gaz.*, Oct. 17, 1745; Lin label in Landauer
Coll.; Drake pamphlet in Rare Book Div., Library of Congress; a bottle of
Carey's remedy in the Rochester (N.Y.) Museum.
[20] Thomas Sammons, "Proprietary Medicine and Ointment Trade in China"
(Special Consular Reports, No. 76, Wash., 1917), 7-8.

Emperor of China, the President of Peru, and the Czar of Russia. For the armies of the Czar, Ayer added several bushels of cathartic pills.[21]

The list of alien areas with which nostrums have been christened reads like a gazeteer. The hardy soul could dose himself around the world. What combination of diseases, howsoever dire, could hold out against such an international therapeutic arsenal as Bragg's Arctic Liniment, Hayne's Arabian Balsam, Bavarian Malt Extract, Brazilian Bitters, Carpathian Bitters, Castillian Bitters, Crimean Bitters, Kennedy's East India Bitters, Hoofland's German Tonic, Good Hope Bitters, Hoofland's Greek Oil, Buchan's Hungarian Balsam, Wyncoop's Iceland Pectoral, Osgood's Indian Cholagogue, Mecca Compound, Peruvian Syrup, Persian Balm, Roman Eye Balsam, Redding's Russian Salve, South American Fever and Ague Remedy, Jayne's Spanish Alterative, Hart's Swedish Asthma Medicine, Tobias' Venetian Liniment, and Westphalia Stomach Bitters?[22]

To the ordinary American looking for a remedy to cure his aches and pains, distance seemed to lend enchantment. Sometimes the magic of the faraway was buttressed by folk beliefs to which medicine men could appeal. Everyone knew about Chinese longevity, and Dr. Lin could tout his Chinese Blood Pills by asserting that "such immense ages" resulted from purification of the blood. Everyone knew, too, that Chinese hair was long and black and beautiful, and this gave Dr. Drake a cue in promoting his Canton Chinese Hair Cream. Nor did it take much perception to get the point about Turkish Wafers, advertised with the device of star and crescent and phrases like "For Men Only / Turkish Method / The Sultans / and Harems."[23]

The long ago also had its mysterious appeal. Yadil was an esoteric form of garlic with a history of marvelous cures running back five and a half millennia. Almost as ancient was a Druid Ointment "handed down from . . . mystic days when Stone-

---

[21] *N.Y. Daily Advertiser*, Sep. 18, 1800; *Mexican Mustang Liniment* (n.p., 1850), N.Y. Academy of Med.; Frederick A. Gay, *Sketches in California* . . . also *Interesting Information in Relation to Canchalagua* (n.p., 1848), in the Collection of William Robertson Coe, Yale Univ. Library; Grindle's brochure in Prints and Photographs Div., Library of Congress; N&Q, I, 588; Holcombe, "Private Die Proprietary Stamp Notes," *Scott's Monthly Jnl.*, Dec. 1937, 348-49.

[22] Many sources, with the bitters chiefly from Thompson.

[23] Turkish Wafer brochure, Landauer Coll.

henge was a busy temple." Jew David's Honey Coated Pills were imbued with the sanctity of the Holy Land. Dr. M. S. Watson's Great Invincible Birgharmi Stiff Joint Panacea had been recently rediscovered along the Nile. When, in 1880, a genuine Egyptian obelisk was erected in New York's Central Park, a new interest in Egyptology made itself evident among the nostrum makers. Vaseline put out a trade card picturing the obelisk, and Ayer's Sarsaparilla issued a pamphlet describing "A Night with Rameses II."[24]

The glamor of the long ago and the fascination of the faraway united in the American Indian. The Indian, to be sure, had once been both here and now. The fact that he had really contributed so bountifully of his own healing lore to the white European, enriching regular medicine (even unto today) with therapeutic plants, would in itself have prompted a whole host of imitative quacks. Yet the heyday of the Indian vogue in quackery was not to come until the red man had been pushed far to the west. People who dosed themselves with patent "Indian" remedies had never or seldom seen an Indian. If not quite so distant as a Japanese Emperor or so long gone as a Pharaoh, the Indian profited from the same sort of glamor, with a fillip of patriotism—for he was an American—to boot. As earlier he had been for Europeans, so now he became for non-frontier Americans, the noble savage. The romanticizing process represented in the novels of James Fenimore Cooper took place, and at about the same time, on a lower literary level, in patent medicine promotion. Unspoiled creature of Nature's original domain, the Indian was strong, virile, healthy. "The Art of Healing had its origin in the Woods," opined the author of a nostrum pamphlet, "and the Forest is still the best Medical School." From it had come Wright's Indian Vegetable Pills. Upon the wrapper was engraved a symbolical scene: a majestic Indian sat against a mighty tree and gazed across a river, on which churned a side-wheeler, toward a thriving city on the opposite shore. The gift from Nature to Civilization was made explicit, for on a banner held by the Indian were the words, "Wright's Pills." Another remedy,

---

24 N&Q, III, 136-37; Thomas H. Jones, "Patent Medicines," *Good Words*, 2 (1861), 371-75; *Frederick* [Md.] *Wkly. Times*, Oct. 4, 1832; Jew David's Pill Wrapper, Rare Book Div., Library of Congress; Pickard and Buley, 280; obelisk items in Landauer Coll.

Southern Balm, made the same point in a different way. It pictured an Indian handing a healing plant to Aesculapius.[25]

Another folk notion was used to bolster the Indian's prowess. Since the best cures for diseases native to a country are always to be found within its borders, and since venereal disease was discovered in America by the sailors of Columbus, then America must be the source of the sovereign remedy for syphilis. After centuries of search, proclaimed one nostrum maker, that blessed cure had now been found. He did not explain why, considering that the sailors had met the ailment in the West Indies, the cure was continental, discovered among "the remnant of the once powerful Cherokee."[26]

From the 1820's onward for a century the Indian strode nobly through the American patent medicine wilderness. Hiawatha helped a hair restorative and Pocahontas blessed a bitters. Dr. Fall spent twelve years with the Creeks to discover why no Indian had ever perished of consumption. Edwin Eastman found a blood syrup among the Comanches, Texas Charley discovered a Kickapoo cure-all, and Frank Cushing pried the secret of a stomach renovator from the Zuni. (Frank, a famous ethnologist, had gone West on a Smithsonian expedition.) Besides these notable accretions to pharmacy, there were Modoc Oil, Seminole Cough Balsam, Nez Perce Catarrh Snuff, and scores more, all doubtless won for the use of white men by dint of great cunning and valor.[27]

Indeed, the Indian vogue in the last half of the 19th century conformed to the traditions of the Wild West and often revealed itself in documents at first glance indistinguishable from dime novels about savages not always quite so noble as they once had been. Both bad Indians and good Indians peopled the pages of the adventure story *The Rescue of Tula* issued in 1859.[28]

[25] Kremers and Urdang, *History of Pharmacy*, 128; Wright's pamphlet, Rare Book Div., Library of Congress; Wright wrapper in author's possession; Southern Balm brochure, Prints and Photographs Div., Library of Congress.

[26] Cherokee Medicines pamphlet, Landauer Coll.

[27] *Harper's Wkly.*, 8 (1864), 128; *Frank Leslie's Popular Monthly*, 43 (1897), 5; *Springfield Ill. State Register*, Nov. 2, 1839; *Captured and Branded by the Comanches* (n.p., 1876), Landauer Coll.; *Life and Scenes among Kickapoo Indians* (New Haven, 189-), and *Almost a Life* (New Haven, 1882?), Coll. of William Robertson Coe, Yale Univ. Library; Oregon Indian Medicine Co. pamphlet, Landauer Coll.; Florida Balm brochure, Prints and Photographs Div., Library of Congress.

[28] B. L. Judson & Co., N.Y., in Library of Congress.

The hero of this paperback was Dr. Cunard. Son of a wealthy father, the physician had traveled throughout the world seeking cures for the ailments of men. He became fluent in more than thirty languages. He classified more than 10,000 plants in the Rocky Mountains alone. Living for years with various Indian tribes, Cunard met "unheard of perils and hardships, hoping only to benefit his race."

One day while among the Navajoes within the borders of Mexico, the doctor came upon a fearful spectacle. "An Indian girl, with her hair floating in the wind was bound to a stake, and around her was piled the fuel, soon to be lighted for her torture." Cunard was frozen by her beauty. "The chisel of Praxiteles never formed a lovelier shape, her face and form were of faultless beauty; but the crowning beauty was her eye; before its lightning glance, her tormentors (soon to be) stood abashed. . . . The chief of the captors begged her to be his squaw."

"Dog of a Navajoe," she replied, "I defy thee. I am the daughter of an Aztec Chief. The Eagle mates not with the thieving Hawk."

The sound of this proud voice awoke Cunard from his rigid trance just as the chief applied the torch. Casting aside botanical specimens, the doctor bounded down the mountainside, scattered the startled Navajoes, hurled aside the burning faggots, cut the binding thongs, and carried the princess to the lodge of the medicine man. Then he turned and confronted the astounded Indians.

"It was well that he did so." For the amazed quiet produced by his bold action had ebbed, and the chief was already fitting an arrow to his bow.

"I demand her for my squaw," Dr. Cunard cried. "The Great Spirit has said it, and I say to you, that if you dare refuse, tomorrow you shall see sudden darkness come at noon-day, and the sun shall change to blood—nay, for a sign that I speak truly, the great sun shall be darkened tomorrow, whether you consent or not. Then keep the girl but twenty-four hours unharmed, and if it does not happen as I say, commit us both to the flames; but if it does so come about, know ye me as the 'Benisontan,' the Great Judge of the pale faces, over whom the 'Manitou' spreads his wing, and whom you cannot harm."

[178]

Cunard, of course, had perused an almanac, and when next day his prediction was borne out and his gestures seemed to restore the sun, ceremonies were held in his honor. Then Cunard and Tula set out for her home in a secluded mountain valley. Welcomed for his heroism, the doctor dwelt with the Aztecs for nearly a year. He observed that a powder dispensed by the medicine man prevented any serious sickness among members of the tribe. Begging the formula of the Sachem Tezucho as a boon for having saved his daughter, Cunard was taken in the dark of night through labyrinthine mountain passages to the aged sorceress who alone possessed the secret. Because of his courage, she yielded to his entreaties.

"[It is] a secret," the doctor cries, "that once in my possession, shall *bring healing and strength upon its wings to all the world.*"

Deeper into the mountain must they yet go, to a gloomy cavern containing an altar bearing a golden image of the Sun. Here Cunard takes an oath never to reveal the location of the hidden valley, and here he is shown the six herbs composing the remedy and told their proper proportions. Then, bidding farewell to the last unconquered Aztecs, he departs for the East.

Cunard returns home to find his mother on her deathbed, but the miraculous herbs effect an immediate cure. The news spreads and the demand expands. The doctor cannot compound the remedy fast enough. In order that all who suffer may be healed, Cunard conveys the secret to B. L. Judson & Co., who now compound it as Judson's Mountain Herb Pills.

According to the pamphlet, Dr. Cunard resumes his investigations "for the cause of science and humanity." But is it too much to hope that he has really returned to Tula, the proud Aztec princess, in her secluded mountain valley, where both of them, partaking now and again of the six magic herbs, remain even now glowing with happiness and radiant with health?

The Indian as symbol for hardihood, the Chinese as symbol for longevity, are but two of many figures from history and mythology who have been called upon to vouch for patent medicines. In word and picture, the blessed name of mother has been invoked, nor has grandmother's proverbial wisdom been neglected. The strength of the ox, the power of the elephant, the mystic potency of the unicorn, the recuperative zeal of the phoenix—all have served their turn. Angels great and small, though mostly female, have borne glad tidings. Ben Hur has fought for kidney vigor; Ponce de Leon has promised youth's renewal; Jack has killed the Giant Constipation. Knights have gone forth to battle, sometimes with Red Cross emblazoned on their shields.[29]

The mighty of mythology have been invoked. There was a Minerva Pill to conquer syphilis, a Juno Cordial to banish barrenness. Mars and Jupiter were also called upon. Hercules was an impartial hero, going forth to battle in many a nostrum cause besides that of William Swaim. With equal impartiality Hygeia hovered at the elbows of numerous proprietors, and Aesculapius bestowed his blessing far and wide.[30]

As there are symbols of strength to encourage, so are there symbols of evil to frighten. A fearsome array of creatures have slithered and crept through patent medicine advertising, serpents and dragons, fantastic misshapen imps from the nightmares of the damned, even old Beelzebub himself. The demonic might be subtly suggested with mere words. Under the headline, "Reverend Imposter!!!" an advertisement for the Matchless Sanative told of a New York minister who had been ejected from his church because of improper conduct. This devil's disciple had begun the manufacture, "with his own unholy hands," of a spurious sanative, which he was employing swindling peddlers to palm off on the public. The ex-minister, moreover, had a cloven foot.[31]

The realm of death was replete with symbols, none more awe-

[29] Mother's Friend brochure, Rare Book Div., Library of Congress; N&Q, III, 25; Belmont Med. Soc., *Transactions, for 1850-51*, 50; *Davy's lac-elephantis*, pamphlet cited in *Index-Catalogue of the Library of the Surgeon-General's Office*, series 1, IX (Wash., 1888), 57; Unicorn Drops brochure, Prints and Photographs Div., Library of Congress; Moffat's Phoenix Bitters brochure and Baldwin's Infallible Embrocation brochure, Rare Book Div., Library of Congress; *Ayer's American Almanac, 1885*; N&Q, I, 587, and III, 102; Pierce's Pleasant Purgative Pellets poster (Jack) and Dorman's Original Red Cross Bitters brochure, Prints and Photographs Div., Library of Congress.

[30] *Phila. Democratic Press*, Oct. 25, 1827; Dr. Larzetti's Juno Cordial brochure, Rare Book Div., Library of Congress; Mars and Jupiter referred to in Proprietary Assoc., *18th Annual Report*, 184; Potter's Vegetable Catholicon handbill, Landauer Coll.; wrapper for Force, The Master Rebuilder Tonic, Museum of the State Hist. Soc. of Wis.; Morison ad in back of part 20 (May 1855) of William M. Thackeray, *The Newcomes*; Jewett's Health Restoring Bitters poster, Prints and Photographs Div., Library of Congress; Holcombe, "Private Die Proprietaries," *Wkly. Philatelic Gossip*, Aug. 1, 1942, 490, 497.

[31] Dr. Cheever's Life-Root Mucilage brochure, Rare Book Div., Library of Congress; *Ayer's American Almanac, 1859* and *1885*; Dr. Carter broadside, 1844, Amer. Antiquarian Soc.; Potter's Vegetable Catholicon poster, Landauer Coll.; N&Q, I, 39; Rowell, 388-89; Dr. Jayne's Alterative poster and Wolcott's Instant Pain Annihilator poster, Prints and Photographs Div., Library of Congress; *Vandalia Ill. Sentinel*, Mar 14, 1840.

some than the grim reaper. Whatever dread disease he represented, the robed skeleton, escorting his victim toward an open grave, was a sobering figure. Tombstones stood watch, engraved with skull and crossbones. Yet, despite the atmosphere of almost overwhelming disaster, there still was hope. A knight stood by with sword unsheathed, or an angel hovered ready to reach across the grave to any mortal willing to pay a dollar for the saving remedy.[32]

One gloomy proprietor felt impelled to ransack the caverns of the foreboding. A man is collapsed on the ground, one hand holding his stomach, the other pressed to his despairing face. He lies at the edge of a murky stream, in which crocodiles swim and from which protrudes the skull of a steer. A snake slithers along the bank amidst noxious weeds. Vultures soar overhead, and jagged lightning rends a russet sky, clouds veiling the sun. A grinning skeleton, robed and with scythe, approaches. But, behold, barring his path stands a sturdy maiden, her face aglow, her left arm boldly pushing death away. She is wrapped in a diaphanous robe, but her bosom and midriff are bare, and around the latter she wears Parr's English Pad.[33]

The symbol of evil—simple or compounded—was only one way of frightening a customer into buying a medicine. Nostrum makers found more direct ways of confronting the layman with the grim consequences of inattention to his symptoms. Neglect might bring embarrassment, pain, moral decay, even death itself.

"Humiliating Eruptions" or foul breath could offend friends and lead to social isolation. Baldness could shatter prestige. "How strangely," began an ad for Aldridge's Balm of Columbia, "the loss of . . . [the hair] changes the countenance, and prematurely brings on the appearance of old age, which causes many to recoil at being uncovered, and sometimes even shun society to avoid the jests and sneers of their acquaintance." Maladies of this sort might hurt the purse; an anti-eczema treatment headlined one appeal: "Preacher Itched So He Had to Quit." Even romance might be jeopardized. Witness the poignant tale of Kate.[34]

[32] N&Q, I, 96, and II, 96; Von Graef Sexual Troche pamphlet, Toner Coll.; Folger's Hygeiangelos pamphlet, Ntl. Library of Med.

[33] Landauer Coll.

[34] *Harper's Wkly.*, 29 (1885), 414; *Springfield Ill. State Register*, Oct. 12, 1839; N&Q, II, 622; Dr. I. J. O'Brien ad, *N.Y. Herald*, Mar. 1, 1860.

Kate never smiles, no happy thought
Lights up her pensive eye,
The merry laugh from lip to lip
Passes unheeded by.
Frozen forever is her heart,
The sparkling fount of gladness,
And o'er it pours in rapid flood
The ebon wave of sadness.

She never smiles, has frowning grief
With her stern magic bound her?
Has care her long lean finger raised,
To cast her fetter round her?
Has one so young the lesson learned,
That love is oft betrayed?
Ah no! she never smiles because—
Her front teeth are decayed!

Worse than humiliation was pain. In vivid prose and grim picture, nostrum makers displayed the epileptic falling in the path of a speeding vehicle, the heart sufferer tumbling from a ladder, the madman flailing his arms against the bars of his cell, the cancer victim with nose and cheek eaten away. Nor were externals enough. The body was entered, explored, dissected, its hideous lesions revealed for all to see. It mattered not that Dr. Haines, whose Golden Remedy would "cure" the liquor habit, had stolen his hob-nailed liver from a temperance poster; it was just as sobering for all that. The many worms that dwelt in man's insides were displayed with all their sinuous convolutions, staring at the reader with big round eyes. Happily there was no cut to illustrate one advertising headline: "Another Monster Parasite Over Sixty Feet Long." Expert illustrators were well paid to draw horrendous worms and germs, and to change photographs so as to fake or intensify the ravages of cancer and other dire maladies.[35]

Diseased organs printed on a flat surface in black and white

[35] McAlister's Ointment pamphlet and Beekman's Pulmonic Syrup poster, Rare Book Div., Library of Congress; *Alarming Truths* (N.Y., 1891), Toner Coll.; N&Q, i, 56, 109, and ii, 158, 281, 615; *Life and Scenes among Kickapoo Indians*, inside front cover; Dr. Sherman's Messenger of Health pamphlet, Landauer Coll.; Dr. Stanway's Professional Mark brochure, Prints and Photographs Div., Library of Congress; Secy. of Agric. to Postmaster Gnl., Dec. 9, 1908, Letterbook, Records of the Office of the Secy. of Agric., RG 16, Ntl. Archives; Alvin F. Harlow, "The Career of an Artist," *Amer. Mercury*, 4 (1925), 305-18.

were frightening enough. In three dimensions and with color added they were worse. Profiting from such a morbid lure were anatomical museums, a quack venture that flourished in the dingier streets of cities. The New-York Museum of Anatomy issued a catalog in 1868 listing its 2,167 exhibits. "Here . . . are presented," the proprietors announced, "the numerous lesions, contagions, and disorders which infect all parts of this beautiful mechanism—maladies belonging to the skin, the muscles, the joints, the glands, and to all the internal viscera—every disease deranging the functions, corrupting the blood, decomposing the tissues, deforming the structure and defacing the beauty of the human form divine." Along with exhibits of sickness went samples of sin, sadism, and sex to lure the curious to the wax-works show—the deformed foot of a man executed for murdering his wife and mother-in-law, the French general who lingered on awhile in agony though flayed alive, the female generative organs before and after copulation. But the main stress was upon grue-some renditions of all parts of the body ruined by disease, especially private parts ravaged by unmentionable maladies. Agents haunted the gallery to watch the spectators and exhort those who appeared shamed and stricken back behind scenes where the "doctor" waited with his high-priced "cures."[36]

The fear of death was preyed upon in numerous ways. Death-bed scenes pointed up the utter anguish of the earthly parting. Vivid cuts pictured men putting bullets through their brains—in one case "the result of neglected nervousness." One ad showed a corpse sitting bolt upright in a coffin, with the legend "Killed by Catarrh!" And how much more maudlin was it possible to get than in this verse?

> Grim death has taken darling little Jerry,
>   The son of Joseph and Seveva Vowels;
> Seven months he suffered with the dysentery,
>   And then he perished with his little bowels.
> Perhaps was weaning little Jerry,
>   His bottle seemed to hurt his stomach's tone;
> But with the angels he'll get plump and merry,
>   For there's no nursing bottles where he's gone.[37]

[36] N&Q, I, 23, and II, 375; *Catalogue of the New-York Museum of Anatomy* (N.Y., 1868), Emory Univ. Library.

[37] N&Q, II, 95, 300, and III, 183; *Standard Remedies*, 17 (1930), 6; *Alarming Truths; Nation*, 20 (May 20, 1875), 343; poem cited in Holcombe, "Private Die Proprietaries," *Wkly. Philatelic Gossip*, June 27, 1942, 375.

"Oh, what a pity," the moral is pointed, "that Mrs. Vowels did not know about CASTORIA."

"The medical ad," opined an advertising executive at the turn of the century, "which gives symptoms and tells the progressive stages of a disease, saying plainly what it will lead to if it is not checked, is the one which will produce the most effect on the ordinary mind. I believe most ailing people get a morbid satisfaction from reading vivid descriptions of the symptoms of their sickness."[38]

Disease may indeed lead to pain and death, but not infrequently nostrum promoters predicted these dire consequences when they were by no means the logical outcome of symptoms listed in the advertising. All back-pains did not denote kidney disease, all pimples did not signify poisoned blood, all coughs did not indicate consumption. Quacks exaggerated small symptoms and turned normal physiological phenomena into dread signs of incipient pain and death. They recognized that nearly every man is vulnerable to the power of suggestion and sought to make him sick so they could make him well. When sickness was widespread and men more than usually worried, nostrum makers worked overtime. From yellow fever epidemics in the 18th century to sieges of influenza in the 20th, promoters tied their remedies to the prevailing fear. "Scare" advertising indeed sold medicine. Now and then a healthy person, brooding over the agonized future which his symptoms foretold—according to the quack—turned to suicide.[39]

It was all very well to frighten the customer, but it was also necessary to reassure him. The two moods were often combined in the before-and-after sequence, and not infrequently Miss After-Using might have luxuriant tresses whereas her alter ego, Miss Before-Using, had been bald as a billiard ball. In this field of the before-and-after, tampering with photographs was particularly rife.[40]

Even stronger bastions for encouragement were deemed necessary. As nostrum advertisers bolstered their appeals with the

[38] Charles A. Bates, *Good Advertising* (N.Y., 1896), 439.
[39] N&Q, I, 802-803, II, 432-33, and III, 120; *N.Y. Eve. Post*, Aug. 18, 1804; *Food and Drug Bull. of the* [N.Y. City] *Dept. of Health*, 2 (1920), [2]; *Printer's Ink*, 240 (Sep. 26, 1952), 10.
[40] *Black Cat*, Mar. 1898, xx; Harlow, 307-308.

magic name of science and the lure of the exotic, so they seized the symbols of patriotism. Early in the 19th century, the American eagle appeared in nostrum advertising. So too did the Stars and Stripes, until the practice was declared illegal by that same Congress whose place of meeting was represented on a bitters label. One firm printed the text of the Constitution in small type and black ink. Advertising slogans were added along the borders and run into the main body, in larger type and red ink. Thus the powers of Congress were interrupted for the message: "Pendleton's Calisaya Tonic Bitters Is used by the most delicate Females." Joined to the article on the judiciary was the counsel that the Bitters be used "for Impaired or Exhausted Vital Energy." During the Spanish-American War, a pamphlet cover displayed a sailor and a soldier flanking a man-sized bottle of Pe-Ru-Na. "The Three Safeguards of Our Country," the legend said. "The Navy protects our Country against foreign invasion, The Army protects our Country against internal Dissension, PE-RU-NA protects our Country against Catarrhal Diseases."[41]

Uncle Sam, after his invention, became a favorite figure in patent medicine advertising. For one proprietor he sat at a table and affixed his signature to a document which read: "This is to certify that I am using 100,000 boxes of Ex-Lax every month."[42]

So much for patriotism.

Religion was also a mighty fortress in which the nostrum maker took refuge. Testimonials from ministers continued to rank with those from physicians at the summit of prestige. By eating a bowl of Grape-Nuts "after my Sabbath work is done," observed one pastor, ". . . my nerves are quieted and rest and refreshing sleep are ensured me." Whether those among the clergy who had wandered farthest from the decrees of the Council of Trent were the most susceptible to quackery, as Sir William Osler postulated, might be difficult to demonstrate. Ayer's Sarsaparilla managed to get a testimonial from the Sisters of Charity who ran St. Mary's Infant Asylum in Massachusetts. Remedies

[41] Benjamin Morange Medicated Oil Silk broadside [1826], N.Y. Academy of Med.; Brandreth Pills glass sign, Landauer Coll.; Congress Bitters card, Marion W. Sterling Coll. of Advertising Cards, Enoch Pratt Free Library, Baltimore; Clark, *The Southern Country Editor*, 73; Pendleton brochure, Map and Print Room, N.-Y. Hist. Soc.; Pe-Ru-Na pamphlet, Ntl. Library of Med.
[42] Landauer Coll.

were named for St. Anne and St. Joseph, not to mention Pastor Koenig and Father John.[43]

Failure turned to success for one proprietor when he began to tell the public that his formula had been "revealed in a providential manner." Dr. Munyon, the purveyor of a kidney cure, confronted millions of Americans with his grim visage, lifted arm, and elevated finger. "If the Sign of the Cross Were to Be Destroyed," he cried, "the Next Best Sign Would Be 'The Index Finger Pointing Heavenward.'" Signs and symbols abounded from the religious realm. Besides angels, Eve also appeared, picking fruit in a garden. The Good Samaritan had a career that spanned the centuries. Nostrums were marketed bearing such names as Balm of Gilead, Paradise Oil, Resurrection Pills, and 666 (see Revelation 13:18).[44]

The Bible was often quoted. One proprietor reprinted the sermon of a noted Brooklyn divine on a text from the Proverbs (7:23): "Till a dart strike through his liver." Whenever this organ was mentioned in the sermon, Warner broke in with a plug for his Safe Cure for liver ailments.[45]

Even the troublesome factors in religious life could be turned to account. The makers of a multi-purpose liniment called Merchant's Gargling Oil got out a trade card showing a grinning gorilla who boldly announced:

> If I am Darwin's Grandpapa,
> It follows don't you see,
> That what is good for man and beast,
> Is doubly good for me.[46]

Found more frequently than doggerel in nostrum advertising has been the appeal to statistics: the proofs of time and territory and total cures. Indian Balsam of Liverwort had proved its efficacy for ten years, LaMott's Cough Drops for a full score, and Pond's Extract, "The Universal Pain Extractor," (as of

43 *The Commoner*, July 14, 1906; Osler cited in *British Med. Jnl.*, 1 (May 27, 1911), 1250; *Ayer's American Almanac, 1885*; N&Q, II, 16, 91, 144, 622.
44 Rowell, 384; N&Q, I, 513; Eve in Proprietary Assoc., *18th Annual Report*, 184, and *Woman's A, B, C of Health* (n.p., 1860), Rare Book Div., Library of Congress; Moffat's *The Good Samaritan* (1842), *ibid.*; Dr. Peabody's *The Good Samaritan* (1865), Chicago Hist. Soc.; *N.Y. Eve. Post*, Aug. 25, 1804; Resurrection Pills, Radway & Co. circular in author's possession; N&Q, III, 70; *N.Y. PM*, Apr. 23, 1944.
45 Landauer Coll.
46 *Ibid.*

1878) for over thirty. In frontier Illinois, the purveyors of Garlegant's Balsam boasted of its success in Maryland, Virginia, Pennsylvania, Ohio, New York, Kentucky, Missouri, South Carolina, Alabama, Georgia, and New Orleans. A later proprietor issued a pamphlet suggesting an amazingly expansive therapy, *Half the People in the World.* This was, nonetheless, only half as encompassing as the odyssey of pain-killing circumnavigation undertaken by Perry Davis.[47]

Potter's Vegetable Catholicon, in the 1830's, produced cures so numerous "as to preclude insertion in any newspaper." In the next decade Dr. Townsend of Sarsaparilla fame was bold enough to try. Within two years, he said, his remedy had cured over 35,000 cases of severe disease, of which at least 5,000 had been deemed incurable. Included were more than 3,000 cases of chronic rheumatism, 2,000 of dyspepsia, 5,000 of consumption, 2,000 of scrofula, 2,500 of kidney disease and dropsy, 1,500 of liver ailments, 1,000 of female complaints, 400 of general debility and want of energy, and thousands more of ulcers, erysipelas, pimples, headache, spinal afflictions, etc., etc. Countless other proprietors resorted to the overwhelming impact of huge numbers in the hope of luring individual readers to join the crowd.[48]

Big numbers were impressive, but—by themselves, at any rate —they did not have the emotional impact of the individual case. The face was made to stand out in the crowd through the drama of the testimonial. President Jackson spoke well of an ointment, and Vice-President Colfax praised a throat lozenge. "Congressmen," observed a 20th-century commentator, "are notoriously easy to get, and senators by no means beyond range." Peruna managed to get out an ad naming fifty members of Congress who were voting its anti-catarrhal ticket. Doctors and ministers, authors and athletes, have testified. Vin Mariani ventured into the arts, citing compliments from Charles Gounod and Emile Zola. From the theater Edwin Booth and William Gillette, Julia Marlowe and Sarah Bernhardt—all spoke their lines for various remedies.[49]

[47] *Springfield Ill. State Register*, Aug. 4, 1837, and Sep. 21, 1839; *Alton* [Ill.] *Spectator*, Nov. 5, 1834; *N.Y. Spirit of the Times*, Nov. 16, 1878; Pineoline pamphlet, *Half the People in the World* (St. Louis, 1896), Toner Coll.; Davis pamphlet, *Around the World in 40 Years*.

[48] *Shawneetown Ill. Gaz.*, May 29, 1830; *Frederick* [Md.] *Republican Citizen*, Apr. 7, 1848.

[49] *Standard Remedies*, 8 (June 1922), 8-9, and (July 1922), 8, 10, 12; Adams, *Great American Fraud*, 65; *Harper's Wkly.*, 24 (1880), 112, and 39

Not all the testifying by the famous, to be sure, could be taken at face value. Muckraking journalists were to discover that praise might be bought, or pried from the reluctant by various shrewd ruses, some of them smacking of blackmail. Outright fakery was sometimes resorted to, with testimonials from famous men fabricated out of whole cloth. The German bacteriologist Robert Koch was one of many treated to this indignity.[50]

The same sort of trickery was used by nostrum makers in printing praise from humble citizens. Some simply did not exist, except in the imagination of the copywriter. There was one touching tale of an old resident who had been given up by five physicians until cured by Mayr's Wonderful Remedy. This cheering narrative was sent out to newspapers all over the nation, with a headline containing a blank space in which to insert the name of the city in which the ad was run. But these extremes were not really necessary. Patent medicine men knew from the beginning that they could get all the genuine certificates of cure they needed. Testimonials could be purchased for a pittance. More often they were given free. Men and women, persuaded they had been cured, were eager to volunteer their thanks. Others among the unsung, whether or not they were quite aware of it, were looking for a boost in self-esteem, attention from the neighbors. "If your brains won't get you into the papers," advised a newspaper editor, "sign a 'patent medicine' testimonial. Maybe your kidneys will."[51]

Commendation from representatives of America's millions, on farm and in factory, has been much esteemed by nostrum makers. "It is generally agreed among experts," noted a newspaper writer at the beginning of the 20th century, "that nothing is more effective as a business getter than the much derided 'testimonial.' Personal statements of that kind have a tremendous influence in small communities, and those signed by plain, everyday working people are at present regarded as more valuable than the indorsement of celebrities." So it had been two centuries before with Bateman's Pectoral Drops.[52]

(1895), 1,101, 1,122; Holcombe, "Private Proprietary Stamp Notes," *Stamp and Cover Collectors' Review*, Oct. 1938, 249-50; Adams in *N.Y. Tribune*, Feb. 21, 1915, reprinted in Amer. Med. Assoc. pamphlet, *Testimonials Medical and Quasi-Medical*.

50 N&Q, I, 686; Mark Sullivan, "The Inside Story of a Sham," *Ladies' Home Jnl.*, 23 (Jan. 1906), 14.

51 N&Q, II, 528-32; *Toronto Star*, cited in *ibid.*, III, 197.

52 *New Orleans Time-Democrat*, cited in *Druggists Circular*, 45 (1901), xi.

With thousands of testimonials appearing in hundreds of papers, it is not surprising that now and then the same page of the same issue of the same paper should reveal both the testimonial and the obituary of the testator. More often, testimonials continued running in newspaper columns long after the satisfied users had gone to their graves.[53]

If greater stress was placed on the authority of the other fellow in nostrum advertising, there were proprietors willing to let the reader himself be judge. Few have had courage enough to suggest so dramatic a demonstration of therapeutic merit as that proposed by the maker of Riga Balsam in 1801. "The trial of it is this," he advertised in a Savannah paper. "Take a hen, drive a nail through it's scull, brains and [t]ongue, then pour some of it into the wound it will directly stop the bleeding, cure it in 8 or 6 minutes, and it will eat as before." On the whole, advertisers wanted readers to try the medicine out not on chickens but on themselves. If the remedy did not work, money would be cheerfully refunded. As one proprietor slyly put it:

> While Quacks are robbing mortal clay,
> My motto is *"No cure, no pay."*

The money-back guarantee was a perennial pitch. Sometimes the ante was raised. The manufacturer of a hair restorer went so far as to announce that his product could grow hair on John D. Rockefeller's head or he would forfeit $1,000.[54]

Thus the patent medicine fraternity ran the gamut of appeals to human psychology. Critics might rant, the judicious might grieve, but the nostrum promoter pursued his wily way. "Advertisers and flourishers know perfectly well," wrote an editorialist in 1871, "that even the gravest and most cautious are to a certain extent touched by their appeals, and that even in the act of denunciation, the most careful often find themselves seduced."[55]

[53] N&Q, I, 139, 644, II, 178, and III, 198-200; *Testimonials Medical and Quasi-Medical; Printer's Ink*, 172 (Sep. 5, 1935), 106.

[54] *Columbian Museum & Savannah Advertiser*, Mar. 3, 1801; *Phila. Public Ledger*, Sep. 26, 1836; *Standard Remedies*, 23 (June 1937), 13; *Amer. Druggist*, 47 (1905), 358.

[55] "Thoughts on Puffing," *All the Year Round*, 25 (Mar. 4, 1871), 330.

12

MEDICINE SHOW

"And they like to pay a little for a tonic and an evening's entertainment rather than pay a lot to a doctor who gives you no fun at all."—VICTOR HOLMES, *Salt of the Earth*[1]

NOTHING in God's world is the matter with most of you but worms, worms, worms."[2]

Such a startling pronouncement, set in bold-faced type, might well give pause to any newspaper reader and urge the eye on down into the smaller print in search of whys and wherefores. How much more disturbing were the same words when heard rather than seen, delivered with pontifical assurance by the resonant voice of a commanding figure in a tall hat and cutaway coat, who gained in majesty through the flickering illumination of gasoline flares.

Patent medicine promoters, during the same years that they pioneered in print the many psychological lures that might sell their wares, often went out to meet their customers face to face. Because the effort of orating an appeal was more profitably expended on a group than on an individual, some enticement to attract a crowd was necessary. Exotic costume might help, but most itinerant vendors did not rest content with dressing themselves up. They added entertainment. They put on a show.

Colonial America had her mountebanks selling their wares, just as did Europe of the same day. They came to towns and villages especially at such times as fairs, when the native population was swollen by outsiders. They set up their platforms, performed their shows, delivered their harangues, sold their remedies, and went their ways. The tone of their entertainment sometimes offended ministers, and the quality of their medicines sometimes disturbed physicians. If the two groups could agree,

1 Holmes [Kenneth H. Kitch], *Salt of the Earth* (N.Y., 1941), 214.
2 Robert B. Nixon, Jr., *Corner Druggist* (N.Y., 1941), 66.

as in Connecticut on the eve of the Revolution, restrictive legislation might be enacted. Medical declamations by mountebanks, the colonial assembly decided in 1773, as well as their "plays, tricks, juggling or unprofitable feats of uncommon dexterity and agility of body," had harmful social results. All this fostered "the corruption of manners, promoting of idleness, and the detriment of good order and religion," and also ensnared people into buying "unwholesome and oftentimes dangerous drugs." So mountebanks were outlawed.[3]

But laws did not stop them. During the first half of the 19th century there were many men like William Avery Rockefeller who brought both entertainment and nostrums to backwoods towns. Rockefeller circulated through the Midwest and, according to legend, used his talents as marksman, ventriloquist, and hypnotist to attract the crowds to whom he sold his packaged herbs. (When William's son, John D., died in 1937, his physician reported that the aged millionaire had taken "several patented articles religiously, to aid his health.")[4]

The heyday of the medicine show came during the last two decades of the 19th century. Solo performers like Rockefeller continued to operate. But there was a tremendous expansion in the size and variety of the business. Nevada Ned, a big-time showman, summed up the colorful scene: "Here full evenings of drama, vaudeville, musical comedy, Wild West shows, minstrels, magic, burlesque, dog and pony circuses, not to mention Punch and Judy, pantomime, movies, menageries, bands, parades and pie-eating contests, have been thrown in with Ho-Aug-Nan, the great Chinese herb remedy, and med shows have played in opera houses, halls, storerooms, ball parks, show boats and tents, large and small, as well as doorways, street corners and fairs."[5]

So large and complex did the cast of characters become that caste lines developed, from the prestigious performers in large shows vending innocuous remedies like liniments down to the

[3] Richardson Wright, *Hawkers & Walkers of Early America* (Phila., 1927), 57-58, 199-200 [the Conn. law]; Shafer, *The American Medical Profession, 1783 to 1850*, 206; John Keevil, "Coffeehouse Cures," *Jnl. Hist. of Med. and Allied Sciences*, 9 (1954), 195; *The Harangues, or Speeches, Of Several Celebrated Quack-Doctors in Town and Country* (London, 1762).

[4] Allan Nevins, *John D. Rockefeller* (N.Y., 1940), I, 16-18, 37-38; *Standard Remedies*, 23 (June 1937), 13.

[5] N. T. Oliver (as told to Wesley Stout), "Med Show," *Sat. Eve. Post*, 202 (Sep. 14, 1929), 12.

"jamb workers," the sheer frauds, like the Duke and Dauphin encountered by Huckleberry Finn.[6]

The grandest spectacle of all was the Indian show born of the joint imaginations of a Connecticut Yankee and a Texan. The New Haven Irishman, John E. Healy, had been a Civil War drummer boy who took a liniment down to Savannah in Reconstruction days. Temporarily side-tracked with a troupe of non-therapeutic Irish minstrels, Healy had gotten back to medication in 1879 with a liver pad. This was his first venture with "Texas Charley" Bigelow, a farm boy who had served a med show apprenticeship with Doctor Yellowstone. The experience had given him long hair and beard and useful if suspect Indian medical lore. The liver pad did well, especially among the newly liberated Negroes of the South, who attributed to it conjuring powers. Healy and Bigelow, however, dreamed of even bigger things. In 1881, along with "Nevada Ned" Oliver, they formed the Kickapoo Indian Medicine Company to vend a remedy called Kickapoo Indian Sagwa. The original Sagwa, according to a legend in the business, was made of aloes and stale beer. Whatever it may have been, the formula through time did not stray far from herbs and alcohol. It was not the constituents but the promotion that brought this tonic fame. Healy and Bigelow began hiring Indians by the hundreds—none of them Kickapoo—to put on a show.[7]

Healy and Bigelow could traffic not only on the long-established connection between the red man's vigor and the white man's nostrum. They could also count upon the Easterner's awed curiosity about a bronze-skinned people he no longer knew at firsthand but was much aware of through reports of constant Indian fighting in the West.

The standard Kickapoo show traveled with half a dozen Indians and as many white performers. The show opened with the Indians sitting stoically in a half-circle, in front of a backdrop painted to reveal an Indian scene, the more realistic because of torchlight illumination. Nevada Ned, or some other "scout" wearing long hair and buckskins, introduced the Indians one by one,

[6] Violet McNeal, *Four White Horses and a Brass Band* (Garden City, N.Y., 1947), 43-44; N. T. Oliver (as told to Wesley Stout), "Alagazam, The Story of Pitchmen, High and Low," *Sat. Eve. Post*, 202 (Oct. 19, 1929), 76.

[7] Information on the Healy-Bigelow shows is from the Oliver articles; Harlowe R. Hoyt, *Town Hall Tonight* (Englewood Cliffs, N.J., 1955), 247; McNeal, 53; an early 20th century bottle of Sagwa in author's possession.

briefly describing their past heroism. Five of the redskins acknowledged their introduction with a mere grunt, but the sixth delivered an impassioned oration in his native tongue. As interpreted by the scout, the tale described the dramatic origin of the remedy which had saved countless Indian lives and which was about to be offered, after great sacrifice, to the white members of the audience. When the sales pitch was finished, half the Indian and white members of the company went out among the crowd to sell, while the remaining whites played musical instruments and the Indians beat their tom-toms and broke into wild war whoops. In such a noisy atmosphere, medicine and money changed hands.

Some seventy-five such Kickapoo shows might be touring the country at a time during the eighties. Now and then Healy and Bigelow promoted an even more majestic spectacle, a stationary show with up to a hundred performers. Nevada Ned presided over one such venture that played a whole season in New Jersey. A wagon train attacked by Indians was saved by cowboys who in turn were threatened by a prairie fire. The final outcome was the sale of up to $4,000 worth of Kickapoo Indian Sagwa every week. Among the show's spectators was numbered Buffalo Bill himself, but there is no record as to whether or not he bought a bottle.

The peer of Healy and Bigelow ventures, in commerce if not in showmanship, were the troupes traveling to boost the sale of Hamlin's Wizard Oil. John Austen Hamlin, the founding father, had been a magician pure and simple, according to legend, until he discovered that the take was greater when he used his prestidigitation to promote a liniment. Magic there was for sure in the name Wizard Oil, which he affixed to the remedy he vended. Moving from Cincinnati to Chicago during the Civil War, Hamlin built up his product to one of the best-known liniments in America. In doing so, he rather forsook magic for music.[8]

Hamlin's emissaries sang for their sales. Touring the highways and byways of the country were numerous troupes, each

8 Information on the Hamlin enterprise is from William P. Burt, "Back Stage with a Medicine Show Fifty Years Ago," *Colorado Mag.*, 19 (1942), 127-28; Oliver, "Med Show," 174; McNeal, 54-55; *Chicago Tribune*, May 21, 1908; John W. Leonard, ed., *The Book of Chicagoans* (Chicago, 1905), 258; Chicago city directories, 1864-1905, in the Chicago Hist. Soc.; *Missouri Hist. Rev.*, 45 (1951), 375; *Hamlin's Wizard Oil Song Book* in author's possession. That the concern did not entirely forsake magic is evident from Hoyt, 248.

made up of a lecturer, a driver, and a male quartet. The group traveled in a special wagon, pulled by a four- or six-horse team, into which was built a parlor organ. The wagon, in the torch-lit evening, became a stage, from which the quartet sang and played. A stylish sight they were, clad in silk top hats, frock coats, pin-striped trousers, and patent leather shoes—with spats. At times the assembled audience sang with them. One of Hamlin's stunts was the lavish distribution of pamphlets in which the words of such songs as "I'se Gettin' Up a Watermelon Party" and "Is Life Worth Living?" were interspersed with promises as to how Wizard Oil could grapple with asthma and neuralgia. These song books were carried into thousands of homes. During the week or more that a troupe stayed in a town, the members were busy during the day as well as at night. While the lecturer sought to place supplies of Hamlin's liniment with local drug-gists, the quartet displayed their talents for church and charity groups.

Hamlin, a man of substance in Chicago, fittingly spent some of his Magic Oil income, soon after the great fire, to build an opera house that bore his name.

There were other major entrepreneurs like Hamlin and the Healy-Bigelow team. There were also innumerable small-time free-lancers of all shades of repute. One of the better sort was Dr. C. M. Townsend with whom the young James Whitcomb Riley traveled for a season. The doctor was a kind and generous man with a gift for coining moral aphorisms. During the winter he prepared and packaged his Magic Oil, his King of Coughs, and his Cholera Balm, in Lima, Ohio, and in the spring set out with a covered wagon containing side seats for the members of his troupe. Nearing a town, they would arouse the population with blasts from a horn and then distribute broadsides. At the edge of town they formed a band and paraded through the main streets.[9]

Dr. Townsend gave two "lectures" a day, one in the after-noon, the main speech at night. The versatile Riley did so many things that he was presented as the "Hoosier Wizard." He beat the bass drum, played the violin, sang ballads, gave poetic readings, and used his sketching talent to draw cartoons on blackboards affixed to the wagon while his employer extolled the

---

[9] Dickey, *The Youth of James Whitcomb Riley*, 193-212.

merits of his remedies. "Last night at Winchester," the poet wrote, "I made a decided sensation by making a rebus of the well-known lines from Shakespeare—

'Why let pain your pleasures spoil,
For want of Townsend's Magic Oil?' "

Most small-scale medicine shows were neither so moral nor so literary. Bad liquor flowed like water. One lecturer took swigs of the alcohol in which were preserved the repulsive tapeworms. Drug addiction was not infrequent. Performers were people with skill too limited to make the big time, or with temperaments, habits, or pasts which doomed them to dreary, ill-paid, nomadic lives. Most of the "doctors," for that matter, died broke. Expensive habits, poor management, a run of bad luck, drained off the proceeds. Not that each individual sale did not yield a handsome dividend. Few of the small operators were as conservative as the O. Henry pitchman who "respected his profession, and . . . was satisfied with 300 per cent. profit." The sky was the limit. The operators filled salve boxes with axle grease. They mixed powdered herbs in hotel bathtubs. They colored and flavored and bottled water. "Water," explained the brooding "doctor" in a Jim Tully story, "is the great healer—three-fourths of the earth's surface is water."[10]

Whatever medicine was sold, and whatever attractions were used to lure the citizenry, the sales pitch was always sandwiched in between entertainment. It would not do to begin selling at once, for the audience would feel themselves short-changed. A proper mood needed creating. This mood was not one thing. It might be awe at expert marksmanship. It might be delight at black-face comedy. It might be the slightly naughty shock of seeing a magician pull lingerie from grandpa's pocket.[11] The mood was something that beguiled a crowd, drove from their minds extraneous concerns, and focused attention upon a novel and entrancing spectacle. Thus they were made receptive. Even

[10] McNeal, *passim*; Malcolm Webber, *Medicine Show* (Caldwell, Idaho, 1941), 14, 47-48, 82-83; O. Henry, "Jeff Peters As a Personal Magnet," in *The Gentle Grafter* (N.Y., 1908), 22; Charles L. Pancoast, *Trail Blazers of Advertising* (N.Y., 1926), 178; Jim Tully, "The Giver of Life," *Amer. Mercury*, 14 (June 1928), 154-60.

[11] Claude Gamble, "The Medicine Show," manuscript sketch written for the *Peoria Star*, in possession of Robert Gamble, Sea Cliff, N.Y.; Oliver, "Med Show," 173; Holmes, 225.

with such a build-up, no medicine man was cocky enough to count on holding his audience during the sales pitch without the promise of more free entertainment to come. The after-piece was a fixed part of every show.

When the pitchman took over, he did not begin by mentioning medicine. Showmen there were, indeed, like Doctor Silver Dollar, who haughtily denied they were what they really were. When a village editor referred to Dollar's Famous Carnival of Health as a "medicine show," the doctor disdainfully replied: "You sully us. We deal in no back lots and gutter water." Most pursuers of the profession did not go to this extreme. But they might deny that they were *selling* medicine—they were giving it away and using the small mandatory contribution to finance a missionary journey. Or they might deny that they were selling *medicine*—rather, it was healthful minerals extracted from Nature's purest water. If it was medicine and if they were selling it, the price was "introductory" and seldom half as high as the figure printed on the label.[12]

Any talk of medicine and money was gradually and gingerly approached. Skilled haranguer that he was, the pitchman had a big job to do first. He had to scare the living daylights out of the people in his audience. However hale and hearty they might feel, he must make them sick and frightened enough to buy his sovereign remedy. The variety of fright was infinite. The false symptom was a popular approach. For example:

"Do you ever feel like it is almost impossible to get up in the morning? You eat well and sleep well, but you hate to get up. You hate work. Do you ever feel that way? . . . Well, folks, you may not know it, but that's the first sign of gallopin' consumption!"[13]

Or again: "You laughing, happy audience; you mother, you father, you young man, woman and child, every one of you—within you are the seeds of death! Is it cancer? Is it consumption? Is it perhaps some unknown malady?"[14]

Often was cited the horrible example: "Kidney trouble sneaks up on you like a snake in the grass. Like a thief in the night. It spares neither rich nor poor. The Archbishop of Canterbury was

[12] *Ibid.*, 216-22; Thomas J. LeBlanc, "The Medicine Show," *Amer. Mercury*, 5 (June 1925), 234; W. Lee Provol, *The Pack Peddler* (Phila., 1937), 87-88; McNeal, 167-79.

[13] LeBlanc, 235.

[14] David Edstrom, "Medicine Man of the '80's," *Reader's Digest*, 32 (June 1938), 77.

descending the steps of that great English cathedral when he fell down like an ox smitten in the shambles, stone dead! They held an autopsy; there was nothing wrong with his stomach, heart, or lungs. But gentlemen, when they turned him over and looked at his kidneys . . . gentlemen, they looked just like a rotten tomato."[15]

In addition to the power of his personal magnetism, the traveling "doctor" had another advantage over his rival who advertised in the press. The medicine showman could contribute to the atmosphere of panic by means of horrendous exhibits. The massive hookworm—bought by the bucketful from local slaughterhouses—was indeed a shocker. Curled up in alcohol in large glass jars, the sobering creatures mutely performed for months. There were showmen specializing in making the hookworm the root of all evil, who performed clandestine feats of legerdemain that let them later exhibit worms in public and tell the names of local dignitaries who had allegedly harbored them.[16]

A pitchman who battled against catarrh planted one of the company in his audiences to step up when an appeal was made to test the potency of the salve on sale. "My friend, have you catarrh?" the doctor would inquire. "Yes, sir," the shill replied in a snuffly voice. "Please put a small application of this salve in each nostril," the doctor directed. The shill did as he was bade. Finally the pitchman handed the sufferer a spotless handkerchief. "Now blow your nose hard," he said. The noise could be heard hundreds of feet away. What the audience did not know as they were shown the revolting result was that the doctor's anonymous assistant had earlier stuffed a nostril with stiff custard.[17]

This sort of "proof" showmen often resorted to. It was a common stunt to flatter an audience by remarking on their intelligent faces. Most crowds, the showman would say, looked much less bright. The present company could not be persuaded by mere words, he was well aware, so he would present an irrefutable demonstration. This might require calling the huskiest man from the crowd to take the tuberculosis test, which consisted of blowing through a straw into a sensitive diagnostic fluid (limewater). Of course, the fluid turned milky, and of course the cloudiness denoted raging consumption. The healing potency of the doctor's remedy could also be scientifically proved. A few

15 McNeal, 66.   16 *Ibid.*, 69-70; LeBlanc, 234.   17 McNeal, 118-19.

drops (of vinegar) dispelled the cloud and restored the water to its pristine clarity.[18]

Other demonstrations relating to body chemistry were equally persuasive, and the site of their internal occurrence might be graphically portrayed by means of anatomical models and charts which showmen carried. It was effective, when orating about the dire afflictions which might assail the lungs, the liver, and the bowels, to point to pictures of these organs printed in gaudy reds and purples. Diamond Dick displayed a series of such charts— the muscles, the veins and arteries, the skeleton, the inward organs, even the nerves shining in silver within a dark human frame. Another pitchman used an "Alas, poor Yorick" routine. He came forth holding in one hand an inhalator and in the other a skull. Nervous laughter swept his audience. "This isn't a joke, friends," the showman said. "It is far from a joke. This is the skull of a man who died from catarrh. He wouldn't have died if he'd had one of these inhalators. Put it in your nose and it goes where you can't get with anything else. . . . Spinal meningitis germs enter the nasal passages. Science says that over fifty disease germs, many of them deadly, enter the nose and mouth. Here's something that won't make them feel so good, but will make you feel a lot better."[19]

Quick cures were sometimes wrought before the very eyes of an audience. Liniment could relieve deafness (if due partially to impacted wax) when the showman, in addition to inserting the potent fluid, performed some sleight-of-hand with an earspoon. Snake oil could vanquish arthritis of the elbow if, during its vigorous application, the victim's arm was numbed by pressing tightly against the back of a chair. Stunts of this sort were not devoid of risk. On one occasion a showman had made a man's rheumatism temporarily disappear by vigorous rubbing. But the pain returned, and the dissatisfied customer came back with a gun. The frightened doctor fled the town on foot. Out in the country, he heard dogs baying in the distance. Fearful of a posse, the showman climbed a tree. Soon two hounds ran by chasing a rabbit. Safe but completely unstrung, the pitchman gave up his profession.[20]

[18] *Ibid.*, 159-60; LeBlanc, 233-34.
[19] *Ibid.*; Gamble; Theodore Pratt, "Good-Bye to the Medicine Show," *Medical Economics*, 20 (Oct. 1942), 50, 124.
[20] LeBlanc, 233; article on El Brendel, *Atlanta Jnl.*, Apr. 17, 1954; Burt, 132-33.

From time to time, of course, there were skeptics who had to be dealt with. Most pitchmen were quick thinkers endowed with a brazen manner, and they had a store of stock remarks to deal with various untoward situations. It was deemed wise to heap a scornful scolding on the first member of the audience who sought to wander off after the spiel began. The rest of the crowd, fearful of being made so embarrassingly conspicuous, generally stood rooted to their spots. Sarcasm was also employed to silence the smart aleck who voiced his doubt. Many pitchmen sought to ward off hostility from one quarter by praising the local disciples of Aesculapius and suggesting that the nostrum for sale had the blessing of reputable medicine. One street-corner sharper, indeed, posed as a virtual agent for the American Medical Association. But there had to be a certain ambivalence regarding orthodox medicine, for with showmen as with newspaper-advertisers, their remedies had to succeed where regular doctors failed. Surgeons especially were belabored. The operating doctor was a lower form of creature than a butcher, quick to engage in such a dastardly adventure as to "cut open your umbilicus and take out your tweedium."[21]

Fantastic tales to explain a remedy's healing potency often formed part of a showman's speech, varied to fit the flavor of the show. Many were the medical secrets that had been lured from the Indians by devious stratagems. God's hand was frequently at work, for there were medicine shows that traveled in the name of religion. Pitchmen in somber Quaker garb vended remedies with much thee-ing and thou-ing. The Shakers also were in the field, similarly clad—and this sect really did exercise some supervision over the quality of the herbal mixtures vended. The Oriental theme was also popular. One "professor" spent his first evening in a new town saying not a word. Swathed in robes, he sat silent as a statue, staring straight ahead, while two aides, one on either side, pounded away at kettledrums. Phosphorescent banners bore his name and a weird mixture of unintelligible letters and symbols. The scene was illumined by green fire.[22]

21 Jerome Renitz, "Med Shows on the Main Stem," New Republic, 63 (1930), 366-68; McNeal, 155-57, 161; Oliver, "Alagazam," 76; Tully, 157.

22 Holmes, 219-21; Burt, 133-34; Hoyt, 246-47; McNeal, 53-56; Oliver, "Med Show," 173-74; Oliver, "Alagazam," 79; George Jean Nathan, "The Medicine Men," Harper's Wkly., 55 (Sep. 9, 1911), 24.

[199]

The wonders of the Oriental healing art were relied upon by one of the noted women who plied the medicine trade in the early 20th century. Violet McNeal, in her autobiography, *Four White Horses and a Brass Band*, describes her debut as Princess Lotus Blossom. Wearing a mandarin coat and Chinese skullcap, she told her street-corner crowd the sad "story of peril, of overwhelming danger, of a dread and mysterious ailment which threatened to wipe from the face of the earth the great people of the Chinese nation." This dire disaster was loss of male vitality. "To the horror of all who were aware of this impending tragedy, it seemed inevitable that this mighty race might perish. Its life force was gone. Its manhood no longer possessed the strength for perpetuation of the strain which had existed throughout history."[23]

The Emperor, faced with the crisis, proclaimed that he would give a princely fortune to anyone who found a means of restoring Chinese vitality. Many famous physicians and scientists tried and failed. One astute sage, He Tuck Chaw by name, while exploring a volcanic region encountered a variety of turtle, the Kup Ki See, in which the golden-striped male was outnumbered by the female 1,000 to 1. What was the secret of this incredible vitality? He Tuck Chaw pushed his researches with vigor and hope. At last he discovered that the male turtle differed from the female in possessing a small pouch, the Quali Quah pouch, at the base of the brain. "He removed the pouches. . . , dried and powdered them, and gave tiny portions to the Chinese people. The reaction was both swift and effective." The nation was saved.

Princess Lotus Blossom, of course, had come into possession of the secret. "There is, gentlemen," she told her listeners, "a sufficient quantity of this same substance in these Vital Sparks I am going to offer tonight to restore you to health, virility, and happiness."

The Vital Sparks had really been no closer to a turtle than had the Princess to China. She and her husband had made them by pouring buckshot candy into a hotel bureau drawer, dampening it, and rolling it around in powdered aloes. This was what made "old men young and young men stronger."

After the pitchman had terrified his hearers and given the romantic credentials of his remedy, the moment came for selling.

23 McNeal, 73-74, 91-94.

Sales went best amid noise, turbulence, and confusion. Nevada Ned's Indians whooped and his musicians played. Most showmen sought for a similar atmosphere. The beating of drums and blaring of horns produced a frenzied accompaniment for the pitchman's continued harangue, rendered in a bull-like roar. Members of the troupe ran madly here and there among the audience, sometimes turning cartwheels to add to the excitement. Getting one bottle of medicine from the doctor, each minion would hurry out and sell it, shouting "S-o-o-o-l-d!" or "Another bottle gone!" or "More medicine, Doctor!" as he pocketed the money and ran back to get another bottle. A sort of mob hypnotism swept spectators into the buying mood. Sometimes they bought and later went away, leaving the medicine behind.[24]

Restrictive legislation—federal, state, and local—was to put serious restraints on the free-wheeling medicine showmen in the 20th century. As rural areas became less culturally isolated, the shows lost some of their appeal. Moving pictures and, in time, the radio offered competitive amusements that took some of the fresh zest away. Though the medium continued, it did not possess the glamor and the daring of late 19th century ventures sponsored by Healy and Bigelow and their imaginative rivals.[25]

Seldom did an outsider get on the inside of the medicine show. On those rare cases when he did, he may well have been as astounded as was the fictional pedagogue in a novel of Harry Leon Wilson. Fleeing the routine of his campus and the dreariness of his home, Professor Copplestone winds up as an "Indian" in a flea-bitten show vending Aga-Jac Bitters among the farming folk of Iowa. At the first night's performance the yokels are carried away by the professor's medley of Greek iambics which passes for an aboriginal tongue. But they are not more impressed by Copplestone's contribution than is he by theirs. At the end of the evening, the professor's partner, a rogue named Sooner Jackson, counts out the money.[26]

"Forty-two iron men," he cries, "only thirty-two of which are profit, however, because those bottles cost money. Therefore, old bean. . . , you are sixteen plunks . . . to the mustard. Not bad for a start, eh?"

24 Oliver, "Med Show," 173; Webber, 28; Pratt, 122; Edstrom, 78.
25 Oliver, "Med Show," 12; Oliver, "Alagazam," 76; McNeal, 105-106; *Missouri Hist. Rev.*, 45 (1951), 375.
26 Wilson, *Professor How Could You!* (N.Y., 1924), 123-33.

"I, for one, consider it excellent," the amazed professor replies, and he muses to himself: "Indeed, reckoning time and energy invested, it was so far in excess of my ordinary stipend that I felt my previous years had been frittered away."

PART FOUR

LEGISLATION

13

"THE GREAT AMERICAN FRAUD"

"Ponce de Leon, groping toward that dim fountain whence youth springs eternal, might believe that he had found his goal in the Peruna factory, the Liquozone 'laboratory,' or the Vitae-Ore plant; his thousands of descendants in this century of enlightenment painfully drag themselves along poisoned trails, following a will-o'-the-wisp that dances above open graves."—SAMUEL HOPKINS ADAMS[1]

THE most famous series of articles in American patent medicine history began on October 7, 1905, in the pages of *Collier's, The National Weekly*. They were written by a free-lance journalist named Samuel Hopkins Adams, and his conclusions were succinctly rendered in the title he gave to the series, "The Great American Fraud." Adams did not say much that had not been said before in the long decades during which patent medicines had been criticized. But in the *Collier's* series he made a major campaign out of what had been an occasional skirmish, and he reached an audience not only vastly larger than had ever before heard nostrums castigated, but one enthusiastic about supporting reform.

Adams' "muckraking" journalism came during the Progressive period. The first major attack on patent medicines had been part of that earlier upsurge of reform sentiment associated with Jacksonian democracy. It had been led by perceptive physicians and pharmacists, who belabored Swaim's Panacea and saw hazards to American health in other packaged pills and potions. Denunciation of nostrums continued in the years that followed, as in the case of R. G. Eccles, that relentless foe of Radam's Microbe Killer, who was both doctor and druggist. He and his fellows in both professions could aim anti-nostrum weapons of improving accuracy, as medical science and pharmaceutical

---

[1] Adams, "The Fundamental Fakes," *Collier's* 36 (Feb. 17, 1906), 22.

chemistry advanced. The target also kept expanding, as the volume of patent medicine production boomed and the blatancy of advertising increased during the last quarter of the 19th century. In view of these circumstances, although nostrums came in for a great deal of criticism, it is perhaps surprising that there was not more.

To be sure, the patent medicine evil remained an acceptable theme for an indignant oration before the annual meeting of the medical society, to be printed soon thereafter in the society's transactions. The reform-minded physician, however, became so obsessed with quackery within the profession that the trend was toward fewer speeches and articles on nostrums advertised direct to the lay public. As scientific standards developed, there was much concern that state licensing procedures did not reflect these advances so as to eliminate unskillful practitioners like the seventeen kinds of non-regular "doctors" imposing upon the residents of Indiana. Equally disturbing to competent medical men was the rise of the quack remedy promoted direct to physicians.[2]

The old days of simple prescribing were fast passing as the manufacturing of medicines became a major American business, and physicians of the best intent had a hard time deciding what was good and what was spurious. In the 1870's they were confronted with a host of new products to assay. The "ethical" proprietary made its appearance, a non-secret packaged product, unpatented but sometimes bearing a distinctive copyrighted name, prepared in the laboratory of a reputable pharmaceutical manufacturer. These medicines were primarily elegant preparations of standard formulas—elixirs, pills, syrups—aimed at performing essentially the same roles as the official preparations of the *Pharmacopoeia*. In the same decade new German synthetics came to America, chemical pain-killers and fever-reducers, the formulas of which were known. These drugs were patented and marketed under special arrangements with the German producers. The advertising for these new remedies might promise too much, but it was essentially honest. The serious trouble came when doctors, not well trained in the materia medica in any case, sought to keep

---

[2] Titles cited in the *Index-Catalogue of the Library of the Surgeon-General's Office*, first two series; William H. Loppe, cited in Pickard and Buley, *The Midwest Pioneer*, 168-69.

the new ethicals apart from countless pseudo-ethicals which quickly appeared to imitate new pharmaceutical approaches and steal their thunder.[3]

"Far more iniquitous [than the maker of ordinary patent medicines]," warned a Philadelphia physician in 1892, "and far more dangerous to society is the wily manufacturer that advertises 'to the profession only.' Whether he ostentatiously holds secret the composition of his nostrum, or whether with pretended frankness he describes it with an appellative that means nothing, or publishes a formula that cannot be carried out, his object is the same; he seeks to make the physician's the hand whereby he may reach pockets shut from the coarser methods of the Warners, the Pinkhams, and the Jaynes. . . . [A sick man] certainly deserves better [from his physician] than to be handed over to the mercies of 'antikamnia,' or 'Quickine,' or 'gleditschine,' or 'Freligh's tablets,' or 'Listerine,' or any other of the unholy crew."[4]

This rebuke by Solomon Solis Cohen to his muddled or careless colleagues was one of many attempts to keep the pseudo-ethicals off medical prescription pads. Vain efforts had already been made to curtail one of the worst features of these proprietaries, the way in which their makers advertised in medical periodicals and, in some cases, influenced editorial policy. Even the *Journal of the American Medical Association* harbored suspect advertising. During the eighties and nineties, criticism of such a course led leaders of the Association to reform policy somewhat, but never altogether and not for long. Publishing deficits led to a relaxation of standards. A new promise as late as 1900 was not completely kept: the Association did require advertisers to supply formulas, but these lists of ingredients sometimes proved false. In 1905 *JAMA* did not have as many bad ads as many medical journals, but this is only faint praise. In the field as a whole, the situation was shocking. Out of some 250 medical journals, only a few could not be "bribed into defrauding their readers" by hearkening to the quack advertiser's demand that plugs appear disguised as articles or editorials.

3 Kremers and Urdang, *History of Pharmacy*, 320-23; George H. Simmons, "Work of the Council on Pharmacy and Chemistry," *Southern Med. Jnl.*, 7 (1915), 259; *JAMA*, 32 (1899), 910; 44 (1905), 718-19, 1,047-48.
4 Solomon Solis Cohen, "Shall Physicians Become Sales-Agents for Patent Medicines?" Phila. County Med. Soc., *Proceedings*, 13 (1892), 215.

Some journals were "owned openly or covertly" by the men who marketed pseudo-ethical remedies.[5]

With so much to straighten out in the front room of their own house, physicians of critical bent paid less attention to the old-fashioned type of patent medicine aimed direct at the consumer. Only "sporadic attempts have been made from time to time, by medical associations and medical journals," wrote the editor of *JAMA* in 1900, to expose patent medicines, and "but little progress has been made in checking the evils. . . . In fact, but little light has so far been shed on the subject." That little light, so far as the lay public was concerned, had been hid under a bushel, for the criticism was printed in the pages of medical journals which laymen rarely if ever saw.[6]

The same was true of drug periodicals. What condemnation of patent medicines there was in the late 19th century did not meet the eyes of steady nostrum buyers. When criticism came before the gaze of the druggist, it forced him to face up to an old dilemma. As a man of science, he must admit grave evils in the nostrum trade. As a merchant, he found the sale of proprietary remedies bulking large in his gross income. It was not impossible to find plausible ways of resolving this pressure. One oft-repeated argument held that there were good patent medicines and bad patent medicines and a druggist should confine his stock to bottles of the former. The view was also ventured that the public was bound to buy quack stuff, and if pharmacists stopped selling it less competent merchants, like grocers, would.[7]

Despite vested interests and inertia, a valiant corps of pharmacists continued the attack. They appealed to their colleagues not only with humanitarian arguments but through a more careful analysis of self-interest. "Do we not recognize," a Chicago druggist asked, on the floor of the 1893 American Pharmaceutical Association convention, "that this [patent medicine] industry is one of our greatest enemies, and that there are millions of dollars' worth sold all over the country, thus diverting money which

[5] Morris Fishbein, *A History of the American Medical Association, 1847 to 1941* (Phila., 1947), 112-13, 115, 161-63, 168-69, 198-99; *JAMA*, 22 (1894), 95-96, 396-97, 438-39, 480; 34 (1900), 986-88, 1,041-43; 44 (1905), 1,982-86; 45 (1905), 264-65.

[6] *Ibid.*, 34 (1900), 1,420.

[7] *Druggists Circular*, 50 (1906), 61-63; *Bull. Pharm.*, 21 (1907), 446; *Amer. Jnl. Pharm.*, 48 (1876), 10-18, and 46 (1874), 89-91.

rightly belongs to the retail drug trade, in the way of prescriptions and regular drugs?"[8]

How stupid can pharmacists be? another druggist asked a decade later. "They give away valuable window display space to show goods which are making their sworn enemies rich; they hang the pictures and tack signs of their biggest rivals in the most conspicuous place in their stores; they plaster their windows with transparencies and give place on the sidewalk to all kinds of signs and bicycle racks, to the end that a quack living in a distant city, a doctor who is too sick to practice, or a 'retired missionary' who is too strong to work, may wax opulent."[9]

Year after year patent medicine quackery was debated on the floor of American Pharmaceutical Association meetings. Strong resolutions were passed condemning nostrum evils, and pleas were issued for remedial legislation. A handful of drug trade journals also kept up a constant attack. One of the most vigorous, the *Druggists Circular and Chemical Gazette*, looked backward from 1905 and expressed satisfaction over its career of "active and uncompromising opposition to fraud and sham in the drug business." Not only had it met the Microbe Killer head on. It had revealed that the advertising photograph of the alleged discoverer of a purported brain tonic was really the picture of a notable German musician. There had been many other blasts at quackery.[10]

Yet at times even the most devoted crusader was overwhelmed with a sense of despair. "Of what avail," a pharmacist had queried in 1883, "are teachers of science, and schools of learning, and the lives devoted to the study and application of materia medica, and the bringing to light of the hidden resources of nature, for the alleviation and cure of human maladies, when such cabalistic signs as St. X, 1860, can be made to invest rum with wonderful healing properties, or a bearded man in a pine forest, kneeling beside an open book and alembic, effect the wonderful transformation of turpentine into an 'elixir of life'?"[11]

Pharmacists and physicians who continued to fight patent medicines, despite such occasional discouragement, were joined in the late 19th century by a new brand of scientist. The same

8 Amer. Pharm. Assoc., *Proceedings, 1893*, 41 (Phila., 1893), 287.
9 *Druggists Circular*, 49 (1905), 30.
10 *Proceedings, 1885*, 33 (Phila., 1886), 394-98, and *1893*, 41 (Phila., 1893), 284-88, 345-52; *Druggists Circular*, 49 (1905), 417-18.
11 *Amer. Jnl. Pharm.*, 55 (1883), 565.

chemistry that developed the German pain-killing drugs had widespread applications to the food which Americans were eating. The Civil War had launched a boom in canned and packaged foods. Greater remoteness of producer from consumer, with complicated processing in between, coupled with new chemical techniques, provided temptations which many manufacturers were unable to resist. Chemicals were employed to heighten color, to modify flavor, to soften texture, to deter spoilage, indeed, to transform ingredients like apples and hayseeds into concoctions labeled strawberry jam. Farmers in agrarian states were aroused at the use of chemistry to deodorize rotten eggs and to revive rancid butter. What chemists had learned to disguise, the farmers began to realize, chemists could learn to detect. On state payrolls, there began to appear agricultural chemists, men who sometimes went to Germany to improve their techniques, whose task was to discover and publicize the tricks of shady processors. In 1884, seeking strength through collaboration, the state men banded together into an Association of Official Agricultural Chemists. These scientists began to turn out official reports by the dozen, exposing the fraud in food. Some of them did not confine their energies to investigating the things which people ate. Any crookedness involving chemistry interested them, and no more fertile field for probing existed than that of patent medicines. From Connecticut to North Dakota state chemists began to test tonics for alcohol, soothing syrups for morphine, headache powders for acetanilide. In their official pamphlets they published the results of their analyses, tearing the mask of secrecy from scores of nostrums and exposing the brazen falsity of label claims.[12]

Not all the criticism of patent medicines after the Civil War was written by natural scientists. There were lay critics, too, as there had been in antebellum days. To find this condemnation of nostrums, the newspapers were hardly the place to look, at least not until the 20th century. Rural newspapers, crammed to the margins with remedy ads, were so completely devoid of criticism that William Allen White's anti-nostrum *Emporia Gazette* was a

[12] Mark Sullivan, *Our Times* (N.Y., 1926-35), II, 501-10; W. B. White, "A.O.A.C. Methods of Analysis," *Food Drug Cosmetic Law Quarterly*, 1 (1946), 443-45; *Dictionary of American Biography*, X, 120-21, and XX, 215-16; Erling N. Rolfsrud, *Lanterns over the Prairies* (Brainerd, Minn., 1950), 113-22; interview with Samuel Hopkins Adams, April 5, 1955.

startling exception. City papers continued to rely on the *caveat emptor* policy, taking what ads were offered and letting the reader exercise his own due diligence. When there was criticism, it was often temporary or half-hearted or both, a one-shot campaign against an unusually notorious quack whose cousins might be advertising in adjacent columns. Some papers did hold to something like consistency in excluding remedies for venereal disease and sex weakness, while accepting tuberculosis and cancer cures. Still, with all their caution, enough editors were sufficiently independent-minded to cause medicine proprietors sleepless nights, especially after nostrum control bills began to appear in state legislatures. If the press had been considered as indisputably safe, patent medicine advertisers would have had no need to develop ways of making criticism costly.[13]

What the nostrum manufacturers had invented to protect themselves was a "red clause" in advertising contracts. Frank J. Cheney, whose company made Hall's Catarrh Cure, boasted to his fellow members at a Proprietary Association meeting that the clause was "pretty near a sure thing." "It is mutually agreed," the red type in the advertising contract read, "that this Contract is void, if any law is enacted by your State restricting or prohibiting the manufacture or sale of proprietary medicines." Cheney told his colleagues how he had used the contract in Illinois to call the tune for newspapers when a tax on proprietaries was threatened by the legislature. These words to the wise were sufficient, and "muzzle-clauses" proliferated.[14]

As the 19th century changed into the 20th, the press became bolder. On many papers the advertising exclusion policy toughened up considerably, and some publishers publicly flaunted the "red clause" which had hitherto held them in restraint. These newspapers, it is true, represented a minority of the American press: of all the gazettes which Massachusetts boasted, only the *Springfield Republican* had courage enough to report a lively debate in the state legislature over a nostrum-labeling bill. But this journal, the *Chicago Tribune*, the *St. Louis Star*, the *New*

[13] Clark, *The Southern Country Editor*, 77; Lee, *The Daily Newspaper in America*, 321; Presbrey, *The History and Development of Advertising*, 531; *JAMA*, 11 (1888), 863-64; *N.Y. Tribune*, Apr. 1, 16, 29, May 6, June 1, Dec. 8, 1883.
[14] Sullivan, *The Education of an American*, 188-91; *Collier's*, 36 (Nov. 4, 1905), 13-16, 25.

York Post, the *New Orleans Item*, the *Seattle Post-Intelligencer*, and a respectable group of other papers, down to and including the *Telegram* (circulation 500) published in Marine, Illinois, put public service ahead of advertising revenue and fought patent medicine abuses.[15]

Some magazines also had spoken out in opposition to medical quackery. Orange Judd's *American Agriculturist*, begun in 1859, had excluded objectionable nostrum advertising and had set aside a special page on which to expose frauds. Wilmer Atkinson's *Farm Journal*, started in 1877, had adhered to the policy described in the circular announcing the first issue, that it would accept no "quack medical advertisement at any price." *Popular Science Monthly* took a perennial interest in quackery and through the years printed a series of able attacks. Even the staid *Atlantic Monthly* in 1867 published Dr. S. Weir Mitchell's *The Autobiography of a Quack*, a novel which revealed the shabbiness of the fake remedy game so vividly that it was reprinted in the *Century* when the anti-nostrum movement had heated up.[16]

It was during the 1890's that the *Ladies' Home Journal* first got interested in patent medicines. Cyrus H. K. Curtis, the publisher, came to the decision that proprietary ads must go, and, when the treasurer protested, the taciturn New Englander withered him with a look. In full agreement with his publisher and father-in-law was editor Edward Bok. He kept the *Journal* columns clean and occasionally wrote a harsh word about nostrums, particularly the bitters of high alcoholic content. Many of Bok's feminine readers were ardent members of the revived temperance crusade, and WCTU leaders, more sophisticated than they once had been, were now well aware that Hostetter's Bitters and Peruna might provide an unwitting or a secret tipple. Through pamphlets, speeches, and propaganda in the schools, they battled the demon rum disguised as medicine. Bok gave them a helping hand.[17]

[15] *Ibid.*, 36 (Oct. 28, 1905), 29; (Nov. 4), 13; (Nov. 25), 30; *Druggists Circular*, 50 (1906), 191; H. J. Kenner, *The Fight for Truth in Advertising* (N.Y., 1936), 14; *Popular Science Monthly*, 67 (1905), 423.

[16] Kenner, 7; Atkinson, *An Autobiography* (Phila., 1920), 160-63, 179-80, 184; *Popular Science*, issues for June 1883, May 1891, April 1896, August 1897, Sep. 1905, June 1906; Mitchell, *Atlantic Monthly*, 20 (1867), 466-75, 586-98, and *Century Mag.*, 59 (1899-1900), 108-19, 290-98, 385-94.

[17] Bok, *A Man form Maine* (N.Y., 1923), 126; John A. Thayer, *Out of the Rut* (N.Y., 1912), 87-89, 106-107; Bok, *The Americanization of Edward Bok*

The *Journal's* random attacks on nostrums turned into a vigorous campaign in 1904. The change of tempo owed much to a chance error. In an editorial condemning "The 'Patent-Medicine' Curse," Bok listed the ingredients of various nostrums, citing a document issued by the Massachusetts State Board of Health. One of the remedies was Doctor Pierce's Favorite Prescription, and it contained, said Bok, relying on his source, alcohol, opium, and digitalis. The company promptly launched a $200,000 libel suit, asserting that the medicine contained none of these. The editor found he had made a careless and costly mistake. The Massachusetts analysis he had depended upon was a quarter of a century out of date; new analyses run by chemists hired for the purpose confirmed the Pierce contention. So did a visit to the manufacturing plant. Bok printed a retraction, prepared for the trial, and stepped up his denunciation of the patent medicine business.[18]

The *Journal* editor hoped that he might be able to find an old bottle of Pierce's remedy, perhaps in some isolated rural store, which would contain alcohol, opium, and digitalis. To make this hunt he needed an able and trustworthy man, and Bok hired a young Harvard-trained journalist and lawyer named Mark Sullivan. Despite a diligent search, the *Journal's* sleuth could find no such bottle as his employer needed for the trial. The woman's magazine lost its suit, and the jury awarded Pierce $16,000. In the meantime Bok had given Sullivan other undercover tasks to do, and, shadowed by detectives, he probed into the workings of the patent medicine business. Using assumed names, Sullivan advertised in the papers of various cities as if seeking to hire men skilled in different branches of the industry. Then he interviewed those who struck at his bait, the chemists, the experts in direct mail selling, the advertising specialists. Eager for better jobs, these men bragged about their own ability, revealing to Sullivan the tricks of the trade, confiding the formulas. He learned that letters written by ailing men and women in response to advertisements were sold, after the company had fully exploited them, to other proprietors. These pathetic and confidential missives

(N.Y., 1923), 340-41; Mrs. Martha W. Allen, Supt. of the WCTU Dept. of Non-Alcoholic Medication, to Harvey W. Wiley, Nov. 5, 1904, and June 10, 1905, Wiley Papers, Manuscript Div., Library of Congress.

[18] *LHJ*, 21 (May 1904), 18, and (July 1904), 18; *Bull. Pharm.*, 19 (1905), 444; Bok, *Americanization*, 342-43.

ended up in huge bundles, packaged according to disease, and brokers sold or rented the letters for several dollars a thousand. Sullivan bought some packages and had them photographed. Another photograph became more celebrated. Sullivan soon learned that, although advertising showing Lydia Pinkham's maternal face might be read as suggesting that she would answer letters of inquiry from suffering women, the venerable lady had long been dead. Accompanied by a friend who owned a camera, he set out on a tour of the Pine Grove Cemetery near Lynn, Massachusetts, and found the imposing tombstone inscribed with the date of Mrs. Pinkham's passing, May 17, 1883. The picture soon appeared in the pages of the *Journal*.[19]

It was Sullivan who found out about the "red clause" in advertising contracts. As a result of some delicate maneuvering, he secured a copy of the minutes of the Proprietary Association meeting at which Cheney had made his boastful speech. With this clue, Sullivan tracked down and photographed similar "muzzle-clauses" in the contracts of several major medicine advertisers. He also obtained pictures of letters written by proprietors to newspapers when danger loomed, and he secured direct quotations from Dr. Pierce's son praising the newspaper publishers' association for help in defeating inimical bills.[20]

All of this sensational information Sullivan drafted into an article which he called "The Patent Medicine Conspiracy Against the Freedom of the Press." Bok liked it but felt it too "legalistic" and long for the *Ladies' Home Journal* and offered it to Norman Hapgood, the sober, scholarly editor of *Collier's*. Hapgood took it and Sullivan's article appeared in the magazine during November 1905. At the time that it was printed *Collier's* was in the midst of the most earnest campaign ever waged against patent medicines by an American magazine.[21]

The crusade had started with a jest. William Jennings Bryan had been belaboring corporations in the pages of his personal organ, the *Commoner*, a paper which contained full-page advertisements for Liquozone, a nostrum promising to cure everything from dandruff to dysentery. Hapgood chided Bryan editorially,

[19] Sullivan, *Education*, 183-91; *Bull. Pharm.*, 20 (1906), 138; *LHJ*, 21 (Nov. 1904), 18, 22 (Mar. 1905), 18; (Apr. 1905), 20; (Sep. 1905), 15; (Jan. 1906), 14, 18; (Feb. 1906), 23.
[20] Sullivan, *Education*, 188-91; *Collier's*, 36 (Nov. 4, 1905), 13-16, 25.
[21] *Ibid.*; Sullivan, *Education*, 191-92; Bok, *Americanization*, 344.

asking if it were not inconsistent for him to attack the immorality of corporations and at the same time countenance such an absolute therapeutic monopoly. Bryan did not appreciate the joke and wrote a letter of injured innocence. Liquozone's proprietor did not appreciate the joke and sent his lawyer to talk with Hapgood. "In a short time," the editor later wrote, "we were launched into a field we occupied for years."[22]

The more Hapgood looked into the matter, the more he was affronted by the fraud and effrontery of the patent medicine business. Collier's own hands were not clean, as Bryan had pointed out. The magazine was running advertising for such remedies as Vapo-Cresolene, which promised to cure whooping cough and diphtheria, and Buffalo Lithia Water, which possessed a "Marvelous Efficiency in Gout, Rheumatism, [and] Gastro-intestinal Dyspepsia" lauded by no less a figure than the Physician in Ordinary to the Pope. Such ads Hapgood ordered expunged from his magazine, and he set out to find a reporter capable of digging out the facts and writing a hard-hitting full-scale exposure of medical quackery. The man he found was Samuel Hopkins Adams. The choice was one of the shrewdest in the annals of journalism.[23]

Adams was no doctor, although he was not unfamiliar with matters medical. As an undergraduate at Hamilton College, he had pursued for a time a course in pre-medical studies. Journalism won him away from science, but Adams did not abandon his interest in disease and health. After graduating, he became a reporter, spending nine years perfecting his craft on the staff of one of the nation's distinguished newspapers, the New York Sun. He became adept at crime reporting and covered the major sensational cases of robbery and murder. Sleuthing techniques here developed were later to stand Adams in good stead. In 1900 he left the Sun to enter the employ of that driving temperamental genius of the journalistic world, S. S. McClure. Adams first edited the syndicate that distributed stories and articles to newspapers, and later served as advertising manager for the McClure publishing house.[24]

[22] Norman Hapgood, The Changing Years (N.Y., 1930), 177-78; Collier's, 34 (Mar. 25, 1905), 8, and 35 (Apr. 22, 1905), 9, 27.

[23] Ibid., 35 (Apr. 9, 1905), 32, and (May 20), 28.

[24] Biographical material on Adams is taken mainly from Hamilton Alumni Review, Jan. 1937; National Cyclopaedia of American Biography (N.Y., 1892-1952), XIV, 166; Bookman, 21 (1905), 562-63; and the interview with Adams.

While Adams was associated with these enterprises, *McClure's Magazine* suddenly became the most exciting periodical in America. On its staff were topflight reporters like Lincoln Steffens, Ida Tarbell, and Ray Stannard Baker. They began to write articles asserting that the American dream had been blighted. Big business had grown so huge, these journalists stated, that it had crushed American freedom, ruining small business, thwarting freedom of speech, and subverting all branches of government. Charges like these had been made before, but seldom so explicitly and never with such a wealth of circumstantial detail. *McClure's* authors were not content with generalities. They named names, mentioned places, and cited dates. There was already a reform spirit astir in America, here and there, when *McClure's* writers began to write. With their exposure articles they fanned local fires into a searing national flame. They were joined in this task by other writers on other magazines, for the booming circulation figures of *McClure's* led to widespread imitation. Never before had so many Americans, especially the great middle class, bought so many magazines. Never had the magazines treated the evils of society with such a combination of exact description and moral passion. Never—unless the abolition crusade is excepted—had exposure literature played such a compelling role. The leadership of American thought, said the philosopher William James, was leaving the universities and entering the ten-cent magazines.[25]

In 1904, a year after the McClure authors had brought "muckraking" journalism to fever heat, Samuel Hopkins Adams resigned his post as advertising manager in order to write. No longer on the regular payroll, he continued to receive *McClure's* checks, since his important early articles appeared in the magazine shoulder to shoulder with pieces by Steffens, Baker, and Miss Tarbell. With them Adams shared a dedication to factual accuracy and a zeal for improving the lot of mankind, both of which marked his discussions of certain aspects of the public health. For Adams had turned to his continuing interest in medical science for themes, writing on tuberculosis, yellow fever, typhoid fever, and surgical techniques. These subjects, good as

25 On "muckraking" see Louis Filler, *Crusaders for American Liberalism* (New ed., Yellow Springs, O., 1950), and Cornelius C. Regier, *The Era of the Muckrakers* (Chapel Hill, 1932). James cited in Hapgood, 63.

[216]

they were, lacked one essential ingredient of the full-blown "muckraking" essay: the human evil-doer. Such a sinister figure was by no means absent from the medical scene. So Adams turned to patent medicines.

Ray Stannard Baker, as Adams recalled it, first suggested to him that he prepare a series on American nostrums. The idea struck him most favorably. He had done some thinking but no research when he was approached by Norman Hapgood. Adams owed first loyalty to McClure, who could have published the series, but for some unaccountable reason—his staff could never predict his reactions—McClure was lukewarm to the idea. Hapgood, however, was in earnest. Adams signed a contract and set to work.

The build-up for the Adams series lasted from April to October. Week after week, in editorial, jingle, and picture, *Collier's* whacked away at the nostrum menace. E. W. Kemble drew a "DEATH'S LABORATORY" cartoon, depicting a skull with patent medicine bottles for teeth. Hapgood wrote an article bemoaning the fact that America's most reputable newspapers opened their pages to disreputable ads, and he surrounded his words with a pictorial border linking patent medicine appeals with the mastheads of papers from which they had been clipped. The rhymster, Wallace Irwin, like countless other Americans, perused an advertisement and discovered to his horror

> That mushrooms were growing all over my liver,
>   That something was loose in my heart,
> That due to my spleen all my nerves had turned green
>   And my lungs were not doing their part.
> I wrote Dr. Sharko and got as an answer,
>   "The wart on your thumb is incipient cancer."[26]

Adams, in the meantime, was hard at work. He was gathering and studying examples of nostrum advertising. He was buying the medicines advertised, transporting the bottles to his Hamilton chemistry professor or experts at a pharmaceutical laboratory, and requesting them to find out what was inside. He was getting counsel from state agricultural chemists and consulting editors of pharmaceutical journals. With a list of curative claims and a list

[26] *Collier's*, 35 (June 3, 1905), 5; (July 5), 12, 13, 22; Irwin, "A Testimonial," (July 22), 17.

of ingredients, he was asking experts in medical research if the former could possibly derive from a dose of the latter. Adams was doing lots of leg work. He was selecting choice testimonials and then seeking to find the testators and get their stories at first hand. Nor was the busy journalist diffident about approaching nostrum princes themselves. One of the leading proprietaries of the day, a remedy so influential that babies were named for it,[27] was Peruna. The maker of this much-vaunted tonic was a genial old German named Samuel D. Hartman, a trained physician. Adams journeyed to Columbus, Ohio, to talk with Hartman and was accorded a friendly reception. The medicine man told the reporter everything, even after being warned that the planned article was bound to be critical.[28]

Not all remedy proprietors took such a charitable view of Adams' researches, and he found that his goings and comings were being followed by a private detective. Suddenly events took a nasty turn. One weekend Adams was invited to a house party in Connecticut. In the station in New York, he met the wife of a close friend, also on the guest list, and they rode together on the train. Soon thereafter it was brought to his attention that this episode had been observed and that the story of his train trip with another man's wife might be made public in an unfavorable way if he was so injudicious as to continue his investigations.[29]

The suggestion of blackmail made Adams' blood boil, yet he was worried, for he shrank from any course that might bring embarrassment to the lady. As luck would have it, Adams was well acquainted with the mayor of the city where the nostrum proprietor lived whom Adams believed to be chiefly responsible for the threat. Hastening west, Adams told the mayor his plight. The city official knew just the facts which the journalist required. Not long before, the mayor reported, the nostrum maker had been surprised in a roadhouse room with another man's wife. When detectives had knocked on the door, the startled medicine proprietor had jumped from a window and broken his leg.

Adams cautiously let it be known that he was privy to this tale. Not only did he hear no more of the threat, but the detectives were immediately withdrawn.

27 Elsdon C. Smith, *The Story of Our Names* (N.Y., 1950), 113.
28 Interview with Adams.
29 *Ibid.*

Safely past this contretemps, Adams returned to his researches with a new zest. "A character inherited from a line of insurgent theologians," noted a *Collier's* colleague, "gave him firm conviction in his beliefs." And Adams "gloried in combat." In this respect appearances were perhaps deceptive, for the reporter looked younger than his thirty-four years and his face, rather than being pugnacious, was relaxed and pleasant, with soft contours and rounded features. His hair was cut long and parted just to the right, and he wore a high stiff collar and flowing cravat. Adams' amiable, indeed aesthetic, appearance may have fooled the patent medicine tribe into thinking him a less than worthy foe. No such miscalculations were made after October 7, 1905.[30]

On that date *Collier's* carried the first chapter of "The Great American Fraud." Adams' vigorous words appeared under a page-wide illustration showing a hooded skull in front of patent medicine bottles exuding noxious vapors. Sinewy serpents, so often the nostrum maker's symbol of evil, had now turned coat and slithered among the vials.[31]

"Gullible America," Adams began, "will spend this year some seventy-five millions of dollars in the purchase of patent medicines. In consideration of this sum it will swallow huge quantities of alcohol, an appalling amount of opiates and narcotics, a wide assortment of varied drugs ranging from powerful and dangerous heart depressants to insidious liver stimulants; and, far in excess of all other ingredients, undiluted fraud. For fraud, exploited by the skilfulest of advertising bunco men, is the basis of the trade. Should the newspapers, the magazines, and the medical journals refuse their pages to this class of advertisements, the patent medicine business in five years would be as scandalously historic as the South Sea Bubble, and the nation would be the richer not only in lives and money, but in drunkards and drug-fiends saved."

After this sweeping introduction, Adams got down to cases. He rebuked Pond's Extract for "trading on the public alarm" by running an advertisement boldly headed "MENINGITIS" while New York was suffering an epidemic. Next to his criticism was a reproduction of the offending ad. Adams described how proprietary manufacturers inserted into their advertising contracts with

[30] Will Irwin, *The Making of a Reporter* (N.Y., 1942), 155; portrait in *Amer. Mag.*, 62 (1906), 225, and *Bookman*, 21 (1905), 563.
[31] *Collier's*, 36 (Oct. 7, 1905), 14, 15, 29.

newspapers the restraining clause printed in red ink. Beside Adams' words was a picture of a contract which had been offered by the Cheney Medicine Company to the *Emporia Gazette*. Adams explained that patent medicine testimonials were gathered from gullible ignoramuses or secured through various pressures from people in public life. He told the tale of the visit to the advertising manager of a Chicago newspaper by an agent for Paine's Celery Compound. The agent showed the manager a full-page advertisement with blank spaces in the center.

"We want some good, strong testimonials to fill out with," he said.

"You can get all of those you want, can't you?" asked the newspaper manager.

"Can *you*?" returned the agent. "Show me four or five strong ones from local politicians and you can get the ad."

"The Nostrum Evil," as Adams entitled his initial article, contained other generalizations buttressed by specific instances. It was, indeed, a sort of broad preview of what he intended to treat in more detail in the articles to follow.

Adams followed his first general attack on nostrums with the exposure of Peruna, about which he had warned its friendly proprietor at the beginning of their conversation. The article opened with a quotation from a public health official.[32]

"Let us," the man had suggested to Adams, "buy in large quantities the cheapest Italian vermouth, poor gin, and bitters. We will mix them in the proportion of three of vermouth to two of gin with a dash of bitters, dilute and bottle them by the short quart, label them '*Smith's Revivifier and Blood-Purifier; dose, one wineglassful before each meal*'; advertise them to cure erysipelas, bunions, dyspepsia, heat rash, fever and ague, and consumption; and to prevent loss of hair, small-pox, old age, sunstroke, and near-sightedness, and make our everlasting fortunes selling them to the temperance trade."

"That sounds to me," Adams had replied, "very much like a cocktail."

"So it is," the health official noted. "But it's just as much a medicine as Peruna and not as bad a drink."

Peruna's alcoholic content, Adams discovered, ran about 28

32 "Peruna and the 'Bracers,' " *Collier's*, 36 (Oct. 28, 1905), 17-19.

per cent, and a dollar bottle of the remedy cost its manufacturer—
including the bottle—between fifteen and eighteen cents. As a
medicine Peruna was promoted to cure nothing but catarrh, but
catarrh in Dr. Hartman's pathology was a term encompassing
appendicitis, consumption, mumps, and female complaints. Adams reported on Peruna "alcoholics" he had met, at least one of
them a member in good standing in the WCTU, and he reproduced an Office of Indian Affairs order to Indian agents prohibiting the sale of Dr. Hartman's product as an intoxicant "too tempting and effective." Among the many Peruna testimonials written
by men in high places, Adams was particularly fond of the
assertion by a North Carolina Congressman: "My secretary has
as bad a case of catarrh as I ever saw, and since he has taken one
bottle of Peruna he seems like a different man."

Next in the series came Liquozone, the nostrum which had
started *Collier's* on the muckraking trail. Like numerous other
remedies, it trafficked on the public's wariness of bacilli, and
paraded as a universal antiseptic. Like Radam's Microbe Killer,
Liquozone was 99 per cent water, though devoid of red wine.
The one per cent was made up of sulphuric and sulphurous acids,
with occasionally a trace of hydrochloric or hydrobromic acid.
The risks a sick man ran in relying on Liquozone were those of
neglect; proper medical treatment was not initiated. This was a
serious charge to bring against the fake antiseptics, but it was
still not so brutally fiendish a crime as that of which "The Subtle
Poisons" were guilty.[33]

These were, Adams believed, "the most dangerous of all quack
medicines." They were less transparent in their quackery than
Peruna and Liquozone, so even highly intelligent people fell prey.
Not only did they pose an immediate danger; they also created
"enslaving appetites." What were these insidious poisons? They
fell mainly into two classes, Adams said. One was made up of
catarrh powders that contained cocaine and soothing syrups that
contained opium. Medicines of this sort might threaten sudden
death, but, almost worse, they led innocent victims into narcotic
addiction. It was a "shameful trade," Adams asserted, "that
stupefies helpless babies, and makes criminals of our young men
and harlots of our young women." The second class—nostrums

[33] "Liquozone" (Nov. 18), 20-21; "The Subtle Poisons" (Dec. 2), 16-18.

loaded with acetanilide—were nearly as dangerous. These too were habit forming and sometimes, because of a personal susceptibility or through an overdose, led to death. The names and addresses of twenty-two such victims Adams listed in a box accompanying his article. The symptoms of still-living victims of acetanilide were also grim. Adams quoted a medical report: "Stomach increasingly irritable; skin a grayish or light purplish hue; palpitation and slight enlargement of the heart; great prostration, with pains in the region of the heart; blood discolored to a chocolate hue." And yet Orangeine, one of the acetanilide mixtures in widest use, claimed that it would strengthen the heart and improve the blood. "Thus far in the patent medicine field," wrote Adams, "I have not encountered so direct and specific an inversion of the true facts."

The same statement, however, he might have applied to much of the advertising written by proprietors who were "Preying on the Incurables." "There are being exploited in this country to-day," Adams stated, "more than one hundred cures for diseases that are absolutely beyond the reach of drugs. They are owned by men who know them to be swindles, and who in private conversation will almost always evade the direct statement that their nostrums will 'cure' consumption, epilepsy, heart disease, and ailments of that nature." From two New York Sunday papers of the same date Adams clipped nearly a score of ads categorically promising to cure cancer, consumption, and fits, and reproduced these false promises in "A Fraud's Gallery." He reported the ingredients which some of these purported remedies contained, drugs like chloroform, opium, alcohol, and hashish, which could well hasten the course of the diseases they promised to eradicate. Adams concluded his discussion in somber mood: "Every man who trades in this market, whether he pockets the profits of the maker, the purveyor, or the advertiser, takes toll of blood. He may not deceive himself here, for here the patent medicine business is nakedest, most cold-hearted. Relentless greed sets the trap, and death is partner in the enterprise."[34]

In February 1906 Samuel Hopkins Adams concluded his series on "The Great American Fraud." He set to work immediately on another series, directing his detailed facts, his wit, and his scorn against the advertising doctors with their fake clinics

[34] (Jan. 13, 1906), 18-20.

and institutes. Editor Hapgood, in the meantime, kept up the pressure in his editorial columns, through his own barbed words, letters from grateful readers, and promises from newspapers which, with blinders removed, were joining the anti-nostrum crusade. Opposition evoked by the *Collier's* compaign also was quoted. The magazine was "A Yellow Weekly," said a Philadelphia editor, and its survey of the medical scene "a hideous and ghastly caricature." Medicine makers themselves felt aggrieved. One company threatened to sue *Collier's* for $50,000. The magazine did not court the suit, Hapgood replied, although it did not fear it. "The mere threat . . . will furnish the Proprietary Association of America with material for press notices: 'Another worthy medical firm grossly libeled!' "[35]

Adams, indeed, avoided the embarrassment and *Collier's* the expense which had afflicted Bok and the *Ladies' Home Journal* as a result of carelessness. No statement was printed about a nostrum in Adams' articles, unless the ingredients were listed on the label, without a chemical analysis being made. Some 264 medicines, doctors, and firms were mentioned in the ten articles which Adams wrote. Four months after the last one had appeared, Hapgood asserted, the only damage suffered had been two personal protests "filed" with the magazine and two libel suits still on the docket.[36]

By no means all the medicine men who smarted under the *Collier's* lash protested to the magazine. They had other channels through which to express their anger: the receptive pages of friendly papers, certain drug and medical journals, anonymous pamphlets. One of the latter termed Bok guilty of "gross misrepresentation" and called Hapgood "ignorant or . . . malicious." These men, the pamphleteer charged, "*want a sensation. . . .* They could not make a sensation if they merely told 'the truth and nothing but the truth.' So they simply prevaricate—affirmatively and negatively—directly and indirectly—by implication and by suppression and in every other way which serves their

[35] The last article in the original series, "The Fundamental Fakes," appeared Feb. 17, 1906, pp. 22-24, 26, 28; the second series, 37 (July 14, 1906), 12-14, 22, 24, (Aug. 4), 14-16, (Sep. 1), 16-18, and (Sep. 22), 16-18, 24, 26. The opposition was cited in 36 (Mar. 10, 1906), 8, and (Mar. 24), 22.

[36] Interview with Adams; *Collier's*, 38 (Jan. 5, 1907), 11-12. Regier, 183, says neither *Collier's* nor Adams ever lost a cent from a patent medicine libel suit.

purpose; and they have the presumption to ask reputable publishers of this country to follow their lead!"[37]

This pamphlet and others like it also included harsh words aimed at physicians who condemned proprietary medicines. *Collier's* had been pleased to cite praise received from doctors for the Adams series, although Hapgood believed, just as Bok did, that the medical profession had been tardy in assuming its full measure of responsibility in the fight against medical quackery. "So far," Hapgood editorialized, ". . . the Medical Societies have done little but pass resolutions." It was a sentiment with which even the *Journal of the American Medical Association* reluctantly agreed. Nonetheless, the remedy proprietors were not wrong in fearing both doctors and journalists and in seeing a connection between the two. During the same months that the muckraking of nostrums was at high tide, the medical profession was assuming a much more aggressive role. The American Medical Association began a campaign that would at long last eliminate suspect advertising from its *Journal*. To provide a clear basis for separating proprietaries of value from those of disreputable stamp, a Council on Pharmacy and Chemistry was created. Its members, skilled physicians, pharmacists, and chemists, set about analyzing the ingredients in proprietary products and studying their techniques of promotion. The results, good or bad, not only determined the *Journal's* advertising policy but also appeared in the news pages for all who wished to read.[38]

Nor did the Association limit its scrutiny to nostrums advertised directly to doctors. As proof of their wider concern with quackery, the American Medical Association reprinted Adams' vigorous articles in a booklet which was sold for a nominal price. In time nearly 500,000 copies of *The Great American Fraud* were bought by disturbed Americans. Doctors were also engaging in deliberate and effective pressure to achieve the goal which *Collier's* and the *Ladies' Home Journal* most desired, the action

[37] *Memoranda Concerning Recent Sensational Attacks upon Proprietary Medicines*, 1905 pamphlet in N.Y. Academy of Med. Library.

[38] *Collier's*, 36 (Nov. 18, 1905), 7; Bok to *JAMA*, 44 (May 20, 1905), 1,628-29; editorial, *ibid.*, 1,621; Fishbein, 865-76; *JAMA*, 44 (1905), 718-21; James Gordon Burrow, "The Political and Social Policies of the American Medical Association, 1901-1941" (unpublished dissertation, University of Illinois, 1956), 142-76.

which the nostrum makers most opposed: national legislation regulating the patent medicine trade.[39]

The manufacturers of proprietary remedies were right. There was a plot against them. It included not only muckraking writers and doctors, not only pharmacists and chemists. There was also a governmental contingent. State legislators were seeing the light and feeling the pressure. Members of the national House and Senate were growing increasingly concerned. In the executive branch, President Theodore Roosevelt had said a few words, and down the chain of command, in the Department of Agriculture, was a man who had said a great many more: Harvey Washington Wiley, chief of the Bureau of Chemistry. Wiley had long been pleading for a national law. While gathering material for "The Great American Fraud," Samuel Hopkins Adams had sought help from many sources, one of them Wiley's laboratory.[40] To the red-brick building in Washington also had gone many other men and women desiring to tell the American people why laws were necessary if nostrum abuses were to be restrained.

The manufacturers of proprietary remedies were right. There was a conspiracy against them. And so many American citizens were becoming party to it that the outlook at long last was favorable that a protective measure might be passed.

[39] Interview with Adams; the N.Y. Academy of Med. Library has five editions of *The Great American Fraud*, issued from Chicago and New York between 1906 and 1912.

[40] Adams to Wiley, May 29, 1905, Wiley Papers, Library of Congress; Adams to Wiley, Jan. 8, [1906], Mar. 6, 10, 16, 20, 1906, Incoming Correspondence, Bureau of Chemistry, Record Group 97, Ntl. Archives; Wiley to Adams, Mar. 26, 1906, Letterbook, *ibid.*

14

DR. WILEY'S LAW

---

*"We may extend our lines as a country; we may build
battle ships and navies and constitute great armies; but if the
health of the people is to be undermined by these concoctions
of fraudulent and bogus medicines, of what avail is it?"*

—WELDON B. HEYBURN in the Senate, 1904[1]

MEMBERS of the Proprietary Association of America, assembled in Boston for their annual meeting in September 1903, heard from the Committee on Legislation an ominous report. "At the recent Congress of Physicians and Surgeons held at the National Capital," the Committee stated, "an agitation was begun by Prof. Wiley. . . ." The chief chemist of the Department of Agriculture was not content with a national food and drug bill which limited the definition of drugs to those recognized in the United States *Pharmacopoeia*. He wanted to broaden the definition "to make it cover every kind of medicine for external or internal use," and he demanded "stringent legislation as regards proprietary medicines especially." No remedy should be sold, Dr. Wiley insisted, which did not have its formula printed on the label. No remedy containing alcohol or cocaine should be sold, he said, except by doctor's prescription.[2]

"Such a law," the Committee on Legislation advised their colleagues, "would practically destroy the sale of proprietary remedies in the United States."

For more than twenty years, efforts to secure a comprehensive national food and drug law had been made by members of the Congress. The first measure was introduced in 1879, two years before the Proprietary Association was organized. Neither this bill nor its many successors caused the makers of packaged

---

[1] *Congressional Record*, 58th Cong. 1st ses., 4,350.
[2] Proprietary Assoc., *21st Annual Report* (N.Y., 1903), 52; Wiley's speech was published as "Drugs and Their Adulterations and the Laws Relating Thereto," *Washington Medical Annals*, 2 (1903), 205-28.

[226]

remedies grave concern. There was one flurry of excitement when, during a period of widespread agrarian unrest, the Paddock bill passed the Senate in March of 1892. This measure defined drugs in a sweeping fashion, comprehending "all medicines for internal or external use." Any drug not in the *Pharmacopoeia* was to be considered adulterated if it fell below "the professed standard under which it was sold." This really meant that no medicine maker could say on his label that ingredients were present if in fact they were not, nor could he state that the remedy was made of certain listed substances and then leave actual ingredients off the list. But the proposed law did not require the proprietor to do anything. If he chose to say nothing at all on the label about ingredients, that was his privilege. There was a clause specifically protecting medicine proprietors from any disclosure of their formulas.[3]

Medicine makers professed no worry about Paddock's proposal, but they called it unconstitutional, unenforceable, and a temptation to bribery. "If the business [of manufacturing remedies] was an underhanded one," Charles Fletcher, who made Castoria, told a reporter, "or if in the preparation of these articles injurious substances were used, or if there were anything in the nature of fraud in respect to a large proportion of the well-known proprietary articles, there might be some excuse for special legislation against the manufacturers. No such excuse now exists." As for the few scamps in the business, Fletcher knew what they would do: "I can very well conceive that some one having an article containing more or less opium would feel that he was in danger if the public knew of it, and with a pliable public official it would be easily possible for him to keep this damaging fact from public knowledge."[4]

No such test of the pliability of Professor Wiley's staff occurred, because the Paddock bill did not come to a vote in the House of Representatives. Nor for another decade did a major food and drug proposal pass either the Senate or the House. Toward lesser threats, the proprietors remained alert. When a draft bill to control food and drugs in the District of Columbia

[3] Thomas A. Bailey, "Congressional Opposition to Pure Food Legislation," *Amer. Jnl. Sociology*, 36 (July 1930), 52-64; Charles W. Dunn, "Its Legislative History," *Historic Meeting to Commemorate Fortieth Anniversary of Original Food and Drugs Act* (N.Y., 1946), 9-23; *Cong. Rec.*, 45 Cong. 3 ses., 575; *ibid.*, 52 Cong. 1 ses., 713-15.

[4] *N.Y. Times*, Apr. 15, 1892.

contained an anti-patent medicine provision, the Secretary of Agriculture wrote a Senate Committee that the "active opposition" of the medicine makers was so strong, "The whole bill would probably be defeated with this clause left in." A proposal to keep advertising of "noxious medicines" from going through the mails came to naught, as did an attempt to set up a board of "medical experts" to fix standards for proprietary remedies. On the national level, however, there were few such potentially damaging blows aimed at the patent medicine industry. It was in the states that the Committee on Legislation of the Proprietary Association found its major work to do.[5]

Formula disclosure bills were the main bugaboo. Pushed by physicians and pharmacists, they appeared on state legislative dockets during the 1880's. But the Committee maneuvered so shrewdly that the proposals did not become laws. When Missouri pharmacists made the effort, "it brought down on us," said one of their number, "all the patent medicine men in the State like a flock of wild pigeons." A decline in the number of such bills in 1896 gave the medicine makers hope that their opponents, so often vanquished, had well-nigh quit the field. The joy was premature. The next year the Committee had to confess that "the crop of bills that have swept over the country during the past year has been like unto the locusts that spread over Egypt." They too were crushed, as was the next plague and the next. These victories were won, the Committee told the Association, without spending a cent for bribery or for professional lobbyists. Much of the fighting was done hand-in-hand with newspaper publishers, to whom, in 1899, a vote of thanks was formally rendered by the Proprietary Association. No public reference was made, of course, to the potent "red clause" in advertising contracts.[6]

Despite the victories, it was apparent to medicine manufacturers that rough sledding lay ahead. While rejoicing in their triumphs, the Proprietary Association in 1899 recognized that the time for concessions was near at hand. "The demand for Pure

---

[5] *Adulteration of Foods and Drugs*, 54 Cong. 2 ses., Sen. Rep. 1,458, p. 1; *Advertising Noxious Remedies through the Mails*, 48 Cong. 1 ses., House Rep. 523; *Standard Remedies*, 1 (Feb. 1915), 3-4; *Cong. Rec.*, 52 Cong. 1 ses., 8,603.

[6] *Standard Remedies*, 1 (Feb. 1915), 3-4; 2 (Mar. 1916) 17-18; 1897 Proprietary Assoc. Report, cited in Frederick J. Cullen, "The First Twenty-Five Years" (mimeographed text of address given during May 1956); Proprietary Assoc., *17th Annual Report* (N.Y., 1899), 37, 42, 197; Amer. Pharm. Assoc., *Proceedings, 1893*, 286.

Food laws is growing every year," the Committee on Legislation told the membership, "and, sooner or later, in all of the States such laws are likely to be enacted. . . . Some form of bill . . . should be agreed upon by the members of this Association and the druggists generally. It should be such a bill as will command the support of reasonable men, so that if vicious and ill-considered measures are proposed it can be successfully urged as a substitute." It should *not* be a bill like the one the North Dakota state chemist, Edwin F. Ladd, was soon to persuade his legislature to pass, a measure so severe that proprietary manufacturers set out to boycott the whole state.[7]

Increasingly beleaguered in the states, the medicine men sensed a vast new danger in Harvey Washington Wiley's 1903 pronouncement. For Wiley had developed into the single most powerful figure in the fight to secure a national food and drug law. If he was now insistent that such a law cover proprietary remedies, then the industry had indeed found a foeman worthy of their steel.

Up to this point, the parts of the proposed law which had received Wiley's vigorous attention had concerned food. Raised on a farm in southern Indiana, he had grown up eating whole wheat flour and unbolted corn meal. He had harvested the first sorghum cane and extracted the first syrup in his region. Late starting in his schooling, Wiley pursued it with intensity and variety. His study of the classics at nearby Hanover College was interrupted by a stint as corporal in the Civil War. He then read medicine briefly with a Kentucky doctor, going on to Indianapolis to receive his degree from the Indiana Medical College. Simultaneously he taught Latin and Greek at Northwestern Christian University. Dr. Wiley never practiced as a physician; it was the nutritional side of health that really intrigued him. After some months at Harvard—where he added a B.S. to his M.D.—Wiley taught chemistry at his medical alma mater before accepting, in 1874, the chair in chemistry at the newly opened Purdue. At the same time he became state chemist of Indiana. Better to equip himself for his double task, Wiley went to the heartland of food chemistry. He visited professors at German universities and spent some time at the Imperial Health

7 Proprietary Assoc., *17th Annual Report*, 41; *Amer. Druggist and Pharm. Record*, 8 (1905), 256.

Office, strengthening his passion for food analysis and his antipathy to adulteration. Back home again, Wiley put his enhanced techniques to work, at the request of the state Board of Health, to reveal the extent to which sugars and syrups sold in Indiana were adulterated with glucose.[8]

In 1883 Dr. Wiley was called to Washington as chief chemist of the Department of Agriculture. He took with him his passions and his skills. Enlarging upon the modest studies of adulterated tea and sausage initiated by his predecessor, Wiley launched the famous Bulletin 13. Through ten parts and 1,400 pages issued over a span of sixteen years, this Bulletin revealed the precise ways in which almost every article of food and drink which reached the family dinner table could be modified by "creative" chemistry. Congress, although it was not seriously interested in enacting legislation to curb abuses, was at least agreed in wanting Wiley's work of exposure to go on. In the first appropriation bill for the Department of Agriculture as an executive department, money was provided to "extend and continue" the study of adulteration. Year by year this authorization was repeated, and in 1894 Congress asked the Secretary of Agriculture to report the results of departmental analyses citing the brand names of products.[9]

Five years later Congress—or, at least, one Senator—took another important step. In the years since the Paddock bill, as Wiley later put it, "Pure food bills in the Senate had been regularly committed to the Committee on Manufactures, much as an infant would be left to starve in a barren room." In 1899 a new man on the committee, William E. Mason of Illinois, instigated the first hearings which either House of Congress had held on the pure food question. Throughout nearly a year, Mason's committee took testimony for fifty-one days in three cities from 196 witnesses. Wiley was not only the first witness. He was scientific adviser to the committee, he analyzed 438 food samples submitted to him, and he drafted the bill which Mason introduced into the Senate. "I think if there is any one man in this country,"

[8] Harvey W. Wiley, *An Autobiography* (Indianapolis, 1930), 13-153; Oscar E. Anderson, Jr., *The Health of a Nation, Harvey W. Wiley and the Fight for Pure Food* (Chicago, 1958), 1-31.
[9] Wiley, *Autobiography*, 154-77; Gustavus A. Weber, *The Food, Drug, and Insecticide Administration* (Institute for Govt. Research, Service Monographs of the U.S. Govt., No. 50, Balt., 1928), 2-4.

Mason told his colleagues, "who deserves great credit for trying to furnish the facts for the benefit of the people of this country," that man is Harvey Washington Wiley.[10]

Mason's bill got nowhere, but as the 20th century opened, the hopes of pure food advocates were brightening. Wiley's bulletins and similar attacks upon adulteration by state chemists were having a cumulative effect. Newspaper reports of the Senate hearings aroused public interest. The major segments of the industries which might be controlled by a national law were joining with federal and state officials, and with representatives from organizations as diverse as the American Chemical Society and the WCTU, in National Pure Food and Drug Congresses, seeking to draft a proposed bill that might be mutually agreeable.[11] The temper of the times was changing. To protect the national health by a broad-gauge national law seemed less a violation of the Constitution than it once had seemed. Especially after ebullient Theodore Roosevelt ascended to the presidency, moving the Progressive spirit into the White House, did pure food reformers begin to take cheer.

Wiley increased the pace of his activity. Raised in an evangelical home, the chief chemist applied his moral fervor to the pure food crusade. The science of his bulletins was buttressed by the passion of his oratory. Like an itinerant preacher, he stumped up and down the country, and every woman's club rostrum was a pulpit. His message was not primarily one of fear, for he did not believe that adulteration posed a grave danger to the public health. But his sense of righteousness was offended by fraud, and he inveighed against adulterators as economic cheats. When God's bounty was tampered with, the label at least should say so.[12]

"Dr. Wiley is built on large lines," a journalist wrote of him. "He is tall and massive of stature, with a big head firmly poised above a pair of titanic shoulders. His hair never stays in order, but masses itself forward on both sides of the forehead, giving him at times a somewhat uncouth appearance. The penetrating

[10] Wiley, *Autobiography*, 224; *Adulteration of Food Products*, 56 Cong. 1 ses., Sen. Rep. 516; *Cong. Rec.*, 56 Cong. 1 ses., 4,963.

[11] *Journal of Proceedings of the National Pure Food and Drug Congress Held in . . . Washington, D.C.* (Wash., 1898); *Report of the Proceedings of the Second Annual Convention of the National Pure Food and Drug Congress* (Wash., 1899). The Proprietary Association was represented.

[12] Based on Wiley's *Autobiography* and impressions gained from correspondence in the Wiley Papers, Manuscript Div., Library of Congress.

glance of his rather small eyes, the large and roughly modeled nose, and the severe lines of his mouth add to this impression." Wiley had a light touch and a warm heart. His wit was the talk of the banquet circuit, and he had a gift for clever doggerel. A bachelor, he was free to move about, and he was an ardent club-man, an eager dinner guest. Wiley had the knack of eliciting tremendous loyalty, and his personal associations, tending toward the conspiratorial, were to be as important as his public speaking in the ultimate success of a pure food bill. Endowed with tremendous energy, he could operate without tiring on several fronts at once.[13]

Wiley had a flair for the dramatic and was something of an innovator. At Purdue he had been officially reprimanded for riding a bicycle on campus, and in Washington he was the third man to drive a car, the first to suffer a collision. He could turn a Congressional hearing into high drama by whipping out three bottles of pure Georgia cane syrup which he had seen made, so that he could personally testify they contained no salicylic acid, no glucose. Even Wiley's research could be theatrical. In 1902 he set up an experiment designed to test the effect of various preservatives upon the health of twelve robust young men who worked in the Department of Agriculture. Long before any results were in, the whole nation knew about and worried over the fate of the "Poison Squad."[14]

Congress reacted to the developing pressures. During 1902 both the Senate and the House held hearings on food and drug bills, and in both hearings the chief chemist was a star performer. In December the House bill passed, but Porter J. McCumber of North Dakota strove in vain, during the dying days of the session, to bring the Senate measure from committee to the floor. "I can now see no possible way to get consideration for it," he asserted, "and yet I do not believe there is any bill in which the public is more interested. . . . It seems to me we ought to have, in the course of two years, one hour or two hours in which to consider a bill that has been the first one on the Calendar."[15]

[13] *Ibid.*; the quotation is from Edwin Björkman, "Our Debt to Dr. Wiley," *World's Work*, 19 (1910), 12,443.

[14] Wiley, *Autobiography*, 156, 215-20; Charles T. Tittman, "Harvey Washington Wiley, 1844-1930," *Cosmos Club Bull.*, 5 (May 1952), 2-5; *Adulteration, Etc., of Foods, Etc.*," 57 Cong. 1 ses., Sen. Rep. 972, 112-14. Wiley himself objected to the term "Poison Squad."

[15] *Ibid.*; *Hearings before the Committee on Interstate and Foreign Commerce*

The pressure of many interests had been brought upon Senators to produce this stalemate. Some patent medicine makers viewed any pure food and drug measure with jaundiced eye, but the abortive bill would not have placed their own products in immediate jeopardy. The bill that had passed the House, in accord with the recommendation of the Pure Food and Drug Congresses, limited the coverage of drugs to those in the *Pharmacopoeia*. Upon this definition the Proprietary Association, which was represented in the Congresses, could lay its blessing.[16] The medicine men, indeed, had faired most fortunately thus far amid the quickening of interest in legislation by some members of Congress. Food and liquor had held the center of the stage. During several protracted hearings and some debate in both Houses, the references to patent medicines could be numbered on the fingers of one hand, and these comments were casual and oblique.[17] Nonetheless, the Committee on Legislation of the Proprietary Association was quite right in viewing with grave alarm Dr. Wiley's criticism of patent medicines in his speech before Washington physicians. This betokened a turning of the tide.

Wiley had never been a friend of quackery. As a boy he had known of a neighborhood nostrum dispensed to quiet malarial chills. As chief chemist in Washington he had collected "bales of advertising of fraudulent remedies." His bureau had tested several "lost manhood" treatments for the Post Office Department and had investigated suspicious remedies shipped in from overseas. Wiley's main concern, however, had been with fraudulent food, and this had monopolized his research time and public oratory. Now, in joining his voice to those already decrying patent medicines, Wiley was giving a sort of governmental sanction to the criticism. As the main champion in the fight for a national law, he was lending his personal prestige to the suggestion that patent medicines should be regulated by such a law. His adherence to the anti-nostrum crusade was no temporary allegiance. Wiley spoke out against patent medicines again and

---

of the House of Representatives on The Pure-Food Bills (57 Cong. 1 ses., 1902); *Cong. Rec.*, 57 Cong. 2 ses., 457-58, 2,647, 2,964-67. The best available discussion and analysis of the Congressional battle leading to the 1906 law is in Anderson, 120-96.

16 Proprietary Assoc., *22nd Annual Report* (N.Y., 1904), 93-99.

17 See, for example, *Adulteration of Food Products*, 56 Cong. 1 ses., Sen. Rep. 516, pp. 193-95, 484.

again, even at the International Congress of Applied Chemistry in Berlin. On March 1, 1903, he set up, within the Bureau of Chemistry, a drug laboratory which devoted increasing attention to the analysis of proprietary remedies.[18]

It would be giving one man too great credit to say that Wiley's anti-nostrum addresses loosed the flood of criticism which soon flowed forth across the land. The American Medical Association's thorough house-cleaning of its *Journal's* advertising, Bok's revived attack on patent medicines in the *Ladies' Home Journal*, and, especially, Hapgood's fresh campaign in *Collier's* with Samuel Hopkins Adams as his leading general—all these events would have taken place in any case. With a spirit of exposure in the air and the need for revelations so patent in the nostrum field, muckraking was inevitable. Without Wiley's lead and help, however, the task of exposure would have been more difficult.

Adams went to Wiley at the very start of his researches, and the chemist gave the reporter counsel, lent him clippings, and read drafts of his articles. The two men became firm friends and co-conspirators regarding patent medicine features of the food and drug bill. Bok too sought Wiley's advice and persuaded the chief chemist to write an article on headache powders. When the American Medical Association set up its Council on Pharmacy and Chemistry, Wiley was made a member. His laboratory helped in testing medicines advertised to doctors, and in 1905 Wiley and the Association officers managed to get the relationship between the Bureau and the Council put on a semi-official basis. From these contacts, Wiley was enabled to call the timing of powerful AMA lobbying efforts in behalf of a food and drug bill.[19]

Wherever there might be support for the kind of law he wanted, there Wiley was active. "He had become the commander of a heterogeneous army bound together in a curious amalgam of self-interest and principle." He kept in close touch with agricultural chemists in the states. He corresponded with trade

[18] Wiley, *Autobiography*, 53, 205; manuscript entitled "Federal Control of Drugs," Misc. Papers, III, Bur. of Chem. Records, Record Group 97, Ntl. Archives; speech drafts in Wiley Papers, boxes 188-190, Library of Congress; Weber, 5; Lyman F. Kebler to Wiley, Nov. 30 and Dec. 15, 1902, Bur. of Chem., Incoming Corres., RG 97, Ntl. Archives.

[19] Adams to Wiley, May 29, 1905, Wiley Papers, Library of Congress; *ibid.*, Jan. 8 [1906], Mar. 6, 16, 20, 24, 1906, Bur. of Chem., Incoming Corres., RG 97, Ntl. Archives; Wiley to Adams, Mar. 26, 1906, Letterbook, Bur. of Chem., General Corres.; Bok to Wiley, Apr. 27, Oct. 15, 1906, Bur. of Chem., Incoming Corres.

editors and trade association officials who had come to recognize
the need for protective legislation. He helped devise activities for
the Pure Food Committee of the General Federation of Women's
Clubs. Most significantly of all, Wiley continued to work hand
in glove with members of the House and Senate who favored a
rigorous law.[20]

The expanded public criticism of patent medicines began to
make its weight felt early in 1904. A House bill, passed in
January, still covered no drugs but those of the *Pharmacopoeia*.
But the bill presented by McCumber to the Senate defined drugs
in a sweeping way and stated that any drug was adulterated
which fell below the professed standard under which it was sold.
For the first time in a Congressional hearing, proprietary
remedies were extensively debated. Manufacturers and some
wholesalers objected strenuously to the mere mention in the draft
bill of their wares, while anti-nostrum spokesmen feared that the
phraseology was too fuzzy for effective regulation. Senator Mc-
Cumber, believing the opposition to this clause might jeopardize
the whole bill, sought to retreat, but his colleague, Weldon Heyburn from Idaho, prevented it, and the bill went to the Senate
floor with the expanded drug definition. Lobbying pressures
from industries, now including the drug trade, were still too
powerful to be denied. McCumber and Heyburn could not get
the Senate to take up the measure. Heyburn's last two efforts,
indeed, were cut off in mid-sentence. And so the bill died.[21]

The pure food advocates were disheartened but they did not
falter. One major task of recruitment still faced them. President Roosevelt, for all his reforming zeal, had not yet spoken out
in behalf of a food and drug law. Perhaps the reason was, as

[20] R. M. Allen, Ky. chemist, to Wiley, Feb. 23, May 2, Dec. 5, 1904;
A. C. Morrison, Amer. Baking Powder Assoc., to Wiley, June 11, 24, 30, 1902,
Apr. 5, Dec. 22, 1905, Bur. of Chem., Incoming Corres.; F. N. Barrett, *Amer.
Grocer*, to Wiley, Apr. 24, May 21, June 3, 1902, Feb. 1, Mar. 3, 16, 1904;
Gaswell A. Mayo, *Amer. Druggist*, to Kebler, Oct. 27, 1904; numerous letters to
Wiley from Alice Lakey, chrmn., Pure Food Committee of the General Fed. of
Women's Clubs; Hepburn to Wiley, Mar. 2, 3, 1902, Nov. 30, Dec. 5, 1903;
Heyburn to Wiley, Feb. 11, Apr. 15, 29, May 2, July 7, 28, Nov. 20, 1904,
Apr. 10, Dec. 30, 1905, Bur. of Chem., Incoming Corres., RG 97, Ntl. Archives;
Annals of the Amer. Acad. of Pol. and Social Science, 28 (1906), 296-97. The
quotation is from Anderson, 147.
[21] *Adulteration of Foods, Etc.*, 58 Cong. 2 ses., Sen. Rep. 1,209; *Cong. Rec.*,
58 Cong. 2 ses., 4,349-50; 3 ses., 126-27, 3,754-55, 3,845-47, 3,852-55, 3,943-
44; Proprietary Assoc., *22nd Annual Report*, 93-99; Edward Lowry, "The
Senate Plot against Pure Food," *World's Work*, 10 (1905), 6,215-17; *Ntl.
Druggist*, 35 (1905), 54.

Samuel Hopkins Adams believed, that pure food "wasn't political enough to interest him, at least he thought it wasn't." Senator Heyburn had sought to persuade him, and had then urged Wiley to use his blandishments. The chemist had talked with the President and had been instrumental in arranging a visit from a committee of six of the most persuasive pure food advocates. Roosevelt was sympathetic. Nine months later, in November 1905, when the President had not yet made a public statement, the committee called at the White House again. This time he promised that he would endorse pure food legislation in his annual message. The next month Roosevelt devoted three sentences to the matter: "I recommend that a law be enacted to regulate interstate commerce in misbranded and adulterated foods, drinks, and drugs. Such law would protect legitimate manufacture and commerce, and would tend to secure the health and welfare of the consuming public. Traffic in foodstuffs which have been debased or adulterated so as to injure health or to deceive purchasers should be forbidden."[22]

The President did not mention patent medicines, but both reformers and proprietors felt sure that he had them in mind. He had acquiesced in a decided stepping-up by the Post Office Department of its attacks against medical frauds. He had agreed to the Treasury Department order which plagued the Hostetters, expanding the internal revenue taxes levied on whiskey to cover patent medicines containing a high proportion of alcohol. When Roosevelt sent his brief message to Congress, Adams' first *Collier's* series was at the halfway point. Public excitement was rising.[23]

The pressure on the medicine men had begun to tell. The *National Druggist* of St. Louis, at the most violent extreme, increased the tempo of its strident attacks. Several Proprietary Association stalwarts, on the other hand, felt that concession was called for. Charles Stowell told the annual meeting that the Ayer firm was going to print on the labels of all its remedies the complete formulas, using plain English and giving exact quantities.

[22] Interview with Adams; Heyburn to Wiley, Nov. 20, 1904, Bur. of Chem., Incoming Corres., RG 97, Ntl. Archives; Sullivan, *Our Times*, II, 530; Charles A. L. Reed to Wiley, Oct. 25, 1905, Bur. of Chem., Incoming Corres.; *Cong. Rec.*, 59 Cong. 1 ses., 102.

[23] "Mr. Roosevelt's Views on 'Patent Medicines,'" *Ladies' Home Jnl.*, 23 (April 1906), 21; *Report of the President's Homes Commission*, 60 Cong. 2 ses., Sen. Doc. 644, pp. 281-83.

He pleaded with other proprietors to join him. A few did, but the majority refrained. The breach was widened when Stowell and others opposed the launching of a vigorous newspaper campaign to fight hostile legislation. Even the main wing of the Association was forced to give some ground. They forsook their adamant opposition to a national bill that controlled proprietary remedies in any way and centered their ire on versions sponsored by the Wiley-led reformers. "If the Federal Government should regulate Inter-state traffic in drugs on the basis of their therapeutic value," the Committee on Legislation inquired rhetorically, "why not regulate traffic in theology, by excluding from transportation, all theological books which Dr. Wiley and his assistants, upon examination, should find to be 'misleading in any particular'?" At a special secret meeting early in December 1905, the Proprietary Association called for an end to nostrums containing narcotics and remedies over-loaded with alcohol. They urged their Committee on Legislation to work for a law that would exercise restraint in these respects. The Association also advised its members to avoid promotion inflated with falsehood. This led a drug trade journal which long had fought nostrum abuses to editorialize: "The warning to the members . . . to be more guarded in their published claims is unfortunately not so valuable now as it would have been a year or even six months ago."[24]

There was evidence that a feeling of pressure had helped to motivate the more compromising position. Well represented at the Association's meeting were officers of firms which the muckrakers had handled savagely. These men displayed a hesitancy in talking to newspaper men which looked to one reporter "like real fear."[25]

Hardly had the Proprietary Association adjourned its meeting in New York when the new Congress convened in Washington. The next day after hearing Roosevelt's plea for action, Senator Heyburn reintroduced his pure food and drug measure. This time the Senate dared not give the bill the silent treatment. During January and February the debates were long and heated.

[24] *Ntl. Druggist*, 35 (1905), 35-56; [Henry R. Strong], *The Arrogance of Ethics* (St. Louis, 1905: reprinted from *Ntl. Druggist*); *Amer. Druggist and Pharm. Record*, 46 (1905), 255-56; 47 (1905), 244, 315; *Druggists Circular*, 49 (1905), 311; Proprietary Assoc., *23rd Annual Report* (N.Y., 1905), 34; *Bull. Pharm.*, 20 (1906), 5.

[25] *Amer. Druggist and Pharm. Record*, 47 (1905), 315.

Patent medicines were a central theme. McCumber and Heyburn, using material furnished them by Wiley, castigated the nostrum evil, but they differed somewhat in their views as to how tightly the bill would control therapeutic claims made on medicine labels. The chief champion for the proprietary interests was J. A. Hemenway of Indiana, a friend of A. R. Beardsley, treasurer of the Miles Medical Company and leading figure in the Proprietary Association. Hemenway did not want to kill the measure, he said, but to modify it. He cited Beardsley's opposition to a law which would attack "statements made in good faith regarding the therapeutic qualities of medicine or its ingredients." McCumber and Heyburn objected to a Hemenway amendment but finally accepted a modification of it, as they did other Senatorial suggestions that seriously crippled the patent medicine provisions of the bill. Having striven in vain for years even to get a measure to the floor, the Senators from North Dakota and Idaho compromised where necessary in the hope that at last some bill might be accepted by their colleagues. When the moment approached Heyburn could scarcely believe it. Senator Albert J. Beveridge of Indiana recalled the circumstances:

"The Senate was in a jam and public feeling had become intense. Aldrich [Republican leader in the Senate, to whom Roosevelt had made a personal appeal to withdraw his opposition to the bill] came to me one afternoon and said: 'Tell Heyburn if he asks consideration for the Pure Food bill there will be no objection.' (Some fight was going on between us [Progressives] and the Old Guard, and this was obviously a manoeuvre, to save something else they thought more important; I think perhaps they counted on killing the Pure Food bill in the House later. . . .) So I went to Heyburn and told him to bring up the Pure Food bill instantly and the Old Guard would not block him. Heyburn could not believe it and said he was tired of being made a fool of by asking useless consideration which he had asked so many times before. However, I insisted. . . . I told Heyburn there was no time to waste, and to act without any questions. . . . Finally, about the middle of the afternoon, Heyburn got up. . . ."[26]

[26] *Cong. Rec.*, 59 Cong. 1 ses., 140-2,773 *passim; Chicago Tribune*, Feb. 21, 22, 1906; Beveridge cited in Sullivan, *Our Times*, II, 533-34.

On February 21, 1906, with Wiley sitting in the balcony, the pure food and drug bill passed the Senate. Hemenway joined Heyburn in voting for the measure.[27]

If staunch opponents of patent medicines were not happy with the terms, they rejoiced that at least the Senate had done something and hoped that the stronger anti nostrum provisions in the House bill might eventually prevail. But would the House act at all? Advocates of the bill began to wonder as the days went by. Then a discouraging sign was noted. Lobbyists for interests fighting restrictive legislation were checking out of their hotels and leaving town. A reporter learned from a leading House Republican the decision to keep the bill from coming to debate during that session.[28]

If death by inaction was the sentence intended for the pure food and drug bill by its enemies, fate entered in to reverse the judgment. The circumstances had nothing to do with patent medicines, but they certainly helped to achieve tighter drug provisions in the final bill. A book was published by an obscure Socialist writer named Upton Sinclair. He had gone to Chicago to write a tract in fictional form about the miserable life of immigrants who labored in the packing houses. He had aimed at people's hearts, as he said, but he had hit their stomachs. For *The Jungle* incidentally described the filthy conditions under which America's meat was processed, how inspectors blinked while tubercular carcasses were brought back into the line, how rats and the poisoned bread put out to catch them were ground up with meat for public consumption, how employees now and then slipped into steamy vats and next went forth into the world as Durham's Pure Leaf Lard. The public was staggered, and the sale of meat fell by half. Roosevelt was angry. When an investigation revealed that Sinclair had not overdrawn the case, the President insisted that Congress act to insure clean meat and pure food for the American people.[29]

The sense of urgency influenced the drug clauses in the bill brought to the floor of the House by the Committee on Interstate

[27] *Cong. Rec.*, 59 Cong. 1 ses., 2,773; Wiley, *Autobiography*, 229.
[28] Sullivan, II, 534. This may not have been so; Speaker Cannon's position was not fully clear. Anderson, 188.
[29] *Ibid.*, 471-83, 535-52; Sinclair, *The Jungle* (N.Y., 1906).

and Foreign Commerce. Indeed, James R. Mann, a physician from Illinois, who with William P. Hepburn of Iowa had the bill in charge, felt the time was ripe for a grandstand play. He wrote into the measure, with Wiley's and Adams' help, the toughest anti-patent medicine provisions that any draft ever had contained. Among other things, the bill would require medical labeling to report the presence and quantity of alcohol, opium, cocaine, "or other poisonous substances." Medicine makers, at the mere thought of what Wiley might deem to be poison, broke out in a cold sweat. "The officers of the proprietary association started at once for Washington," as Mann narrated the tale. "They insisted that the provision was absolutely new, had been adopted without any hearings, and would be ruinous to their business if enacted into law. Our subcommittee gave them courteous, full and patient hearing. They presented to us an amendment."[30]

The manufacturers' proposal would require the listing on labels of certain specified drugs if they were present above a certain minimum amount. Modeled after a Massachusetts law, this plan represented the greatest concession yet made by the Proprietary Association. But Wiley did not think much of it. "The bill might as well not contain anything in regard to patent medicines," he wrote Mann after an interview with fifteen medicine makers, "as to allow the quantities mentioned in the proposed amendment to be used without notice. . . . It would simply make the bill a joke." He did feel it might be shrewd to change the "other poisonous substances" to a specific list. Thus Wiley the crusader urged upon Mann the legislator some modification, but he was fearful, nonetheless, that Mann might yield too much. The medicine proprietors, Wiley wrote to Adams, "I think will get their amendment . . . practically just as they have written it." In conference and letter Wiley kept supplying Mann with clippings, nostrum analyses, and other data, and Adams came to Washington to help keep the Illinois Congressman staunch for a strongly worded bill.[31]

Mann went on with his grand strategy. He seemed to yield by accepting a weaker patent medicine amendment, knowing all

[30] *Cong. Rec.*, 59 Cong. 1 ses., 8,889-9,801 *passim*, with Mann explaining his strategy especially at 8,892-93 and 9,739-40.

[31] *Ibid.*; Wiley to Mann, Mar. 19, 23, 29, Apr. 2, 1906; Wiley to Adams, Mar. 26, 1906, Letterbooks, Bur. of Chem., General Corres., RG 97, Ntl. Archives; Adams interview.

the time that his committee was willing to support more vigorous controls when the moment seemed propitious to reinsert them in the bill. News of this scheme leaked out, however, when a newspaper reporter overheard Mann explaining it to Adams.

The revelation stirred the medicine makers to strenuous action with respect to a master plan of their own. "Not daring to fight this bill in the open," Mann charged on the floor of the House, "not daring to say that they were afraid to state the quantity of narcotics in their drugs, they have falsified in some way about this bill and endeavored to give the country the impression that it was the Senate bill which provided for labeling the narcotics . . . and that it was the House bill that proposed to strike it out, when, as a matter of fact, the Senate bill has nothing upon the subject, and it was the House committee which put it in." This trick was remarkably effective. Many tried and true supporters of rigorous legislation were fooled. Pro-pure food newspapers, like the *New York Tribune*, pleaded in editorials to pass the Senate bill and quash the House version. Doctors wrote letters to the same effect. Even officials of the American Medical Association were briefly befuddled. But Mann and Hepburn managed to keep House members from succumbing to this complete reversal of the facts.[32]

The House debate in June made clear how much wider was the awareness of the nostrum menace than it had been five years, even a year, before. To be sure, no attention need be given meat, for a separate inspection bill had recently passed the House. There was still much discussion about the food, whiskey, and administrative provisions of the bill. An adamant states rights minority reiterated their opposition to any national law: "The Federal Government," said a Georgian, "was not created for the purpose of cutting your toe nails or corns." Some suspicion of Wiley and the sophisticated science he stood for remained: "I believe," asserted the same Congressman, "there are millions of old women, white and black, who know more about good victuals and good eating than my friend Doctor Wiley and all his apothecary shop." But the main theme of the House debate was the patent medicine evil. "Of all the great civilized nations of the earth," stated a Texan, "the United States is about the only one that has not a strict law on the subject." Even Russia did, he

[32] *Cong. Rec.*, 59 Cong. 1 ses., 8,892-93 and 9,739-40; *N.Y. Tribune*, June 21, 1906.

added. For every illness caused by unclean meat, insisted another member, there were a hundred cases of poisoning and death from nostrums. More than that, tainted meat was not habit-forming. Congressmen were chided for giving testimonials to proprietary concerns. "Indeed," jibed a member, "Peruna seems to be the favorite Congressional drink." The anti-nostrum provisions, asserted the Congressman from Samuel Hopkins Adams' home district, were "the most important subjects of the bill." Others expressed the same sentiment, and the name of Adams came frequently into the debate. Mann acknowledged with appreciation that the list of dangerous drugs which must be named on medicine labels had been drawn up with the journalist's assistance.[33]

Many uncomplimentary adjectives, on the other hand, were hurled at the heads of the medicine makers, who seemed to have no champion on the floor brave enough to speak out. On June 23 the bill passed the House, with only the states-righters casting negative votes. The House and Senate reconciled their different versions in conference, and the nostrum provisions emerged more stringent than they had been in either bill. On June 30 Theodore Roosevelt put his signature to the Pure Food and Drugs Act.[34]

Dr. Wiley sought to get the pen with which the President signed, but found that Senator Heyburn had put his name in first. This priority was not the one that counted most. In a tribute that in American annals is extremely rare, this piece of legislation came to bear, not Heyburn's name, nor that of any other member of the Senate or the House who had worked so diligently. The act became known as the Wiley law. Heyburn himself concurred in such recognition. Even before the law was passed he had written the chemist: "You may rely upon it that for all time your name will be closely associated with . . . any 'Pure food' legislation whatsoever named." On the House side, Mann had ended his remarks before the vote on the conference report with praise of Wiley. Wiley returned the compliment, saying that to Mann "the principal credit must be given." The chief chemist also expressed appreciation for the unflagging zeal of other Congressional stal-

---

[33] *Cong. Rec.*, 59 Cong. 1 ses., 8,889-9,801.

[34] In the House bill the amount of alcohol could be withheld from the label if it did not exceed the quantity required as a solvent or preservative for the active ingredients. Even this exception was eliminated in conference with the Senate.

warts. He recognized the crucial importance of the publication of Sinclair's *The Jungle*. The major influences upon Congress that brought success, Wiley believed, were two: "the medical profession, the American Medical Association with 140,000 members, and the 700 women's clubs in the country."[35]

Almost all segments of opinion greeted the new law with approval. The pure food and drug advocates were too optimistic in their appraisal. As a result of the act, editorialized the *New York Times*, "the purity and honesty of the food and medicines of the people are guaranteed." The patent medicine provisions, predicted the *Nation*, would deal a "death-blow" to harmful nostrums. The law was "far better in every respect," asserted the *Journal of the American Medical Association*, than its most ardent supporters could have hoped. "Certainly the powerful Proprietary Association of America has not proved to be so powerful after all."[36]

Yet the Proprietary Association was not unhappy. Frank J. Cheney, its president, thought it was "silly" to require him to put a new label on Hall's Catarrh Cure just because it contained "a trifling amount of alcohol." But the general effect of the law, he said, would be good. "People generally will reason, and reason correctly, that preparations which come up to the requirements of a congressional enactment must be all right, or, certainly, that they are not harmful or dangerous." Even the *National Druggist*, most acrimonious foe of legislation, termed the final result "not such a terrible thing after all." "But let it not be supposed," the editor added, "that the law would have been enacted in its present rather innocuous form but for hard, intelligent and most tactful work on the part of the representatives of the interests it is intended to regulate."[37]

What did the new Wiley act have to say about proprietary remedies? It required that the labels which manufacturers put

[35] William Loeb, Jr., Roosevelt's secretary, to Thomas R. Shipp, July 12, 1906, Wiley Papers, box 60, Library of Congress; Heyburn to Wiley, Dec. 30, 1905, Bur. of Chem., Incoming Corres., RG 97, Ntl. Archives; *Cong. Rec.*, 59 Cong. 1 ses., 9,740; manuscript of Wiley address before Atlas Club, Chicago, Dec. 14, 1906, Wiley, Papers, box 61; Wiley, "The Value of the Food and Drug Act to the Consumer," *Chautauquan Daily*, July 29, 1908, clipping in Wiley Papers, box 191; Anderson's judicious appraisal of Wiley's role is given at 195-96.

[36] *N.Y. Times*, July 1, 1906; *Nation*, 82 (1906), 523; *JAMA*, 47 (1906), 42, 116.

[37] *Ntl. Druggist*, 36 (1906), 210, 372.

upon their medicines must tell the truth—not the whole truth, but the truth in certain significant respects. The presence and amount of certain dangerous drugs—alcohol, the opiates, chloral hydrate, acetanilide, and several others—must always be stated on the package. Other ingredients need not be named unless the proprietor wished to, but if he did choose to indicate that certain substances were present, they must be there, and in the quantity claimed. If he asserted that certain ingredients were not present—denying that a nostrum contained opium was a favorite promotional device—then they must in fact be missing. As the law put it, a remedy was adulterated "If its strength or purity fall below the professed standard under which it is sold." If a proprietor could not beguile consumers with respect to ingredients, neither could he deceive in other respects or be guilty of misbranding. He could not misinform about the state, territory, or country in which his product was made. Nor, indeed, could he put upon his label "any statement, design, or device" regarding the medicine or its ingredients which was "false or misleading in any particular."[38]

Keep quiet on the label or do not lie, the law said. Respecting the listed dangerous drugs, silence was forbidden. Thus the act did not strike a blow against self-medication, but sought to make it safer. It was based on a favorite Progressive assumption, an assumption as old as American independence, that the average man was intelligent enough to plot his own course and would avoid risks if he was aware of them.

Time was to reveal serious shortcomings in the 1906 law and to challenge optimism about the common man's capacity. Nonetheless, the Pure Food and Drugs Act marks a mighty turning point in patent medicine history. For more than a century, American proprietors had been free to mix whatever they wanted and promote it however they wished. In such an atmosphere "the toadstool millionaires" had flourished. Now, with Dr. Wiley's law, the concept of control over proprietary remedy promotion was firmly written into national policy.

[38] Ch. 3,915, 34 Stat. 768.

PART FIVE

EPILOUGE

15

HALF A CENTURY LATER

"I know it is common to speak of the 'good old days' of snake oil and soothing syrup as though they were gone forever. The amazing fact is that to a very great extent those good old days, so-called, are still with us."

—COMMISSIONER GEORGE P. LARRICK,
Food and Drug Administration, 1955[1]

PRIOR to 1906, the only inhibition upon American patent medicine proprietors, except for an occasional critical article, was self-restraint. This did not prove an adequate force for the protection of the medicine-consuming public. In the half-century since 1906, the Pure Food and Drugs Act and subsequent legislation have provided agencies of the federal government with increasingly rigorous controls over drugs and devices for self-medication. Henry T. Helmbold and his 19th-century competitors would be astounded at the restraints placed upon the freedom of action of their successors. Yet, despite all the differences between the 1860's and the 1960's in the science of medicine and in the laws of medication, there are, in pseudo-medicine, disturbingly strong continuities. Quackery is not only not vanquished; never in previous history—regulatory officials are the first to say it—has medical quackery been such a big business as now.

This sad fact does not minimize the significance of federal regulation. There is today a vast proprietary industry that operates within the law. Before 1906 the most respectable proprietors considered it not improper to market medicines containing unmentioned narcotics—like Mrs. Winslow's Soothing Syrup—or a high proportion of alcohol—like Hostetter's Bitters. Nor did they feel any great compulsion to restrain curative claims. One of Lydia E. Pinkham's sons, surveying the possibilities of a New

[1] "Our Unfinished Business," *Food Drug Cosmetic Law Journal*, 10 (1955), 168.

York market, wrote home suggesting that "Kidney Complaints" be added to the ailments listed in their pamphlets, "as about half of the people out here are either troubled with . . . [them] or else they think they are."[2] Today major producers of remedies for over-the-counter sale would not think of including powerful drugs not mentioned on the label, or of letting the state of the market dictate the diseases for which their remedies are treatments. To be sure, when Asian flu reached epidemic proportions several years ago, the Food and Drug Administration and the Federal Trade Commission did find it necessary to issue a public warning to advertisers of aspirins, cough syrups, and ointments not to exaggerate how firmly these American proprietaries could close with the Oriental invader.[3] But kidney disease or cancer would not find its way into the advertising of large-scale proprietary manufacturers today.

The Proprietary Association, which had fought during the first years of the century the enactment of stringent legislation, came to boast that few of its members had lost contests with the government.[4] Voluntary compliance was proving profitable. Sales were booming. The public, encouraged by the existence of a law to think self-medication safe, were buying more proprietaries than ever. By battling the unscrupulous nostrum maker, the government agency was an ally of the more respectable proprietor, reducing his competition. What happened in the aftermath of 1906 was to happen again after the extensive revision of the law in New Deal days. Major producers, opposed to a new law at first,[5] were to accept the 1938 act and find it profitable. There still sometimes appears a lack of circumspection in the advertising practices of some of the most respectable firms in the proprietary industry. There are occasional differences of opinion between major proprietors and regulatory officials about interpretations of the various laws. The head of the FDA's Division of Medicine, in addressing the Proprietary Association during 1958, could state: "There are still too many proprietary products

2 Burton, *Lydia Pinkham Is Her Name*, 89.
3 *FDCLJ*, 12 (1957), 681-82.
4 *Standard Remedies*, 1 (Sep. 1915), 8-9.
5 *Ibid.*, 20 (July 1933), 2; the requirements today for membership in the Proprietary Association and the organization's Code of Ethical Practices in Proprietary Advertising Copy reveal the acceptance of the 1938 law by the major manufacturers.

not acceptable for advertising in first-rate medical journals."[6] But federal agencies and major proprietors are today both on the same side in decrying the really vicious practices of unmitigated quacks.

Another difference between 1906 and today is that the unscrupulous nostrum promoter could not then be caught and punished for his transgressions, and now he can be. In their constant warfare against quackery, the Food and Drug Administration, the Federal Trade Commission, and the Post Office Department do win significant battles.

The FDA can act against drug, device, food, or cosmetic labeling if it bears misleading therapeutic claims, and the courts have approved the agency's ever more elastic definition of what labeling means. Posters in a drugstore may become labeling, and the oral claims of door-to-door salesmen may cause their wares to be misbranded. An important weapon against quackery is the 1938 law's provision that drug labels must bear adequate directions for use. Again because of elastic interpretation, this provision permits the FDA to exercise some influence over drug advertising, a province which Congress in 1938 withheld from the FDA and gave for policing to the FTC. Nonetheless, if a proprietor's advertisement should claim that his pill can cure arthritis, the label on the pillbox must state—as, of course, cannot be genuinely done—just how the pills are to be taken to accomplish the cure. The law also forbids the marketing of a new drug until the FDA has approved tests by the producer demonstrating its safety: this clause has helped the agency to squelch promotions like the vending of pega palo, a Dominican vine, for restoring virility. Many drugs are so powerful that they are considered safe for use only upon the prescription of a physician; a proprietor who includes such a drug in his formula for direct sale to the public violates the law and runs into trouble with the FDA.[7]

[6] Albert B. Holland, "Who Will Be First?" *FDCLJ*, 13 (1958), 472.

[7] The act is reprinted, with the principal regulations relating to it, in Vincent A. Kleinfeld and Charles Wesley Dunn, *Federal Food, Drug, and Cosmetic Act, Judicial and Administrative Record, 1953-1957* (Chicago, 1958), 465-531; David F. Cavers, "The Food, Drug, and Cosmetic Act of 1938: Its Legislative History and Its Substantive Provisions," *Law and Contemporary Problems*, 6 (Winter 1939), 2-42; Kleinfeld, "The 1938 Act—A Decade and a Half of Growth," *FDCLJ*, 9 (1954), 528-43; James C. Munch, "A Half-Century of Drug Control," *ibid.*, 11 (1956), 322-31; FDA Monthly Report, May 27, 1957, *ibid.*, 12 (1957), 325-26; "Bimini Fué Descubierta!! Is 'Pega Palo' the Answer?" *JAMA*, 165 (1957), 695-96.

The trouble may be of various kinds, for the FDA has a choice of weapons which it may ask the Department of Justice to wield. A nostrum or gadget may be attacked directly, by seizing one or more interstate shipments and lodging a libel against them. If the manufacturer fails to contest the seizure, the misbranded or adulterated product is destroyed, or brought into compliance, as it may be if the proprietor does contest and loses the legal action. Multiple seizures are a means by which the FDA affords prompt protection of the public against an unusual hazard to health. An egregious or persistent violator may be personally prosecuted in a criminal suit, with fine or possibly imprisonment as penalities upon conviction. Or the charlatan may be taken to court and enjoined from continuing his quack promotions, with civil and criminal remedies available to the government should he violate the injunction and continue in wrong-doing. More phony operators are in jail for vending drugs and devices labeled with false curative claims than ever before in history.[8]

The Federal Trade Commission keeps a watchful eye on drug advertising in newspapers and magazines and on radio and television. A medicine proprietor who engages in deceptive practices, like exaggerating the curative potency of his product, may find himself confronted with an FTC complaint. He may consent to abandon the shady practice, or he may decide to fight the matter, first through hearings within the Commission, then by appeal to a circuit court. Victory for the FTC means a cease-and-desist order to the advertiser, demanding that he stop the misrepresentation complained of. Violation of the order can result in contempt proceedings and the risk of a fine.[9]

Early in the century Dr. Wiley's laboratories had analyzed "lost manhood" remedies for the Post Office Department. Through its Mail Frauds Division, the Department continues policing medical quackery. The main weapon is a fraud order, issued after an administrative proceeding, which forbids the quack to ship his nostrum through the mail and decrees further that all

[8] Frederic P. Lee, "The Enforcement Provisions of the Food, Drug, and Cosmetic Act," *Law and Contemporary Problems*, 6 (Winter 1939), 70-90; John L. Harvey, "Administration of the Federal Food, Drug, and Cosmetic Act," *FDCLJ*, 10 (1955), 441-48.

[9] Milton Handler, "The Control of False Advertising under the Wheeler-Lee Act," *Law and Contemporary Problems*, 6 (Winter 1939), 91-110; Charles A. Sweeny, "Federal Trade Commission Control of False Advertising of Foods, Drugs, and Cosmetics," *FDCLJ*, 12 (1957), 606-16; FDA 1957 Annual Report, *U.S. Department of Health, Education, and Welfare 1957 Annual Report*, 194.

letters addressed to the quack's address be returned to their senders stamped "Fraudulent." Since a 1949 Supreme Court decision, Reilly v. Pinkus, the Department has confronted a demanding burden of proof to secure a fraud order: unless scientific opinion universally condemns the promoter's claims, his intent to deceive must be established. In rare cases of outrageous fraud, the Post Office asks the Department of Justice to undertake criminal actions, which may send charlatans to jail.[10]

Besides the federal statutes, there are state and local laws aimed at medical quackery.[11] The legal environment today, therefore, is fraught with perils to the unscrupulous or careless proprietor which Swaim selling his Panacea and Radam his Microbe Killer did not confront. The scientific environment is also different. Many medical matters fuzzy in Swaim's and Radam's century have been clarified by modern research. Many quack claims that then could not be combatted with scientific certainty can now be shown to be ridiculous. Pseudo-medical promotion of remedies for diabetes or syphilis, for example, cannot today possess the specious plausibility that their predecessors once enjoyed. Modern medical science, of course, is an indispensable bulwark to effective governmental regulation.

Despite laws and science, however, medical quackery continues to flourish. Indeed, according to former Postmaster General Arthur Summerfield, more money is being made today in medical quackery than in "any other criminal activity." No precise, reliable statistics exist to measure its magnitude. The "take" each year to promoters of specious medication certainly exceeds a billion dollars. Half a billion alone goes into the nutrition racket, wasted on foods and food supplements promoted with therapeutic overtones. Another quarter billion is spent for medicines and gadgets falsely purporting to promote recovery from arthritis and rheumatism. A hundred million goes for ineffective reducing remedies, fifty million for fake cancer cures, and millions more for other panaceas that hold out the vain promise of curing ailments ranging from the common cold to heart disease.[12]

---

[10] James Cook, *Remedies and Rackets, The Truth About Patent Medicines Today* (N.Y., 1958), 196-98; Frederick M. Hart, "The Postal Fraud Statutes: Their Use and Abuse," *FDCLJ*, 11 (1956), 245-61.

[11] The March 1959 issue of *FDCLJ* (vol. 14) has a series of articles on state food and drug laws.

[12] Summerfield cited in Cook, 196; *FDCLJ*, 13 (1958), 677-78; Ruth Walrad, *The Misrepresentation of Arthritis Drugs and Devices in the United States* (N.Y., 1960), 1; Jonathan Spivak, "Crusade on Quacks," *Wall Street Jnl.*, June 22, 1960.

One reason for this astounding state of affairs is that there are shortcomings in legal regulation. Many states and cities lack adequate laws, and others tend to leave the matter of quackery to federal agencies. The Food and Drug Administration, the Federal Trade Commission, and the Post Office Department have many tasks to perform besides seeking to keep proprietors of drugs and devices respectable. The budgets and staffs of these agencies are limited. The FDA, even though its operations have recently been augmented, has been given added responsibilities, and the bulk of its efforts goes into protecting the nation's food supply. So expensive is litigation, and the arduous preparation for it, that the FDA can afford only a few major anti-quackery cases at once. Court contests are protracted, sometimes taking years, for legal processes intended to safeguard the innocent can postpone punishment for the guilty. The FDA may halt a quack's activity by injunction while the merits of the charge are being tried. The FTC may also appeal for an injunction to curtail especially risky advertising pending the adjudication of the issue, but very seldom does. A 1960 law provides the Post Office Department with similar authority to seek an injunction, not yet used. Thus proprietors of questionable medications continue to reap profits while legal maneuvering proceeds along its weary way.[13]

It may be questioned also, in the regulation of medical quackery, if the penalty fits the crime. At the worst, under FTC regulations, when the case is over and the advertiser is defeated, he is told that at long last he must stop disseminating the offending claims. There are no other sanctions. The Commission says, in effect, "Go and sin no more." If the proprietor is foolish enough to repeat the same sin, his fine may reach five figures. But a somewhat different sin requires a new beginning. A more serious deterrent is the denial of mail privileges, coming at the end of a mail fraud action, but this is not necessarily ruinous to the quack. He may continue with over-the-counter sales. But often the wily proprietor, caught in this trap, changes his product's name and

---

13 Melvin E. Mensor, " 'SNAFU' in State Food Laws," *FDCLJ*, 12 (1957), 690-704; E. L. Randall, "Factors Affecting the State Adoption of the Food-Additives Law," *ibid.*, 14 (1959), 174-76; *ibid.*, 13 (1958), 72, 250; William W. Goodrich, "Searching for Medical Truths in the Courtroom," *ibid.*, 11 (1956), 492; David H. Vernon, "Labyrinthine Ways: The Handling of Food, Drug, Device and Cosmetic Cases by the Federal Trade Commission since 1938," *ibid.*, 8 (1953), 367-93; Tobias B. Klinger, "Conflict with Quackery," *ibid.*, 8 (1953), 777-91; Sweeny, 606-16; Cook, 184-95, 198.

address and launches a new campaign. The Mail Frauds Division, like the other regulatory agencies, finds itself involved over and over again with men who make medical quackery a life-long career.[14]

The FDA's multiple seizure weapon is a grave threat to the medicine proprietor, not so much because he may lose the shipments seized, as because his entire interstate operations are quickly and effectively halted. But only when the hazard to health is significant can the agency employ this decisive action. In a criminal suit, the FDA, unlike the Post Office Department, does not need to prove fraudulent intent. Therefore its legal task is easier. For the most part, however, convictions have brought only modest fines, and prison sentences, when given, have been short. More than that, prison sentences are more often than not suspended, so long as the convicted violators abstain from promoting their useless remedies. One recent judgment decreed a fine of $750 and five days in jail—this was the penalty for vending a magnetic ray device in deliberate violation of a permanent injunction. The heaviest prison sentence ever given as result of court action undertaken by the FDA was nine years. The customary lighter penalties, it has been suggested, are regarded by quacks as a sort of license fee for doing business. FDA efforts to force restoration of the purchase money spent by the gullible for fraudulent wares have so far not been granted by the courts.[15]

Another reason for the persistence of quackery lies not in the nature of legal restrictions but in the nature of man. As he did in the 19th century, so does man still yearn desperately for things that cannot be. If the science of medicine could ever win a total victory over disease, then the pseudo-science of medicine might wither away. Medical advances during the 20th century, remarkable as they have been, have not abolished illness and ended death. The pattern of disease has been much modified, the advent of

[14] *Ibid.*, 65, 115-16, 193.

[15] Harvey, 441-48; Francis N. McKay and Benjamin Frauwirth, "The Penalty Provisions of the Federal Food, Drug, and Cosmetic Act," *FDCLJ*, 6 (1951), 575-93; FDA 1955 Annual Report, reprinted in Kleinfeld and Dunn, 707; 1956 Annual Report, *ibid.*, 737; 1957 Annual Report, in *U.S. Dept. of H.E.W. 1957 Annual Report*, 212; 1958 Annual Report, in *ibid.*, 1958, 214; FDA Notices of Judgment (Drugs and Devices), 5076; FDA 1951 Annual Report, in Kleinfeld and Dunn, 596; Goodrich, "Restitution—Modern Application of an Ancient Remedy," *FDCLJ*, 9 (1954), 565-72; Edward Brown Williams, "If There Be Equity. . . ," *ibid.*, 10 (1955), 92-103.

death delayed. But fear of cancer, say, in a man of seventy brings the same anguish that fear of cholera once brought to a man of thirty-five.

Today's physician, despite his greater knowledge and his more effective drugs, is almost as handicapped, in competition with the quack, as was his 19th-century predecessor. The doctor must still confess that disease is a complex phenomenon. The quack continues to say that it is simple. The doctor must often state that treatment will be protracted. The quack says his is speedy. The doctor may have to tell a patient that much expense will be involved. The quack says his remedy is cheap. The doctor must warn of suffering. The quack terms his treatment painless. The doctor, all too often, must confess defeat and admit that all his skill and all the new products of pharmaceutical chemistry are inadequate to the task of restoring health. The quack says his cure is sure. It is the old story over again.

In the last quarter of a century, the medical profession has forsaken virtual therapeutic nihilism and has resumed extensive drug therapy, as pharmaceutical science has produced wonder drugs in an accelerating and—to the layman—bewildering array. This great boon to health has been, perversely, a help to quackery. Just as in William Radam's day, it is hard for John Doe to keep from confusing hopeful headlines about new antibiotics and hopeful advertising about "new" nostrums. "That so much is written and published regarding health topics generally," states Wallace F. Janssen, the FDA's Director of Public Information, "seems to create a climate that is favorable to the spread of quackery—or perhaps one should say, new forms of quackery. More and more people believe in miracles, not only the real miracles of scientific achievement, but also the fake miracles of promoters and charlatans."[16]

One hope of early anti-nostrum crusaders has not been borne out. Education has not made Americans impervious to quackery. In the age of the common man, many physician-reformers believed that honest labeling would sound the death-knell of the nostrum business. This optimism was shared by journalists,

[16] "Statement of Austin Smith, M.D., President, Pharmaceutical Manufacturers Association . . . Before the Senate Subcommittee on Antitrust and Monopoly Legislation . . . February 23, 1960"; Janssen, "Food Quackery—A Law Enforcement Problem," *Jnl. of the Amer. Dietetic Assoc.*, 36 (1960), 111.

doctors, and public officials who waged the successful campaign to put patent medicine provisions into the 1906 law. The goal has never been reached, in that enforcement of this and later laws has not succeeded in making all labeling and advertising honest. Nor has education been adequate, in that anti-quackery propaganda has not come close to equalling patent medicine advertising in its impact upon public attention. Of more basic concern, even the optimistic premise of earlier years is today regarded as too simple. Man's conduct is not so rationally motivated as once seemed true. The state of his psyche, a momentous factor in the state of his health, influences how he pursues well-being. His efforts may be quixotic, anti-rational, contrary to "better" judgment, against the counsel of medical science. Even when panic is not present as a major disorienting factor, many people hope for—and pay for—a cheap, sure protection or relief that does not and cannot exist. Nor is it merely a matter of the nostrum's customers. On grounds that can hardly represent rational conviction, juries, and even judges, turning their backs on scientific evidence and expert opinion, have accepted as true, outlandish claims of impossible cures.[17]

This non-rational bent sometimes leads even men and women with much formal education to the charlatan's door. It has not been uncommon to find the clergyman using and recommending nostrums, the business tycoon espousing a weird religion, and the physician seeking quack counsel on how to invest his gains. "University towns," opined a physician on the staff of the Mayo Clinic, "are hot-beds of quackery." An experienced advertising agent, back in the 19th century, gave this advice on the promotion of patent medicines to a novice in the profession: "You are starting out on a long up-hill journey, and you must write your advertisements to catch damned fools—not college professors." Then, after a moment, he added, "and you'll catch just as many college professors as you will of any other sort."[18]

Education remains a major treatment of choice against quackery, but experience has shown it to be less specific therapy for the malady than once was thought.

[17] Goodrich, "Judicial Highlights of 50 Years Enforcement," *FDCLJ*, 11 (1956), 75-76.

[18] Walter C. Alvarez, "The Appeal of Quackery to the Nervous Invalid," *Minnesota Medicine*, 16 (Feb. 1935), 87; Rowell, *Forty Years an Advertising Agent*, 377.

If the hopes and fears impelling people to irrational therapy are ancient and deep-rooted, so too are the quack's appeals. Now as always he must confront his would-be customers with a message that allays their suspicions and fulfills their expectations. To help him in his task he has available a whole assortment of time-tested lures. Indeed, it would be hard to find a type of appeal pioneered in the 19th century that is not still being put to work—perhaps in modified form—even by reputable proprietary advertisers. Certainly the testimonial is much with us; men and women continue to send voluntary letters of appreciation to medicine makers which they dare not use, so extreme are the curative claims jubilantly reported. The distinction between advertising and non-advertising, that once was hard to detect in newspaper columns, is sometimes blurred on television. Viewers are not always sure when a master of ceremonies is starting to introduce another guest and when he is launching a pitch for some remedy. Television has brought back, too, some of the symbols of evil from the devil's dark domain, and now the fiendish creatures wiggle. Spectators have peered inside the body, watching the race of pain-relievers from stomach to brain. They have seen stomach acid removed, concentrated, and thrown at a napkin with ominous results. They have observed actors impersonating doctors, who report on exciting experiments, lauding in frenetic tones the marvels of scientific progress, of which the product advertised is the prime example. Seldom in polite advertising are physicians debunked—the real quacks continue this ancient war—although there is an occasional sly dig like, "So safe you don't need a doctor's prescription," implying that what the doctor orders is generally risky.[19]

A glance through recent Notices of Judgment from the Food and Drug Administration reveals echoes of other traditional appeals. Religion is represented by Father Francis' Herb Formula—and by the operator who put the Doxology upon his label. Hercules Tonic Tea reveals the symbol of strength. The noble red man continues active in the interest of the white man's health. Capon Springs Water, a gift of the Catauba Indians,

---

[19] Cook, 34, 45, 97, 133, 140; *FDC Reports "The Pink Sheet" Drugs and Devices*, 22 (Jan. 11, 1960), 15. The code of the National Association of Broadcasters was amended in 1958 to outlaw actors in commercials from impersonating physicians, dentists, and nurses, *Drug Trade News*, 33 (June 30, 1958), 1.

caused FDA officials a great deal of trouble. A case in litigation since 1943 had to be terminated in 1954 because "it was discovered that the article under seizure had disappeared." Electricity retains its fascination, and Elisha Perkins' metallic tractors continue to have heirs. One recent gadget bore the name Galvanic Five-in-One Shortwave Oscillotron; another, called more simply Vitalitone, included among the ailments it would vanquish, paralysis, fallen arches, and bags under the eyes—it would also rejuvenate the busts.[20]

Old lures, as always, continue to be supplemented by new approaches, for the ancient adaptability of the quack has lost none of its suppleness. Ask what is exciting public attention, and there you will find the medicine man adjusting his mask. For the hoary question, "Are You Looking for the Fountain of Youth?" there was recently proffered a very modern answer, a device called Atomic-Nu-Life. The atomic age was quick to come to quackery, with uranium tunnels—some lined with ore from the Merry Widow mine—radioactive bath salts, U-235 drinking water, and assorted fission panaceas. One "radioactive" gadget, shaped like an inkwell, could "cure," among other ailments, cancer, diabetes, and arthritis. It operated by enclosing for twenty-four hours a sample of the sufferer's blood which was then re-injected.[21]

Quacks have paid particular heed to major developments in medical science and their impact on the nation's health. Unorthodox as well as orthodox medicine has had its "wonder drugs," and, as infectious diseases have given place to chronic and degenerative diseases in the mortality tables, quackery has increased its attention to arthritis, cancer, and the infirmities of aging.

When the tranquilizing drugs caught hold of national attention, proprietary manufacturers, like Radam before them, sought to make a profit from this medical advance. Advertising strove to create the impression of a distinct resemblance between the prescription tranquilizers, like reserpine and chlorpromazine, on one hand, and proprietaries like Tranquil-Aid, Sleep-eze, Sominex, and NervTabs, on the other. Some of the imitation

[20] Notices of Judgment (Drugs and Devices) 5,071, 4,396, 4,778, 4,667, 4,677; FDA 1951 Annual Report, 597.
[21] N.J. 5,000, 4,579, 4,666; FDA Annual Reports for 1955, 1956, 1957; *Wall Street Jnl.*, June 22, 1960.

tranquilizers were essentially the old-fashioned bromides. Others were antihistamines. This was an intriguing development. A decade ago a whole host of proprietaries burst upon the market, virtually promising that the antihistamines they contained would prevent and cure the common cold. The FTC took action against the most flagrant advertising. Medical observation revealed that a prominent side effect of antihistamine therapy was sedation, a feeling of drowsiness. Thus, as the old market waned, a new one opened up. The side effect was moved to center stage. Antihistamines became non-prescription tranquilizers.[22]

Fraudulent food supplement promotion, currently the major economic front in quackery, demonstrates the flexibility with which the unscrupulous adapt to new conditions. One type of enterpriser in this racket is a salesman who goes from door to door. His medicines are herbal mixtures or vitamin-mineral capsules, accurately labeled as to constituents and bearing no therapeutic claims. A Food and Drug agent, scrutinizing a bottle, can find no fault. Where the trouble arises is in the salesman's oral pitch. To the man or woman who answers the door, he tells a plausible tale of how ill health results from relying on foods grown by the methods of modern agriculture, which drain valuable nutriments from the soil and add poisonous fertilizers to it, or by modern food processing, with its additives and subtractives. There are genuine hazards to health in food about which people are justifiably concerned; Congress expanded the food law in 1958 to require that additives be tested for safety before being introduced to the public diet. However, the food supply of the American people is the best in all history. The quack, distorting the truth and grafting his message to fear, approaches the credulous with words like this, taken down by tape recorder: "You eat food to make blood. You send down junk, your body will be junk. Your body will wind up in the junk pile. You send down vital elements that are needed, you're okay. Whenever you get your body normalized, you won't have no condition. You can't even take a cold. I don't care how you're exposed to freezing temperature, wet feet and cold feet, you'll never take it if you get your blood stream up to par."[23]

[22] Cook, 121-32.

[23] *JAMA*, 167 (1958), 1,745, 2,088; Janssen, 110-13; Horace L. Sipple, "Nutrition Education As An Aid in Counteracting Food Misrepresentation,"

The salesman's pulverized alfalfa or his bona fide vitamins, of course, ward off the danger or cure the complaint—even if it is a broken leg.[24] The court victories expanding FDA's jurisdiction to include control over such oral nonsense are in some ways frustrating. How to catch hold of, for policing, the fleeting words of a hundred thousand salesmen who are working at the nutrition racket?

The problem is so gigantic that the Food and Drug Administration, the American Medical Association, and the National Better Business Bureau launched in 1958 a joint campaign of counter-propaganda. Officials have made speeches and issued press releases. The AMA has urged local medical societies to fight food faddism, and has produced a film demonstrating by case example the dangers of nutritional quackery.[25]

Allied to the food supplement business is the weight reduction craze. Prosperity has permitted the nation to eat high off the hog, with the inevitable result. To embarrassment on aesthetic grounds, as a motive for reducing, has been added fear, spurred by the wide circulation of medical reports showing the high correlation between too much weight and heart and circulatory ailments. Americans have been wealthy enough to pay for expensive drugs and devices which their promoters promise will take off fat without dieting or exertion. To stop the most dangerous and deceptive of reducing racketeers has been a high-priority concern of regulatory agencies. Numerous actions have been taken against "appetite suppressant" drugs, and, according to William W. Goodrich, head counsel for food and drug matters in the Department of Health, Education, and Welfare: "We have seized, I believe, every kind of shaking machine that the mind of man can devise."[26]

As geriatrics assumes greater importance in reputable medicine, so it does in quackery. "It is among the older group," states

FDCLJ, 15 (1950), 65-69; Joseph R. Bell, "Let 'em Eat Hay," Today's Health, 36 (Sep. 1958), 22-25, 66-68, spiel quoted at 24; FDA 1958 Annual Report, 209; nearly every FDA Annual Report of the last decade refers to the problem.

[24] The author has a bottle of vitamins given to him by a student to whose uncle it was sold by a door-to-door salesman as a cure for his broken leg.

[25] JAMA, 167 (1958), 1,745, 2,088; Wall Street Jnl., June 22, 1960.

[26] Secretary Arthur S. Flemming, Dept. of H.E.W., news conference, FDCLJ, 14 (1959), 554, 583; Drug Trade News, 34 (Aug. 24, 1959), 1, 16; Goodrich, "Judicial Progress in 1958," FDCLJ, 14 (1959), 252.

the report to the President from the Federal Council on Aging, "that the unscrupulous operator finds the greatest potential for his wares and services. It is in this age group that we find the diseases with which medical science is not fully capable of dealing—such as cancer, heart disease, arthritis, and others." Florida and California, meccas for the aged, are also the abode of many false medical prophets. Nearly half of America's 11,000,000 arthritis sufferers, according to the Arthritis and Rheumatism Foundation, are spending money for misrepresented drugs and devices. Cancer quackery has risen so alarmingly—there are now some 4,000 practitioners—that it too has been the theme of national warning campaigns.[27]

One of the more persistent operators in the cancer field has been Harry Hoxsey. For over thirty years, though four times convicted of practicing medicine without a license, he has vended his various remedies. In about 1936 Hoxsey set up a clinic in Dallas, promising cancer victims a painless cure without surgery, x-ray, or radium. There his staff gave patients superficial examinations—rarely including biopsies—and prescribed blackish brown or red liquids containing all or some of the following ingredients: sugar, red clover blossoms, prickly ash bark, pepsin, burdock, licorice, potassium iodide, and other substances equally ineffective in cancer therapy. The cost per patient was $400 plus other fees and expenses. Officials of the Food and Drug Administration did not think they could take effective action, since Hoxsey was careful not to ship his medicines across state lines. In 1948 the Supreme Court interpreted the labeling provisions of the 1938 law in a more elastic way so as to give the FDA hope, and in 1950 the agency brought suit for an injunction to stop Hoxsey's cruel deceptions. The District Court refused to grant the injunction, but the Circuit Court of Appeals stated that the evidence was overwhelming and ordered the District Judge to do so. When all the appealing was over, all the counter-suits quashed, the date was 1960. A Pennsylvania Hoxsey Cancer Clinic was closed, the operators of the Dallas clinic were enjoined from ever again selling the medications comprising the Hoxsey

[27] Report to President Eisenhower by the Federal Council on Aging, cited *Drug and Cosmetic Industry*, 85 (1959), 747-48; Walrad, 71; *Wall Street Jnl.*, June 22, 1960; *N.Y. Times*, Oct. 24, 1954.

treatment, and Hoxsey himself was ordered to stop sharing directly or indirectly in the profits of the Dallas operation.[28]

While waiting out the law's inevitable delays, the FDA put out a public warning which appeared in church and farm periodicals, suggesting that anyone planning to take the Hoxsey treatment should first write to Washington to get the facts. Letters of inquiry came in for months at the rate of 50 to 100 a day. To spread the warning even further, the FDA sent copies of a "Public Beware!" poster, lettered in red and black, for display in the 46,000 post offices and substations throughout the land. Hoxsey got out his own propaganda, a book entitled *You Don't Have to Die*, defending his procedures and condemning his enemies. In an ominous show of unity, the major quacks in the business conspired to bring pressure on the FDA. "Using specialists in mass psychology," Commissioner Larrick has said, "the promoters held numerous meetings under the guise of 'scientific lectures' to organize a protest movement among those prejudiced against recognized medical treatment. They used radio, television, circulars, 'religious' publications and even huge barn-side signs, to encourage the public to write to Congressmen and the President, demanding investigations of FDA 'persecution' of their leaders. Many of them did write, for we have had a torrent of belligerent letters to answer."[29]

After the Pennsylvania victory, Larrick had issued a statement of somber import. "The public should know. . . ," he said, "that such actions will not end the menace of this treatment since the Federal Government does not have the power to stop a clinic in any State from treating cancer patients within that State with the nostrums which comprise the Hoxsey treatment. Millions of copies of false promotional literature are still in circulation; much of it reporting cures of persons who are now dead."[30]

[28] Hoxsey information from FDA, "Public Warning against Hoxsey Cancer Treatment," and "Facts Regarding the Hoxsey Cancer Treatment," Apr. 4, 1956; statements by Larrick in FDA releases, Nov. 16, 1956, Oct. 24 and 30, 1957; FDA releases, Jan. 28, 1957 and Sep. 21, 1960; Goodrich in *FDCLJ*, 14 (1959), 253, 501; Larrick in *ibid.*, 13 (1958), 250; *JAMA*, 155 (1954), 667-68, 160 (1956), 55; *Life*, 40 (Apr. 16, 1956), 125-28; interviews with Gilbert S. Goldhammer and Wallace F. Janssen.

[29] Larrick, "Report from the Food and Drug Administration," *FDCLJ*, 13 (1958), 153.

[30] FDA release, Oct. 24, 1957.

So disturbing, indeed, is the magnitude of medical quackery in our disturbing times that a new anti-quackery crusade is well launched to combat it. Regulatory agencies are applying greater rigor to enforcement. Their officials, in collaboration with representatives from the health professions and reputable business, are seeking to warn the public by means of major educational campaigns. Muckraking in lay journals is reviving. Congressional committees are expressing concern. New laws are in the offing.

It is a sad fact that Nicholas Knopp, with his Scurvy Water in 17th-century Boston, and Monsieur Torres, with his Chinese Stones in 18th-century Philadelphia, and William Radam, with his Microbe Killer in 19th-century Austin, are not quaint figures representing outmoded traditions associated with medical ignorance of ancient days. They and their victims are, as it were, still alive, to cast a shadow on the medical brilliance of our own day.

A NOTE ON THE SOURCES

THE PUBLIC posture of the patent medicine maker is easier to observe throughout history than are his private ways. Newspapers, saved mainly for other matter than their advertising, preserve it nonetheless, and nostrum advertising is a fundamental source of the present book, from the *Boston News-Letter* of October 4, 1708, which contained America's "first," to the huge dailies of nearly two centuries later, which contained the blatant appeals condemned by Samuel Hopkins Adams.

The footnotes refer to only a few of the advertisements surveyed in many repositories. Libraries most frequented for their newspaper holdings were the Library of Congress, the New York Public Library, the New-York Historical Society of New York City, the Maryland Historical Society, the University of Illinois Library, the Carnegie Library of Pittsburgh, and the Emory University Library. An effort was made to sample advertising in papers published in different regions, in villages and cities, and for different audiences: hence the *Police Gazette* and *Lookout for Christ and the Church* find a place as well as the *New York Times*.

In addition to advertising in newspapers, patent medicine makers got out countless broadsides, posters, trade cards, handbills, brochures, books, and other promotional literature. Some of this gave the copywriter much more space in which to develop his ideas than was customary in newspaper columns, with not even the deterrent of the mild censorship which publishers sometimes exercised. Throwaway advertising is of great importance as a source for nostrum history, and happily some of it has been preserved.

The richest hoard examined for this work forms part of the Bella C. Landauer Collection of the New-York Historical Society. The best examples of 18th-century broadsides were found in the American Antiquarian Society and the Historical Society of Pennsylvania. Posters, brochures, and labels submitted for copyrighting purposes during the mid-19th century are to be found in the Prints and Photographs Division of the Library of Congress, and in the same library's Rare Book Division, in the Toner Collection, is a fine assortment of pseudo-medical materials mailed to a physician later in the same century. The best collection of nostrum literature of the early 20th century is in the Department of Investigation of the American Medical Association in Chicago. Hundreds of folders, each bearing the name of a medicine, contain thousands of items, the sources for the three useful *Nostrums and Quackery* volumes issued by the Association in 1911, 1921, and 1936.

Other repositories in which significant items of this type were found include the National Library of Medicine and the Folger Shakespeare Library in Washington, the Enoch Pratt Free Library in Baltimore, the College of Physicians of Philadelphia Library, the New York Academy of Medicine Library, the Collection of William Robertson Coe in the Yale University Library, the Yale Medical Library, the Chicago Historical Society, the John Crerar Public Library in Chicago, the State Historical Society of Wisconsin, and the Institute of the History of Pharmacy at the University of Wisconsin. Gerald Carson of Middleton, New York, permitted the author to look over his pamphlet materials. The author has formed his own small collection of patent medicine ephemera discovered in second-hand bookstores and presented by friends. Generous contributions were made by Lawrence B. Romaine of Weathercock House, Middleboro, Massachusetts, and by Norris Goode, Louis Hoeflin, and Charles Jones, of the *Virden* [Ill.] *Recorder*.

One form of nostrum literature that the term "throwaway" did not originally fit was the patent medicine almanac, designed to be kept for a year and, often, with financial accounts scribbled on its margins, made a permanent part of a family's archives. Good files of patent medicine almanacs were examined in the Landauer Collection, the Library of Congress, the New York Public Library, and the Hostetter Corporation of Pittsburgh. A bound collection of 1889 Ayer almanacs in various languages is located in the Peabody Institute Library, Baltimore. Milton Drake of Riverdale, New York, has prepared a Check-List and Census of American Almanacs.

Some pre-1906 patent medicines, as well as literature about them, survive. The author examined many such pills and purgatives in the Division of Medical Sciences of the Smithsonian Institution, the State Historical Society of Wisconsin, the New-York Historical Society, the Rochester [New York] Museum of

Arts and Sciences, the Fort Pulaski National Monument near Savannah, Georgia, and the Samuel Aker, David and George Kass Collection in Albany, New York. The author has his own assortment, found in drugstores in Illinois and Georgia and generously sought out for him in upstate New York by Robert M. Bevan of the Upjohn Company. Friends aware of the research in progress have contributed packages that came within their possession.

Patent medicine promoters have not been forward about giving their private papers to manuscript repositories. Nor have they written memoirs, except for the fictionized accounts of their great discoveries designed as vehicles of promotion. The author has found no manufacturer's account of his career so candid as the perhaps boastful revelations of Violet McNeal concerning the medicine show business, entitled *Four White Horses and a Brass Band* (Garden City, 1947). An occasional newspaper interview, usually anonymous, has claimed to expose the inside of the proprietary business (as in the *New York Tribune* for April 25, 1886), and the muckraking sleuths like Adams uncovered a great deal. But medicine makers themselves have been close-mouthed, except in their wrath at criticism. On the manufacturing level, the annual reports of the Proprietary Association, of which there are some turn-of-the-century examples at the University of Wisconsin, give some insight into the problems of the large-scale producers as they saw them. *Standard Remedies*, begun in 1915 and long the spokesman for the major manufacturers, contains short historical sketches of individual companies, undoubtedly written with information supplied by them. A good file of this magazine may be found in the Library of the Department of Agriculture.

Detailed information on some individual proprietors, the result of careful inquiry, may be discovered in the folders in the American Medical Association offices. Harvey Washington Wiley's Bureau of Chemistry in the Department of Agriculture, as the files reveal, was concerned with nostrums in the years preceding 1906. These records are to be found in Record Group 97 in the National Archives. Helpful counsel with respect to their use came from Helen T. Finneran and Harold T. Pinkett.

The officers of the Hostetter Corporation as of 1956 permitted the author to examine the Minute Book of the corporation's annual meetings, 1889-1935. This contained a record of dividends issued and, occasionally, in the president's report, some comment on the problems confronting management.

Advertising agents, who became the right-hand men of medicine proprietors, have been less reticent. Notable autobiographies are George Presbury Rowell, *Forty Years an Advertising Agent, 1865-1905* (New York, 1926)—Rowell marketed his own remedy—and Claude C. Hopkins, *My Life in Advertising* (New York, 1927).

Helpful in seeing the wholesaler's point of view in the second quarter of the 19th century was a small collection of papers from the Springfield, Illinois, drug firm of Birchall and Owen which the author secured; village general store records were examined for patent medicine references in the Illinois State Historical Society and the State Historical Society of Wisconsin.

The critique of patent medicines has been found primarily in the journals and proceedings of the chief critics—physicians and pharmacists. Exact references are cited in footnotes to Chapters 5, 10, 13, and 14. Especially to be noted are the *Journal of the American Medical Association*, the *American Journal of Pharmacy*, the American Pharmaceutical Association's *Proceedings*, and the *Druggists Circular and Chemical Gazette*. Besides articles, there were issued many separately printed pamphlets and books, written by practitioners of the healing arts, attacking quackery. Libraries used extensively for their journals and pamphlets were the New York Academy of Medicine Library, the National Library of Medicine, the Philadelphia College of Pharmacy Library, the Lloyd Library in Cincinnati, the Library of the American Pharmaceutical Association in Washington, the Library of the Southern College of Pharmacy in Atlanta, and the A. W. Calhoun Medical Library of Emory University.

A force for more decent advertising was the trade periodical *Printer's Ink*, which paid much attention to patent medicines. A card file index which the author was permitted to consult in the New York City editorial offices was very helpful.

The files of the *Ladies' Home Journal* and *Collier's* and other anti-nostrum muckraking magazines were studied. Several engrossing hours were spent in Beaufort, South Carolina, on April 5, 1955, talking with Samuel Hopkins Adams about his famous series, "The Great American Fraud."

A NOTE ON THE SOURCES

The American Medical Association materials and the Bureau of Chemistry records, mentioned above, are, of course, basic sources for the criticism of patent medicines early in this century. The latter must be supplemented by Wiley's private papers in the Manuscript Division of the Library of Congress. Wiley's *An Autobiography* (Indianapolis, 1930) should be mentioned at this point. On the fight for a Pure Food and Drugs Law, pertinent references from these manuscripts, from the *Congressional Record*, and from Congressional documents are given in the footnotes to Chapter 14.

Many conversations have provided the author with information or ideas about interpretation. Especially to be mentioned are those with Oscar E. Anderson, Jr., the Atomic Energy Commission; Jacques Barzun, Columbia University; Thomas W. Christopher, Emory University School of Law; Gerald Carson; Frederick J. Cullen, then executive vice-president of the Proprietary Association; David Donald, Princeton University; John Duffy, Louisiana State University; Oliver Field, Director, Department of Investigation, American Medical Association; George B. Griffenhagen, Director, Division of Communications, American Pharmaceutical Association; Richard Hofstadter, Columbia University; Blake McKelvey, Rochester, N.Y., City Historian; Carl C. Pfeiffer, then Director of the Basic Sciences, Emory University School of Medicine; David M. Potter, Yale University; Richard H. Shryock, Librarian of the American Philosophical Society; Harold C. Syrett, Columbia University; Barbara Young, M.D., Baltimore, and W. Harvey Young, Galesburg, Illinois.

Officials of the Food and Drug Administration of the Department of Health, Education, and Welfare, have been extremely courteous and helpful with their advice. Wallace F. Janssen, Director of Public Information; William W. Goodrich, Assistant General Counsel in the Welfare Department's Office of the General Counsel; Gilbert S. Goldhammer, Assistant Director of the Division of Regulatory Management; and John J. McCann, Jr., Chief of the Communications Standards Branch; should be mentioned particularly. Since the FDA did not begin to operate until after the enactment of the 1906 law, the agency records are not germane to the present volume but to its sequel.

Three theses were of interest: James Gordon Burrow's University of Illinois doctoral dissertation (1956), "Political and

[267]

Social Policies of the American Medical Association, 1901-1941"; David L. Dykstra's University of Wisconsin doctoral dissertation (1951), "Patent and Proprietary Medicine: Regulation and Control Prior to 1906"; and Jacques Marc Quen's Yale University School of Medicine thesis (1954), "A Study of Dr. Elisha Perkins and Perkinism."

In the category of secondary works, two background volumes proved indispensable: Richard H. Shryock, *The Development of Modern Medicine* (New York, 1947) realizes in a brilliant way the intent of its subtitle, *An Interpretation of the Social and Scientific Factors Involved*; Edward Kremers and George Urdang, *A History of Pharmacy* (Philadelphia, 1940), sets the broader stage of pharmacy on which nostrums played their role.

Henry W. Holcombe, during the later 1930's and early 1940's, wrote sketches of all the medicine concerns which issued private die proprietary stamps under a Civil War tax law that was repealed in 1883. These articles appeared in various philatelic periodicals, from which Holcombe took tear-sheets to assemble into a volume which he presented to the New York Public Library. Later Holcombe prepared a series on the stamps of medicine companies during the Spanish-American War, published in *Weekly Philatelic Gossip* from 1955 to 1958. The sketches vary in degree of detail; some contain information learned by Holcombe through visits to the companies.

A brief list of secondary works which have been of help to the author would include the following: Oscar E. Anderson, Jr., *The Health of a Nation, Harvey W. Wiley and the Fight for Pure Food* (Chicago, 1958); Thomas D. Clark, *Pills, Petticoats, and Plows, The Southern Country Store* (Indianapolis, 1944), and *The Southern Country Editor* (Indianapolis, 1948); Morris Fishbein, *Fads in Quackery and Healing* (New York, 1932); Ralph M. Hower, *The History of an Advertising Agency: N. W. Ayer & Son at Work, 1869-1949* (Revised ed., Cambridge, Mass., 1949); John Phillips, compiler, *The Composition of Certain Patent and Proprietary Medicines* (Chicago, 1917); Madge E. Pickard and R. Carlyle Buley, *The Midwest Pioneer: His Ills, Cures & Doctors* (New York, 1946); Frank Presbrey, *The History and Development of Advertising* (New York, 1929); James J. Walsh, *Cures, The Story of Cures That Failed* (New York, 1930).

In preparing the last chapter, especially helpful were the Food and Drug Administration Annual Reports, the files of the *Food Drug Cosmetic Law Journal*, and a book by James Cook that, in its first version, appeared as a series of articles in the *New York Post* during May and June 1957, *Remedies and Rackets, The Truth About Patent Medicines Today* (New York, 1958). The most thorough study of current unorthodox practices with respect to a single disease was made by Ruth Walrad for the Committee on Arthritis Advertising of the Arthritis and Rheumatism Foundation, *The Misrepresentation of Arthritis Drugs and Devices in the United States* (New York, 1960).

My own previous writing on patent medicine history, which reappears in some measure in this book, includes: "Patent Medicines in the Early Nineteenth Century," *The South Atlantic Quarterly*, 48 (Oct. 1949), 557-65; "Patent Medicines: The Early Post-Frontier Phase," *Journal of the Illinois State Historical Society*, 46 (Autumn, 1953), 254-64; "The Origin of Patent Medicines in America," *The Chemist and Druggist*, 172 (Sep. 9, 1959), 9-16; "Patent Medicines: An Early Example of Competitive Marketing," *Journal of Economic History*, 20 (Dec. 1960), 648-56; and two articles written in collaboration with George B. Griffenhagen, entitled "Old English Patent Medicines in America," of which a summary version appeared in *Chemist and Druggist*, 167 (June 29, 1957), 714-22, and a longer version as Paper 10 in United States National Museum Bulletin 218, *Contributions from the Museum of History and Technology*, published by the Smithsonian Institution (Washington, 1959). Three articles were in press: "American Medical Quackery in the Age of the Common Man," *The Mississippi Valley Historical Review*; "Thomas W. Dyott—Pioneer Nostrum Promoter," *Journal of the American Pharmaceutical Association (Practical Pharmacy Edition)*; and "Patent Medicines and Indians," *The Emory University Quarterly*.

INDEX

(Patent medicine and patent medicines are designated by pm)

[271]